442125

KT-399-757

THE MERCERS' SERIES

Oil Paintings in Public Ownership in
Greater Manchester Vol. I

The *Oil Paintings in Public Ownership* series of catalogues is an extraordinary work in progress. Published by The Public Catalogue Foundation, it is the result of the determined efforts of a small team of administrative staff, researchers and photographers spread across the United Kingdom.

Our national collection of oil paintings in public ownership is probably one of the finest anywhere in the world. It is held not just by our museums and galleries but is also to be found in hospitals, universities and other civic buildings throughout the United Kingdom. A large proportion of these paintings are not on display and many have never before been reproduced.

This series of books for the first time allows the public to see an entire photographic record of these works – a collection likely to number some 200,000 in total. In doing so, these volumes provide a unique insight into our nation's artistic and cultural history.

As Patron of The Public Catalogue Foundation, my visits to collections across the country have highlighted to me not only the desire of curators to publicise their paintings, but also the limited resources at their disposal. The Foundation's work goes a long way towards helping to create access to these collections, while at the same time giving the British public the opportunity to see and enjoy *all* the paintings that they own.

I wish The Public Catalogue Foundation every success in its continuing endeavours.

Camilla

Oil Paintings in Public Ownership

in

Greater Manchester Vol. 1

Funding Patron
The Mercers' Company

Coordinator: Pam Walker
Photographer: Gordon MacGregor

The Public Catalogue Foundation

Patron
HRH The Duchess of Cornwall

759.
2
OIL

Contents

Facing page: Nevinson, Christopher, 1889–1946, *Searchlights,* 1916, Manchester City Galleries (p. 179)

Image opposite HRH The Duchess of Cornwall's statement: Brett, Dorothy Eugénie, 1883–1977, *Umbrellas*, Manchester City Galleries (p. 40)
Image opposite title page: Alma-Tadema, Lawrence, 1836–1912, *Silver Favourites*, c.1903, Manchester City Galleries (p. 18)

The Public Catalogue Foundation: People Involved

Trustees & Advisors

Honorary Trustees

Dr Fred Hohler, *Founder*
Dr Alan Borg

Kate Trevelyan

Board of Trustees

Charles Gregson, *Chairman*
Margaret Greeves
Robert Hiscox
Alex Morrison
Richard Roundell

Marc Sands
Dr Charles Saumarez Smith
Graham Southern
Alison Watt

Advisory Panel

David Buckman
Adrian Cooper
Dr Susan Foister
Andrew Greg
Vivien Hamilton
Karen Hosacks

Andy Johnson
Naomi Korn
Dr Andrew Moore
Sarah Saunders
David Saywell
Christopher Wright

Staff

Andrew Ellis, *Director of the PCF*

Online Division
33 Maiden Lane
Covent Garden
London WC2E 7JS
020 7395 0330

Daniel Whibley, *Head of Editorial and Production*
Katey Goodwin, *Head of Research & Digitisation*
Sarah Hilliam, *Development Manager*
Laura Marriott, *Operations Manager*
Andy Johnson, *Photography Manager (England and Wales)*
Iona Shepherd, *Photography Manager (Scotland and Northern Ireland)*
Dr Joanna Meacock, *Regional Research Manager (Scotland)*
Stella Sharp, *Regional Research Manager (London)*
Dr Camilla Stewart, *Regional Research Manager (Wales, SW England & National Trust)*
Edward Bettella, *Production Manager*

Rachel Collings, *Senior Project Editor*
Jade King, *Senior Project Editor*
Adam Jackman, *Project Editor*
Alice Payne, *Project Editor*
Alice Warley, *Production Editor*
Alice Bray, *Production Assistant*
Louis Daly, *Digital Content Producer*
Sarah Fletcher, *Editorial Assistant*
Rebecca Nicholl, *Editorial Assistant*
Katherine Vaughan, *Content & Production Assistant*
Katie Carder, *Press & Marketing Officer*
Sonia Roe, *Editorial Consultant*
Mary Rose Rivett-Carnac, *Copyright Officer*
Martina Stender, *Copyright Manager*
Aidan McNeill, *Copyright Officer*

Printed Catalogue Division
8 Frederick's Place
London EC2R 8AB
020 7600 2920

Dr Fred Hohler
Sophie Kullmann, *Series Editor*
Alison Greenish, *Commercial Manager*

Foreword

Manchester can be most confusing. On my first visit to the Manchester City Art Galllery, a pilgrimage to one of this country's finest public collections, I had not done my research and arrived at its entrance only to find that the gallery was completely closed for a major refurbishment. Not a single painting was available to be seen.

My next visit was more successful. The gallery had been gloriously restored. The paintings were even finer than I had expected. The gallery was spacious and uncrowded. The hang was well considered and the experience hugely enjoyable.

Only one aspect of my visit jarred. Surely, closing the gallery and removing all the paintings into store was a God-given opportunity to photograph and catalogue the collection? Apparently not, for the only hint at a catalogue was a slight pamphlet, covering a few paintings and other items ranging from a Marshmallow Love seat to an early Egyptian funeral jar, which I reluctantly acquired and which I appear now to have lost. It contained the reproduction of a painting, *Summer in Cumberland*, by the late Edwardian artist James Durden. It is a glorious post-Edwardian painting in golden hues: the artist's wife and two children are enjoying a 'high tea', (certainly not the meal they are enjoying), and is a splendid and evocative period piece. More startling was the accompanying comment however that this painting was the Gallery's most popular work, "although it has been seldom exhibited". Which begs a big Why?

I chuckled to myself over that contradiction and used the tale to illustrate to those who needed to understand, how bad the situation had become and how much help even the great galleries now needed, if only to change their hangs more frequently and show the best of their paintings to a public that manifestly wished to see and enjoy them. I little understood in that just-pre-Foundation moment, that this was less a self-inflicted wound by the gallery than a comment on the situation throughout the national collection as a whole, as it was steadily deprived of funds, and focus. A situation that continues to this day (although I understand that the painting in question has since been on view).

Predictably, I suppose, Manchester has required compensation for my hubris. That moment came when the two planned volumes covering Greater Manchester had been laid out and were ready to go to the printers. Whilst establishing the size of the print run, our sales team found themselves talking to a collection that they could not find in the index of either volume. Further investigation showed that it and several other collections amounting in sum to another whole volume, had not been included. The responsibility did not lie with our sainted editor, Sophie, although the remedy did: and that required her to create a third volume and lay out all three of them afresh. Manchester's revenge. But, none of that is begrudged as the three volumes constitute an enduring monument to the magnificence of the collections in the region, and we are proud to be publishing them, whatever the cost.

Particular thanks go to Pam Walker, coordinator and Gordon MacGregor, photographer. In addition, all of us have cause to be grateful to the Mercers' Company, whose generosity has allowed these volumes to be printed.

Fred Hohler, Founder

Catalogue Scope and Organisation

Medium and Support

The principal focus of this series is oil paintings. However, tempera and acrylic are also included as well as mixed media, where oil is the predominant constituent. Paintings on all forms of support (e.g. canvas, panel, etc.) are included as long as the support is portable. The principal exclusions are miniatures, hatchments or other purely heraldic paintings and wall paintings *in situ*.

Public Ownership

Public ownership has been taken to mean any paintings that are directly owned by the public purse, made accessible to the public by means of public subsidy or generally perceived to be in public ownership. The term 'public' refers to both central government and local government. Paintings held by national museums, local authority museums, English Heritage and independent museums, where there is at least some form of public subsidy, are included. Paintings held in civic buildings such as local government offices, town halls, guildhalls, public libraries, universities, hospitals, crematoria, fire stations and police stations are also included.

Geographical Boundaries of Catalogues

The geographical boundary of each county is the 'ceremonial county' boundary. This county definition includes all unitary authorities. Counties that have a particularly large number of paintings are divided between two or more catalogues on a geographical basis.

Criteria for Inclusion

As long as paintings meet the requirements above, all paintings are included irrespective of their condition and perceived quality. However, painting reproductions can only be included with the agreement of the participating collections and, where appropriate, the relevant copyright owner. It is rare that a collection forbids the inclusion of its paintings. Where this is the case and it is possible to obtain a list of paintings, this list is given in the Paintings Without Reproductions section. Where copyright consent is refused, the paintings are also listed in the Paintings Without Reproductions section. All paintings in collections' stacks and stores are included, as well as those on display. Paintings which have been lent to other institutions, whether for short-term exhibition or long-term loan, are listed under the owner collection. In addition, paintings on long-term loan are also included under the borrowing institution when they are likely to remain there for at least another five years from the date of publication of this catalogue. Information relating to owners and borrowers is listed in the Further Information section.

Layout

Collections are grouped together under their home town. These locations are listed in alphabetical order. In some cases collections that are spread over a number of locations are included under a single owner collection. A number of collections, principally the larger ones, are preceded by curatorial forewords. Within each collection paintings are listed in order of artist surname. Where there is more than one painting by the same artist, the paintings are listed chronologically, according to their execution date.

The few paintings that are not accompanied by photographs are listed in the Paintings Without Reproductions section.

There is additional reference material in the Further Information section at the back of the catalogue. This gives the full names of artists, titles and media if it has not been possible to include these in full in the main section. It also provides acquisition credit lines and information about loans in and out, as well as copyright and photographic credits for each painting. Finally, there is an index of artists' surnames.

Facing page: Bacon, Francis, 1909–1992, *Lucian Freud*, 1951, Whitworth Art Gallery, The University of Manchester (p. 354)

Key to Painting Information

Adam, Patrick William 1854–1929 ————
*Interior, Rutland Lodge: Vista through Open
Doors* 1920
oil on canvas 67.3 × 45.7——
LEEAG.PA.1925.0671.LACF ✦ ————

Artist name This is shown with the
surname first. Where the artist is listed on
the Getty Union List of Artist Names
(ULAN), ULAN's preferred presentation of
the name is given. In a number of cases the
name may not be a firm attribution and
this is made clear. Where the artist name is
not known, a school may be given instead.
Where the school is not known, the painter
name is listed as *unknown artist*. If the
artist name is too long for the space, as
much of the name is given as possible
followed by (…). This indicates the full
name is given at the rear of the catalogue
in the Further Information section.

Painting title A painting title followed by
(?) indicates that the title is in doubt.
Where the alternative title to the painting is
considered to be better known than the
original, the alternative title is given in
parentheses. Where the collection has not
given a painting a title, the publisher does
so instead and marks this with an asterisk.
If the title is too long for the space, as much
of the title is given as possible followed by
(…) and the full title is given in the Further
Information section.

Execution date In some cases the precise
year of execution may not be known for
certain. Instead an approximate date will
be given or no date at all.

Almost all paintings are reproduced in the
catalogue. Where this is not the case they
are listed in the Paintings Without
Reproductions section. Where paintings
are missing or have been stolen, the best
possible photograph on record has been
reproduced. In some cases this may be
black and white. Paintings that have been
stolen are highlighted with a red border.
Some paintings are shown with conservation
tissue attached to parts of the painting
surface.

Artist dates Where known, the years of birth
and death of the artist are given. In some
cases one or both dates may not be known
with certainty, and this is marked. No date
indicates that even an approximate date is
not known. Where only the period in which
the artist was active is known, these dates
are given and preceded with the word *active*.

Medium and support Where the precise
material used in the support is known, this
is given.

Dimensions All measurements refer to the
unframed painting and are given in cm with
up to one decimal point. In all cases the
height is shown before the width. An (E)
indicates where a painting has not been
measured and its size has been calculated by
sight only. If the painting is circular, the
single dimension is the diameter. If the
painting is oval, the dimensions are height
and width.

Collection inventory number In the case
of paintings owned by museums, this
number will always be the accession
number. In all other cases it will be a
unique inventory number of the owner
institution. (P) indicates that a painting is
a private loan. Details can be found in the
Further Information section. Accession
numbers preceded by 'PCF' indicate that
the collection did not have an accession
number at the time of catalogue production
and therefore the number given has been
temporarily allocated by The Public
Catalogue Foundation. The ✦ symbol
indicates that the reproduction is based on
a Bridgeman Art Library transparency (go to
www.bridgemanart.com) or that Bridgeman
administers the copyright for that artist.

Facing page: de Maistre, Benjamin, Anthony, 1931–2002, *Senius* (detail), 1962, Manchester City Galleries (p. 27)

THE PAINTINGS

Central
Manchester
University
Hospitals NHS
Foundation Trust

Ashton, Stuart
Manchester Royal Eye Hospital
oil on board 97 x 110
88

Baker, Darren b.1976
Football Crowd 2009
acrylic on canvas 89 x 131
PCF25

Burscough, Lucy
Peter Mount 2012
acrylic on canvas 69 x 49
PCF46

Channon, Fergus b.1979 & **Dickinson, Richard**
Seagulls 2009
acrylic on board 152 x 122
PCF28.1

Channon, Fergus b.1979 & **Dickinson, Richard**
Seagulls 2009
acrylic on board 152 x 122
PCF28.2

D., E.
Robert Barnes' Daughter and Son 1851
oil on canvas 109 x 83
92

El-Assaad, Rached b.1945
Flowers 1996
oil on canvas 53 x 71
PCF43

El-Assaad, Rached b.1945
Poppies 1997
oil on canvas 40 x 50
PCF44

Harris, Rolf b.1930
Snow White and the Seven Dwarfs
acrylic on board 122 x 190
99

Macdonald, Charles b.1943
People on a Beach 2002
oil on canvas 34 x 44.5
PCF38

Macdonald, Charles b.1943
Boats in a Harbour
oil on canvas 60 x 50
PCF37

Macdonald, Charles b.1943
Red-Roofed Village
oil on canvas 30 x 79
PCF35

Macdonald, Charles b.1943
Village and a Rocky Shore
oil on canvas 19.5 x 24.5
PCF32

Macdonald, Charles b.1943
Village and Girl in a Red Dress
oil on canvas 24.5 x 19.5
PCF31

Macdonald, Charles b.1943
Village and Mountain
oil on canvas 18 x 24
PCF41

Macdonald, Charles b.1943
Village, Mountain and Clouds
oil on canvas 34 x 44
PCF30

Macdonald, Geoff b.1950
English Countryside
oil on canvas 24 x 44
PCF40

Macdonald, Geoff b.1950
Fife Fishing Village
oil on canvas 71 x 91
PCF33

Macdonald, Geoff b.1950
Green Door
oil on canvas 38 x 29
PCF39

Macdonald, Geoff b.1950
Island Cottages
oil on canvas 34 x 44
PCF29

Macdonald, Geoff b.1950
Tulips
oil on canvas 30 x 101
PCF36

Macdonald, Geoff b.1950
Where's the Party?
oil on canvas 25 x 25
PCF34

Nash, Martin b.1955
Icon Pictogram I 1990
acrylic on paper 93 x 54.5
PCF27

Nicholson, Alastair b.1956
M. R. I. Band 1984
oil on board 96 x 224
PCF24

Ouless, Walter William (after) 1848–1933
Philip Goldschmidt 1888
oil on canvas 125 x 100
85

R., J.
Landscape
acrylic on paper 62 x 70
PCF45

Scholes, Steven b.1951
Booth Hall
oil on board 50 x 76
96

Shiels, Charles Anthony 1947–2012
Hospitality, Haven Lane 1985
oil on canvas 98 x 158
PCF42

Tate, William 1747–1806
*Charles White (1728–1813), First Surgeon to
the Manchester Royal Infirmary (1752–1790)*
oil on canvas 124 x 99
PCF22

unknown artist
Dauntesey Hulme, Esq.
oil on canvas 60 x 50
36

unknown artist
David Little
oil on canvas 96 x 75
31

unknown artist
*Frank Renaud (d.1904), MD (1848),
Consulting Physician (1866)*
oil on canvas 101 x 76
90

unknown artist
Henry Worrall, Treasurer (1786–1792)
oil on canvas 118 x 94
PCF23

unknown artist
*James Massey, First President of the
Manchester Royal Infirmary*
oil on canvas 89 x 75
PCF19

unknown artist
*John Windsor, Esq., FRCS, Honorary
Consulting Surgeon (1822–1868)*
oil on canvas 111 x 85
87

unknown artist
Richard Thomas Smith, MRCS
oil on canvas 100 x 74
86

unknown artist
Robert Platt
oil on canvas 78 x 60
68

unknown artist
Sir Harry Platt
oil on canvas 76 x 70
69

Chetham's Library

Allen, Joseph 1769–1839
Reverend John Clowes (1743–1831)
oil on canvas 137 x 101.5
PCF10

British (English) School
Elizabeth Leigh (1736–1820)
oil on canvas 46 x 35.5
PCF23

British (English) School
John Egerton Killer (1768–1854)
oil on canvas 48 x 38
PCF20

British (English) School
Martha Taylor
oil on canvas 61 x 45.5
PCF17

British (English) School
Alexander Nowell (1507–1602) c.1650
oil on canvas 61 x 48
PCF6

British (English) School
Humphrey Chetham (1580–1653) c.1650
oil on panel 81 x 63.5
PCF14

British (English) School
*John Bradford (1510–1555), the Manchester
Martyr* c.1650
oil on canvas 58.5 x 43
PCF3

British (English) School
Robert Bolton (1572–1631) c.1650
oil on canvas 58.5 x 43
PCF4

British (English) School
William Whitaker (1548–1595) c.1650
oil on canvas 61 x 48
PCF5

British (English) School
Portrait of a Young Man Wearing a Wig
c.1771
oil on canvas 76 x 38
PCF25

British (English) School
*Reverend John Radcliffe, Chetham's Librarian
(1787–1797)* c.1790
oil on canvas 74 x 61
PCF21

British (English) School
Portrait of an Elderly Lady c.1800
oil on canvas 74 x 61
PCF21

British (English) School
Reverend William Huntington (1797–1874)
c.1850
oil on canvas 109 x 81
PCF29

Hudson, Thomas (circle of) 1701–1779
Captain John Wagstaffe 1712
oil on canvas 129 x 101.5
PCF22

Kneller, Godfrey (circle of) 1646–1723
*Joseph Addison (1672–1719), and Sir Richard
Steele (1672–1729)*
oil on canvas 104 x 152
PCF16

Krusemans (follower of)
*Silence Wagstaffe (1714–1735), as a Child,
with Her Brother*
oil on canvas 129 x 101.5
PCF15

Mercier, Philippe (circle of) 1689–1760
*Portrait of a Young Gentleman Wearing a Blue
Coat*
oil on canvas 127 x 101.5
PCF1

Pickersgill, Henry William 1782–1875
William Harrison Ainsworth (1805–1882)
oil on canvas 89 x 68.5
PCF28

Romney, George 1734–1802
*Robert Thyer (1709–1781), Chetham's
Librarian*
oil on canvas 66 x 48.5
PCF13

Sellaer, Vincent (attributed to)
c.1500–c.1589
An Allegory with Putti and Satyrs
oil on canvas 51 x 76
PCF18

unknown artist
Bosdin Leach, Mayor of Manchester
oil on canvas 110 x 90
PCF26

unknown artist
Portrait of Man with a Red and White Cravat
oil on canvas 70 x 65
PCF19

unknown artist
Reverend Francis Robert Raines
oil on canvas 112 x 86.5
PCF11

Walker, John Hanson 1844–1933
James Crossley (1800–1883)
oil on canvas 101 x 99
PCF12

Walker, John Hanson 1844–1933
Thomas Jones, Chetham's Librarian
oil on canvas 61 x 51
PCF27

Wimpenny, George Henry 1857–1939
Chetham's Kitchen 1921
oil on canvas 35.5 x 61
PCF24

Wimpenny, George Henry 1857–1939
Chetham's Reading Room
oil on canvas 35.5 x 61
PCF9

Greater Manchester County Record Office

Plaxton, T.
Donald Summerfield, HM Coroner for the City of Manchester
oil on canvas 70 x 60
GB124.GMC/11/13

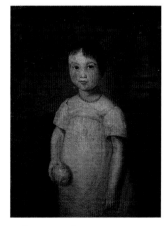

unknown artist
Portrait of an Unknown Child
oil on canvas 57 x 46
GB124.GMC/11/14

Facing page: Renoir, Pierre-Auguste, 1841–1919, *Seated Woman*, 1861–1870, Manchester City Galleries (p. 203)

unknown artist
St James, New Bury
oil on canvas 23 x 31
GB127.L250/1/9/14

Ward, A. A.
Half-Timers 1918
oil on canvas 44 x 29
GB124.GMC/11/12

Greater Manchester Police Museum & Archives

Laycock, James A.
The Moss Side Riots, 1981 1981
oil on canvas 49 x 59
PCF3

Malone, Tom active 1950–1961
Chief Superintendant Jack Wilson, Salford City Police c.1960
oil on canvas 92 x 76
PCF1

unknown artist
Police Dog 'Gunner' 1980
oil on hardboard 59 x 39
PCF2

John Rylands Library, The University of Manchester

Coventry, Gertrude Mary 1886–1964
Portrait of an Unknown Man
oil on canvas 36 x 30
PCF3

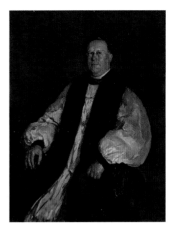

Dugdale, Thomas Cantrell 1880–1952
Archbishop Temple (1881–1944)
oil on canvas 100 x 80 (E)
PCF1

Dunnington, Alfred 1860–1928
The Opening of the Manchester Ship Canal
1894
oil on canvas 26.5 x 22
PCF10

Dunnington, Alfred 1860–1928
The Opening of the Manchester Ship Canal
1894
oil on canvas 26.5 x 22
PCF9

Nowell, Arthur Trevethin 1862–1940
*Arthur Samuel Peake (1865–1929), Chair of
Biblical Exegesis (1904–1929)*
oil on canvas 140 x 110
PCF4

Thompson, Jacob 1806–1879
George John (1758–1834), 2nd Earl Spencer
oil on canvas 44 x 34
PCF8

unknown artist
*'The Grafton Portrait' (Portrait of an
Unknown Man)* 1588
oil on oak panel 44.5 x 38.5
PCF7

unknown artist
George John (1758–1834), 2nd Earl Spencer
oil on canvas 220 x 140 (E)
PCF6

unknown artist
John Rylands
oil on canvas 220 x 140
PCF5

unknown artist
Portrait of an Unknown Scholar in Academic Costume
oil on canvas 120 x 100
PCF2

Manchester City Galleries

Manchester Art Gallery is internationally famous for its outstanding Victorian paintings, particularly works by the Pre-Raphaelites and their associates, but its collection is, in fact, very diverse.

The origins of the collection date back to the Royal Manchester Institution for the Promotion of Literature, Art and Science, (RMI), founded in 1823. The RMI's activities included annual exhibitions of modern art from which purchases were often made, one of the first being Northcote's *Othello, the Moor of Venice*, a portrait of the black actor, Ira Aldridge.

In 1882, the RMI's building and collections were transferred to Manchester Corporation, thus creating the city's first municipal art gallery. One of the conditions of this agreement was that the City should spend £2,000 per annum on purchases of works of art for 20 years. The Art Gallery Committee bought enthusiastically, especially from the Royal Academy exhibitions in London, so that by the end of the century an impressive collection of contemporary art had been accumulated, including a number of well-known paintings: *Work* by Ford Madox Brown, *The Hireling Shepherd* by William Holman Hunt and *Autumn Leaves* by John Everett Millais.

In 1914 Lawrence Haward was appointed the Galleries' first Director and remained in office until 1945. Haward's acquisition of art from both World Wars created one of the most important war art collections outside London. During his directorship, the representation of French art increased with work by artists such as Henri Fantin-Latour, Eugène Louis Boudin, Pissarro and Gauguin. The collection also benefitted from several major gifts and bequests from philanthropic collectors, some of whose wealth derived form the local textile industry and related trade. Notably, in 1917, James T. Blair, a cotton exporter, bequeathed around 200 works of art in the hope that this would inspire others to give. In 1925, the Bradford collector, Charles Rutherston, donated his extensive collection of modern art in order to establish a unique loan service for art colleges in the North West and Yorkshire.

Since 1945, the Galleries have continued to acquire twentieth-century and contemporary art for example, paintings by Fernand Léger, Ben Nicolson, L. S. Lowry, Francis Bacon, Max Ernst, Lucien Freud, David Hockney and Bridget Riley. The holdings of pre-nineteenth-century British art have also been strengthened with the purchase of Stubbs' masterpiece, *Cheetah and Stag with Two Indians*, as well as paintings by, amongst others, Gower, Lely, Gainsborough and Reynolds.

In 1979, the small European Old Masters collection was transformed by the bequest of Mr and Mrs Edgar Assheton Bennett of almost a hundred paintings, mainly by seventeenth-century Dutch and Flemish artists, including Terborch, Ochtervelt, Ruisdael, and Teniers II. The European collection was further developed during Sir Timothy Clifford's directorship by the acquisition of *The Crucifixion* by the school of Duccio and paintings by Bellotto, Bloemaert, Claude and Canaletto.

Today the collection includes some 2,000 oil paintings, plus related studies and archival material. It continues to be enriched by generous gifts and bequests and there is also a renewed focus on collecting contemporary art that will ensure the collection remains dynamic and relevant to modern life.

Ruth Shrigley, Principal Curator: Collections, Manchester City Galleries

Adams, Norman 1927–2005
Angels around the Cross 1961
oil on canvas 172.5 x 152.5
1964.189

Adeney, William Bernard 1878–1966
The Window
oil on canvas 73.4 x 54.2
1925.319

Adin, Charles Waldo 1854–1930
The Verandah 1874–1924
oil on canvas 43.1 x 53.5
1924.8

Adler, Jankel 1895–1949
Composition 1925–1949
oil & sand on canvas 99.3 x 87
1960.215

Adnams, Marion Elizabeth 1898–1995
The Living Tree 1939
oil on panel 61 x 43
1939.207

Adnams, Marion Elizabeth 1898–1995
L'infante égarée 1944
oil on panel 53.5 x 43.3
1944.92

Adshead, Mary 1904–1995
The Picnic 1924
tempera on canvas 75.3 x 100.3
1930.24

Aken, Joseph van c.1699–1749
A Tea Party 1719–1721
oil on canvas 37.4 x 45.7
1979.537

Aldridge, John Arthur Malcolm 1905–1983
River Scene 1915–1946
oil on panel 45 x 53.5
1946.79

Aldridge, John Arthur Malcolm 1905–1983
The Grove Farmyard 1939
oil on canvas 55.8 x 91.3
1940.192

Allan, Robert Weir 1851–1942
Fresh from the Sea 1899
oil on canvas 123 x 182.9
1900.8

Allan, Ronald 1900–1966
Sewing 1929
oil on hessian 46 x 35.6
1930.162

Allan, Ronald 1900–1966
K. Russell Brady 1933
oil on canvas 89.3 x 76.3
1933.13

Allen, Joseph 1769–1839
Peter Clare 1790–1839
oil on canvas 76.7 x 64.6
1927.41

Allen, Joseph 1769–1839
Saint Francis at Devotion 1790–1839
oil on canvas 92 x 71.7
1927.5

Allen, Joseph 1769–1839
Dr Charles White (1728–1813) 1809
oil on canvas 76.2 x 63.2
1920.522

Allen, Joseph 1769–1839
Samuel Ashton of Middleton c.1810–1820
oil on canvas 76.6 x 63.5
1964.275

Allen, Joseph 1769–1839
John Pooley 1820–1824
oil on canvas 76 x 63
1962.17

Allen, Joseph 1769–1839
Hannah Hatfield 1827–1839
oil on canvas 76.5 x 63.9
1957.408

Allen, Joseph 1769–1839
Thomas Hatfield 1827–1839
oil on canvas 76.3 x 63.8
1957.409

Allinson, Adrian Paul 1890–1959
November Fair in Brienz 1924–1936
oil on canvas 69 x 89.4
1937.678

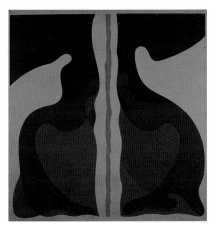

Allinson, Adrian Paul 1890–1959
Farewell to Mallorca 1935
oil on canvas 107.1 x 163.4
1936.132

Allinson, Adrian Paul 1890–1959
Cotswold Autumn
oil on plywood 40.7 x 61
1936.266

Allsopp, Judith b.1943
Number Eight 1967
acrylic on canvas 127 x 121.8
1968.3

Alma-Tadema, Laura Theresa Epps
1852–1909
Sweet Industry 1904
oil on canvas 36 x 35.6
1904.13

Alma-Tadema, Lawrence 1836–1912
A Roman Flower Market 1868
oil on panel 42 x 58
1934.417

Alma-Tadema, Lawrence 1836–1912
Etruscan Vase Painters 1871
oil on panel 42.9 x 28
1980.233

Alma-Tadema, Lawrence 1836–1912
Silver Favourites c.1903
oil on panel 69.1 x 42.2
1917.235

Annan, Dorothy 1908–1983
Christmas, 1944 1944
oil on paper 75.8 x 63.9
1945.271

Ansaldo, Giovanni Andrea 1584–1638
Allegory of the Arts 1590s–1638
oil on canvas 134 x 75
1964.285

Facing page: Dunbar, Evelyn Mary, 1906–1960, *A 1944 Pastoral: Land Girls Pruning at East Malling*,
Manchester City Galleries (p. 44)

Ansdell, Richard 1815–1885
The Chase 1847
oil on canvas 166.5 x 290.5
1882.6

Anthony, Henry Mark 1817–1886
The Village Church 1842
oil on canvas 50.9 x 76.1
1904.12

Archer, James 1823–1904
La mort d'Arthur 1860
oil on panel 43.2 x 50.9
1952.252

Archer, James 1823–1904
Thomas de Quincey (1785–1859) 1903
oil on canvas 102.7 x 86.5
1904.3

Arentsz., Arent 1585/1586–1635
*River Scene with Fishermen in a Rowing Boat
in the Foreground*
oil on panel 28.7 x 58.8
1979.439

Arentsz., Arent 1585/1586–1635
Winter Scene with Numerous Figures on the Ice
oil on panel 25.7 x 50.8
1979.44

Arif Quadri, Saleem b.1949
Carpet of Contemplation
oil on canvas 116 x 303
1993.1

Armstrong, John 1893–1973
September, 1940 1941
oil on panel 47.6 x 76.2
1947.426 ✾

Armstrong, John 1893–1973
Black Pyramids 1942
tempera on hardboard 26.6 x 37.9
1943.7 ✾

Armstrong, Thomas 1832–1911
Manchester and Salford Children 1861
oil on canvas 76 x 61.6
1985.16

Astley, John (attributed to) 1724–1787
Thomas Carill Worsley of Platt 1765–1770
oil on canvas 125 x 97.6
1989.177

Atkinson, Amy B. 1859–1916
Bubbles 1907
oil on canvas 69.9 x 56.2
1907.3

Aumonier, James 1832–1911
The Silver Lining of the Cloud 1890
oil on canvas 105.4 x 181.3
1890.61

Aumonier, James 1832–1911
When the Tide is Out 1895
oil on canvas 108 x 154.2
1895.3

Aumonier, James 1832–1911
Landscape with Sheep
oil on canvas 57.3 x 44.7
1939.21

Aved, Jacques-André-Joseph 1702–1766
A Lady with Embroidery 1720–1766
oil on canvas 127.5 x 101.9
1904.1

Avercamp, Barent Petersz. 1612/1613–1679
River Scene with Fishermen Drawing Nets
1650
oil on panel 33.4 x 52.4
1979.441

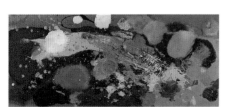

Ayres, Gillian b.1930
Mushroom 1958
oil on hardboard 50.8 x 122.1
1973.161

Ayrton, Michael 1921–1975
Dressing of the Vine c.1940
oil & acrylic on canvas 73.8 x 84.1
2003.167

Ayrton, Michael 1921–1975
The Shepherds 1951
oil on canvas 76 x 101.2
1951.414

Backhuysen I, Ludolf 1630–1708
Seascape 1650–1670
oil on canvas 46.5 x 58.8
1979.443

Backhuysen I, Ludolf 1630–1708
Coast Scene early 1660s
oil on panel 44.2 x 54.5
1979.442

Bacon, Francis 1909–1992
Henrietta Moraes on a Blue Couch 1965
oil on canvas 198 x 147
1979.603

Baellieur, Cornelis de 1607–1671
Martyrdom of Saint Catherine 1627–1671
oil on panel 43.1 x 34
1931.5

Baker, Charles Henry Collins 1880–1959
The Bay 1923–1924
oil on canvas 50.8 x 76.3
1925.53

Ball, G.
Clayton Old Hall 1902
oil on board 28.6 x 45.5
1979.595

Balmford, Hurst 1871–1950
A Cornish Creek 1934–1939
oil on canvas 63.5 x 76.2
1939.149

Balston, Thomas 1883–1967
Geraniums 1937
oil on canvas 40.7 x 51
1938.489

Balston, Thomas 1883–1967
Young Hollyhocks 1938
oil on canvas 40.5 x 50.8
1950.48

Bancroft, Elias 1846–1924
Midday Cheshire 1884
oil on canvas 56 x 77.4
1921.1

Bancroft, Louisa Mary 1864–1948
Wallflowers 1927
oil on canvas 61.8 x 42.2
1928.8

Bancroft, Louisa Mary 1864–1948
Old-Fashioned Flowers 1934
oil on canvas 45.7 x 61.1
1935.7

Barber, Reginald 1851–1928
John Cassidy (RBS) 1900
oil on canvas 58.6 x 107.3
1928.83

Barker, Allen b.1937
Untitled 1973
acrylic on panel 93.4 x 76.9
1974.96

Barker, John Joseph 1824–1904
Landscape with Man and Donkey 1845–1860
oil on canvas 63.1 x 63.1
1951.393

Barker, Thomas 1769–1847
Landscape with Cattle 1790–1847
oil on canvas 48.5 x 66.1
1906.1

Barker, Thomas 1769–1847
Distant View of Malvern 1837
oil on canvas 63.3 x 75.7
1963.352

Barnard, Frederick 1846–1896
A Dress Rehearsal 1868
oil on panel 76.1 x 86.3
1936.117

Barnes, Archibald George 1887–1972
Head of a Boy 1920–1926
oil on canvas 50.8 x 40.9
1926.2

Barnett, John b.1914
Old House, Cheltenham 1956
oil on canvas 40.5 x 50.7
1956.103

Barns-Graham, Wilhelmina 1912–2004
Long Brown 1966
acrylic on hardboard 44.3 x 13.9
1967.243

Barret the younger, George c.1767–1842
The Sketcher 1787–1842
oil on panel 31 x 40.1
1920.542

Barry, Claude Francis 1883–1970
Date Palms 1922–1939
oil on board 46.8 x 57.8
1939.26

Barry, James 1741–1806
The Birth of Pandora 1791–1804
oil on canvas 279 x 520
1882.12

Bateman, James 1893–1959
Somerset Farm 1913–1959
oil on cardboard 25.5 x 35.5
1968.209

Bateman, James 1893–1959
Cottages in the Cotswold Hills 1934
oil on panel 25.3 x 35.3
1968.21

Batoni, Pompeo 1708–1787
Lord Archibald Hamilton c.1755–1765
oil on canvas 75.6 x 70.8
1984.779

Batoni, Pompeo 1708–1787
Sir Gregory Page-Turner 1768
oil on canvas 134.5 x 99.5
1976.79

Bauhof, Frederick active 19th C
A Cattle Market in Pont-Croix, Brittany
oil on canvas 107 x 153.5
1911.28

Bayes, Walter 1869–1956
Cornlands 1914
oil on canvas 26.6 x 35.8
1925.257

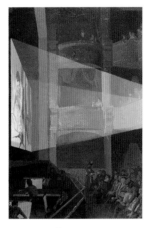

Bayes, Walter 1869–1956
Oratio Obliqua 1918
oil on canvas 91 x 61.1
1926.39

Baynes, Keith 1887–1977
Flowers in a Blue Glass Jug
oil on canvas 45.8 x 35.7
1931.43

Baynes, Keith 1887–1977
Flowers in a Jug
oil on canvas 61 x 51
1932.23

Baynes, Keith 1887–1977
Window, Florence
oil on canvas 41.2 x 33.1
1925.256

Beach, Thomas 1738–1806
Miss Elizabeth Phelips, Dressed as Diana
c.1770
oil on canvas 77 x 64.3
1949.255

Bega, Cornelis Pietersz. 1631/1632–1664
Three Peasants Seated Together 1650–1664
oil on panel 28.5 x 22.4
1979.444

Bell, Robert Anning 1863–1933
The Meeting of the Virgin and Saint Elizabeth
1910
tempera on linen 39.7 x 31.7
1910.42

Bell, Vanessa 1879–1961
Red-Hot Pokers 1921
oil on canvas 80.9 x 54
1925.321

Bell, Vanessa 1879–1961
Still Life with Flowers 1923
oil on canvas 65.7 x 55.6
1940.6

Bell, Vanessa 1879–1961
Still Life
oil on canvas 55.2 x 46.9
1928.5

Bell, Vanessa 1879–1961
The Well
oil on canvas 38.3 x 46
1946.29

Bellot, William Henry 1811–1895
Jane Bellot (1772–1811) 1836–1840
oil on canvas 76 x 64
1969.127

Bellot, William Henry 1811–1895
Frances Bellot (1820–1903) 1848–1850
oil on canvas 51 x 39.5
1969.129

Bellotto, Bernardo 1722–1780
The Fortress of Konigstein: Courtyard with the Magdalenenburg 1756–1758
oil on canvas 133.4 x 238.8
1983.806

Bellotto, Bernardo 1722–1780
The Fortress of Konigstein: Courtyard with the Brunnenhaus c.1756–1758
oil on canvas 133.9 x 238
1982.712

Benjamin, Anthony 1931–2002
Senius 1962
oil on canvas 152.4 x 157.5
1973.183

Benois, Nadia 1896–1975
Quai Anatole, France, La Ciotat 1930
oil on canvas 60.2 x 73
1930.176

Benois, Nadia 1896–1975
Kensington Gardens 1937
oil on canvas 50.8 x 58.2
1937.209

Bentley, Charles 1808–1854
Mont St Michel 1854
oil on canvas 104.3 x 149.5
1927.25

Berg, Adrian 1929–2011
Punchbowl Valley Gardens 1983–1984
oil on canvas 61.1 x 300
1991.46

Bevan, Robert Polhill 1865–1925
The Farmhouse 1917
oil on canvas 52 x 66
1929.2

Bevan, Robert Polhill 1865–1925
Horse Dealers (Sale at Ward's Repository No.1) 1918
oil on canvas 48.2 x 66
1935.157

Beyeren, Abraham van 1620/1621–1690
Fishing Boats off the Coast in a Choppy Sea
1640–1690
oil on panel 42.8 x 56.2
1979.445

Bidlingmeyer, Jules 1830–1893
Apples and a Pan 1850–1893
oil on canvas 38 x 45.7
1917.275

Bidlingmeyer, Jules 1830–1893
Flowers and Apricots
oil on canvas 36.8 x 45.1
1917.276

Birch, Samuel John Lamorna 1869–1955
December 1905
oil on canvas 114.5 x 90.2
1905.23

Birch, Samuel John Lamorna 1869–1955
Lamorna
oil on canvas 122 x 152.5
1919.21

Bishop, Henry 1868–1939
Gravesend 1913
oil on canvas 38.2 x 56.3
1937.29

Bishop, Henry 1868–1939
Sicilian Landscape 1922–1923
oil on canvas 33.8 x 40.7
1937.3

Bissill, George William 1896–1973
Hurstbourne, Tarrant
oil on canvas 63.6 x 77.3
1937.645

Bissill, George William 1896–1973
Winter Landscape
oil on canvas 56 x 76.3
1935.211

Facing page: Greenwood, Orlando, 1892–1989, *The Keeper*, 1922, Manchester City Galleries (p. 110)

Blake, William 1757–1827
Friedrich Gottlieb Klopstock (1724–1803)
1777–1827
tempera on canvas 43 x 79.8
1885.1

Blake, William 1757–1827
Demosthenes (384–322 BC) 1790–1810
tempera on canvas 42 x 105.9
1885.17

Blake, William 1757–1827
Marcus Tullius Cicero (106 BC–43 BC)
1790–1810
tempera on canvas 41.5 x 103
1885.18

Blake, William 1757–1827
Thomas Alphonso Hayley (1780–1800)
1790–1810
tempera on canvas 49 x 58.5
1885.11

Blake, William 1757–1827
Torquato Tasso (1544–1595) 1790–1810
tempera on canvas 51.1 x 91.6
1885.15

Blake, William 1757–1827
William Cowper (1731–1800) 1790–1810
tempera on canvas 55 x 91.5
1885.9

Blake, William 1757–1827
Alexander Pope (1688–1744) c.1800
tempera on canvas 48.9 x 88.1
1885.8

Blake, William 1757–1827
Alonso de Ercilla y Zúñiga (1533–1594) c.1800
tempera on canvas 41.8 x 51.7
1885.12

Blake, William 1757–1827
Dante Alighieri (c.1265–1321) c.1800
tempera on canvas 42.5 x 87.8
1885.16

Blake, William 1757–1827
*Francois Marie Arouet de Voltaire
(1694–1778)* c.1800
tempera on canvas 41.9 x 70.6
1885.13

Blake, William 1757–1827
Geoffrey Chaucer (c.1343–1400) c.1800
tempera on canvas 52.6 x 73.7
1885.4

Blake, William 1757–1827
Homer c.1800
tempera on canvas 40 x 84
1885.19

Blake, William 1757–1827
John Dryden (1631–1700) c.1800
tempera on canvas 40.3 x 80.8
1885.6

Blake, William 1757–1827
Louis vaz de Camoens (c.1524–1580) c.1800
tempera on canvas 41.5 x 56.5
1885.14

Blake, William 1757–1827
Thomas Otway (1652–1685) c.1800
tempera on canvas 40.5 x 76.2
1885.7

Blake, William 1757–1827
Edmund Spenser (c.1552–1599) c.1800–1803
tempera on canvas 42 x 84
1885.5

Blake, William 1757–1827
John Milton (1608–1674) c.1800–1803
tempera on canvas 40.1 x 90.9
1885.3

Blake, William 1757–1827
William Shakespeare (c.1564–1616)
c.1800–1803
tempera on canvas 41 x 79.5
1885.2

Blanche, Jacques-Emile 1861–1942
Thomas Hardy (1840–1928) 1906
oil on canvas 92 x 73.5
1936.134

Blanche, Jacques-Emile 1861–1942
Mrs Sickert 1908
oil on canvas 60.9 x 50
1938.44

Blanche, Jacques-Emile 1861–1942
The Coronation of George V 1911
oil on canvas 92.5 x 73.1
1936.129

Blanche, Jacques-Emile 1861–1942
Walter Richard Sickert (1860–1942) 1935
oil on canvas 80.5 x 61.5
1937.708

Blanche, Jacques-Emile 1861–1942
Miss Winny MacEwan
oil on canvas 74 x 67.1
1936.366

Bland, Emily Beatrice 1864–1951
Flowers in Sunlight 1935
oil on millboard 76.2 x 63.4
1940.142

Bland, Emily Beatrice 1864–1951
The Bouquet
oil on canvas 45.8 x 36
1920.7

Bloemaert, Abraham c.1566–1651
The Raising of Lazarus 1600–1605
oil on canvas 220 x 184
1980.32

Bloemaert, Abraham c.1566–1651
A Man with a Dog in a Landscape c.1630
oil on canvas 50.2 x 64.6
1978.261

Boccaccino, Boccaccio before 1466–1525
Madonna and Child 1473–1524
oil on panel 56.5 x 45.6
1947.132

Bodley, Josselin 1893–1974
Landscape 1941
oil on canvas 33.1 x 41
1947.191

Bohm, Max 1868–1923
Fishermen in a Stormy Sea 1898
oil on canvas 58.4 x 71.8
1912.71

Boks, Marinus 1849–1885
Landscape with a Farmhouse 1867–1885
oil on canvas 13.4 x 29.7
1979.614

Bold, John 1895–1979
A Suburban Landscape
oil on canvas 45 x 55
1980.163

Bold, John 1895–1979
An Aran Landscape (Inishmore)
oil on canvas 40.8 x 50.9
1948.243

Bold, John 1895–1979
An Aran Village
oil on canvas 48 x 62.2
1948.242

Bold, John 1895–1979
Portrait of a Cat
oil on canvas 56.1 x 46
1958.18

Bold, John 1895–1979
The Church, Inishmaan
oil on canvas 61 x 76.3
1955.2

Bomberg, David 1890–1957
Figure Composition c.1913
oil on millboard 36 x 26
1967.113

Bomberg, David 1890–1957
Outside Damascus Gate, Jerusalem 1923
oil on canvas 41 x 51
1928.29

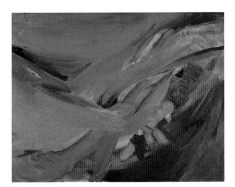

Bomberg, David 1890–1957
Trendrine in Sun, Cornwall 1947
oil on canvas 58.9 x 76.8
1967.112

Bone, Stephen 1904–1958
Hungry Hill, County Cork 1936
oil on canvas 51.1 x 61.4
1937.644

Bone, Stephen 1904–1958
Francis Dodd, RA
oil on canvas 61.3 x 51
1936.237

Bonechi, Matteo 1669–1756
A Concert of Angels c.1725–1750
oil on canvas 23.2 x 30.4
1966.182

Bonechi, Matteo 1669–1756
The Assumption of the Virgin c.1725–1750
oil on canvas 23.2 x 30.2
1966.181

Bonington, Richard Parkes 1802–1828
Pays de Caux: Twilight 1818–1828
oil on canvas 31.1 x 41
1979.529

Bonington, Richard Parkes 1802–1828
*View in Brittany: Bridge, Cottages and
Washerwomen* 1818–1828
oil on panel 31.7 x 40.9
1979.53

Bonnard, Pierre 1867–1947
Palm Trees at Le Cannet 1924
oil on canvas 50 x 48
1987.137

Bonner, Lonsdale b.1926
Rocks, North Wales 1961
oil on millboard 40.2 x 51.3
1973.164

Bonzi, Pietro Paolo c.1576–1636
Landscape with Erminia and the Shepherds
c.1620
oil on panel 37.4 x 53.4
1979.71

Booth, James William 1867–1953
Ploughing 1899
oil on canvas 61.3 x 91.5
1914.86

Booth, James William 1867–1953
The Quarry
oil on canvas 76.2 x 101.5
1905.2

Bordon, Paris (attributed to) 1500–1571
The Holy Family with Saint John the Baptist
oil on canvas 94.3 x 135.9
1971.106

Bosboom, Johannes 1817–1891
Almshouses at Het Hofje van Nieuwkoop
oil on panel 23.9 x 33.9
1979.615

Bottomley, Alfred active 1859–1863
A Little Boy
(said to be Alfred Bottomley, Junior)
oil on millboard 35.1 x 29.7
1972.209

Bottomley, Alfred active 1859–1863
A Little Girl (formerly thought to be
Henrietta Deplidge)
oil on millboard 34.6 x 28
1972.208

Bottomley, Alfred active 1859–1863
Henrietta Deplidge
oil on canvas 91.6 x 71
1972.206

Bottomley, Alfred active 1859–1863
Self Portrait
oil on card 15 x 13
1972.207

Boucher, François 1703–1770
Le galant pêcheur 1768
oil on canvas 49.5 x 64.7
1981.6

Boudin, Eugène Louis 1824–1898
Près de Quimper 1857
oil on panel 42 x 60
1995.39

Boudin, Eugène Louis 1824–1898
Trouville Harbour 1880
oil on canvas 38.4 x 54.5
1947.71

Boudin, Eugène Louis 1824–1898
Étaples 1889
oil on panel 40.5 x 55.2
1908.2

Boudin, Eugène Louis (style of) 1824–1898
A Calm
oil on panel 23.4 x 33.2
1917.225

Bough, Samuel 1822–1878
Edinburgh from Leith Roads 1854
oil on canvas 101.9 x 127.5
1937.125

Bough, Samuel 1822–1878
A Castle 1857
oil on canvas 55.3 x 85.4
1902.13

Bouguereau, William-Adolphe 1825–1905
Innocence 1898
oil on canvas 95.3 x 58
1917.229

Boydell, John 1839–1913
The Lledr Valley near Bettwys-y-Coed 1877
oil on canvas 102.5 x 153.3
1910.4

Bradley, Basil 1842–1904
A Red Squirrel Eating a Nut
oil on millboard 30.5 x 22.8
1918.434

Bradley, William 1801–1857
Sir Benjamin Heywood, Bt 1844
oil on canvas 251.2 x 159.6 (E)
1903.17

Bradley, William 1801–1857
Charles Swain (1801–1874)
oil on canvas 76.3 x 64.3
1888.7

Bradley, William 1801–1857
Eliza Faulkner
oil on canvas 75 x 62.8
1982.152

Bradley, William 1801–1857
George Fraser
oil on canvas 111.8 x 91.5
1930.15

Bradley, William 1801–1857
Isaac Faulkner
oil on canvas 75.5 x 62.8
1982.151

Bradley, William 1801–1857
Lady with a Dog
oil on canvas 77 x 64
1979.599

Bradley, William 1801–1857
Miss Eliza Calvert
oil on canvas 76 x 63.4
1947.13

Bradley, William 1801–1857
The English Belle
oil on canvas 77 x 63.7
1936.118

Bradley, William (attributed to) 1801–1857
A Lady in a Plumed Hat
oil on canvas 56.1 x 45.8
1920.553

Bradley, William (circle of) 1801–1857
Man with a Pipe 1838–1842
oil & chalk on paper 60.7 x 48.5
1982.194

Bradshaw, Brian b.1923
Reflections (Rose Hill, Bolton) 1954
oil on board 63.2 x 76
1954.1136

Bradshaw, Brian b.1923
The Bed 1956
oil on board 112 x 76.4
1957.86

Brangwyn, Frank 1867–1956
Santa Maria Della Salute 1906
oil on canvas 77.5 x 102
1920.9 🐝

Bratby, John Randall 1928–1992
Self Portrait in a Mirror 1950–1957
oil on board 122 x 121.7
1957.509 🐝

Bratby, John Randall 1928–1992
Flower Pots in a Greenhouse 1950–1968
oil on canvas 68.6 x 48.2
1968.145 🐝

Facing page: Byrne, John, b.1940, *Self Portrait*, 1986, Manchester City Galleries (p. 50)

Brekelenkam, Quiringh van b. after
1622–d.1669 or after
Interior with a Lady Choosing Fish 1664
oil on panel 49.8 x 39.4
1979.449

Brekelenkam, Quiringh van b. after
1622–d.1669 or after
A Family Seated Round a Kitchen Fire
oil on panel 41.4 x 55.7
1979.448

Brett, Dorothy Eugénie 1883–1977
Umbrellas
oil on canvas 139.5 x 140.4 (E)
1996.33

Brett, John 1831–1902
Seascape 1881
oil on canvas 17.8 x 35.6
1918.414

Brett, John 1831–1902
The Norman Archipelago (Channel Islands)
1885
oil on canvas 107.2 x 214
1885.25

Brierley, Argent 1893–1960
Bank Holiday 1930–1940
oil on canvas 60.1 x 70
1960.305

Brierley, Argent 1893–1960
Street in Stogumber (near Minehead, Somerset)
1941
oil on canvas 52.4 x 62.7
1942.57

Bright, Henry (attributed to) 1810–1873
On the River Bank
oil on panel 35 x 52.4
1905.28

British (English) School
Charles Worsley of Platt Hall, Manchester
(previously called 'Raphe Worsley of Platt
Hall') 1600–1650
oil on canvas 74 x 61
1946.127

British (English) School
William Chaderton 1602
oil on panel 78.2 x 61
1923.32

British (English) School
Portrait of a Gentleman 1633
oil on panel 78.1 x 61.3
1947.11

British (English) School
Portrait of a Lady Holding a Jewel 1633
oil on panel 78.5 x 61.3
1947.8

British (English) School
Portrait of a Young Lady with a Plumed Headdress 1633
oil on panel 78 x 60
1947.9

British (English) School
Portrait of an Old Lady in a Ruff 1633
oil on panel 76.6 x 65.1
1947.1

British (English) School
A Girl with a Pearl Headdress 1710–1720
oil on canvas 40.8 x 33
1947.56

British (English) School
Horse and Dog in a Landscape 1750–1800
oil on canvas 55 x 61
1908.39

British (English) School
Three Children in a Park c.1750
oil on canvas 91 x 103
1950.296

British (English) School
Portrait of a Lady, Called Mrs Hutchinson of Bristol 1759
oil on canvas 69.5 x 54.4
1917.182

British (English) School
Deborah Worsley of Platt 1765–1770
oil on canvas 153.2 x 125.1
1989.176

British (English) School
A Gentleman in a Green Jacket c.1768–1772
oil on canvas 60.5 x 50.2
1968.27

British (English) School
Portrait of a Lady with a High Headdress
1770–1780
oil on canvas 29.7 x 24.8
1953.114

British (English) School
Two Sisters c.1770–1780
oil on canvas 44.8 x 35.8
1936.204

British (English) School
*A Horse with Groom and Dog in Platt Fields,
Manchester* 1780–1800
oil on canvas 100 x 116
1963.296

British (English) School
Mrs Thomas Barrow 1795–1800
oil on canvas 35.5 x 27.5
1969.132

British (English) School
Thomas Barrow 1795–1800
oil on canvas 35 x 27.5
1969.131

British (English) School
Thomas Bellot (1766–1826) 1800–1810
oil on canvas 66 x 56
1969.126

British (English) School
*On the River Thames (View of St Paul's
Cathedral)* 1800–1850
oil on canvas 25.3 x 33
1917.166

British (English) School
Pope's House, Twickenham 1800–1850
oil on canvas 37.6 x 57.3
1917.181

British (English) School
River Scene with Cows and Timber Waggons
1800–1850
oil on canvas 79.5 x 100.2
1905.2

British (English) School
Venus Rising from the Sea 1800–1850
oil on canvas 68.4 x 54.9
1917.272

British (English) School
Henry Barton Marsden c.1800–1810
oil on canvas 92.3 x 79.9
1964.7

British (English) School
Mrs Henry Barton Marsden c.1800–1810
oil on canvas 92.7 x 79.9
1964.71

British (English) School
'Hunter' in a Stable c.1800–1820
oil on canvas 58.5 x 76.2
1947.97

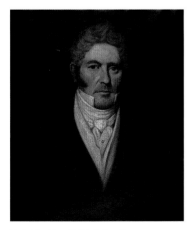

British (English) School
Abraham Bellot 1815
oil on canvas 69.5 x 57.5
1969.13

British (English) School
John Maddox with a Cat 1815–1825
oil on canvas 56 x 45.2
1964.156

British (English) School
Peter Maddox Holding a Bird 1815–1825
oil on panel 55.4 x 44
1964.155

British (English) School
Unidentified Mill Scene c.1820–1825
oil on canvas 65.5 x 91.1
1938.473

British (English) School
Portrait of a Woman Holding a Red Book 1830
oil on canvas 43.5 x 34.5
1962.242/2

British (English) School
William Henry Bellot (1811–1859) 1835–1840
oil on canvas 59.1 x 55
1969.128

British (English) School
Mrs Mary Grimshaw 1840–1850
oil on canvas 117 x 97.4
1973.5

British (English) School
Frances Lee Bellot (1820–1903) 1847
oil on canvas 27.2 x 20.8
1969.135

British (English) School
Edmund Buckley 1850–1870
oil on canvas 110.4 x 87.2
1968.241

British (English) School
Scotland Bridge, Red Bank 1878
oil on canvas 41.1 x 58.4
1936.125

British (English) School
Brenda, Countess of Wilton c.1915–1920
oil on canvas 129.4 x 98.7
1979.582

British (English) School
Boy with Hawk and Dog
oil on canvas 75.5 x 62.5
1951.392

British (English) School
Lady Gordon
(formerly attributed to John Downman)
oil on canvas 96.5 x 71.3
1917.164

British (English) School
Murray Gladstone
oil on canvas 142 x 112.3
1968.242

British (English) School
Portrait of a Lady
oil on canvas 75.2 x 62
1917.185

British (English) School
The House by the Stream
oil on canvas 35.7 x 54.2
1939.18

British (English) School
The 'Wellington Inn'
oil on canvas 59.5 x 75.5
1957.75

British (English) School
Unfinished Study of a Woman
oil on canvas 35.6 x 29.8
1976.52

Brockhurst, Gerald Leslie 1890–1978
Clytie 1920–1924
oil on panel 50.7 x 39.6
1924.21

Brodzky, Horace 1885–1969
Deserted Mills 1922
oil on canvas 47 x 59
1928.41

Bromley, William c.1818–1888
Catherine of Aragon 1866
oil on canvas 107.5 x 153.3
1910.18

Brompton, Richard c.1734–1783
John Horne Tooke (1736–1812) 1777
oil on canvas 126.5 x 102.7
1913.16

Brooker, William 1918–1983
Early Morning 1955
oil on board 40.8 x 50.9
1956.1

Brouwer, Adriaen (follower of)
1605/1606–1638
*Tavern Scene with a Large Crowd of Peasants
Drinking and Merrymaking* c.1623–1638
oil on panel 60.8 x 94.1
1979.451

Brouwer, Adriaen (style of) 1605/1606–1638
Peasants Eating Mussels
oil on panel 42.2 x 33.1
1979.45

Brown, Ford Madox 1821–1893
Frederick Henry Snow Pendleton 1837
oil on panel 16.9 x 13.3
1913.1

Brown, Ford Madox 1821–1893
*The Vicar of Wakefield: Dr Primrose and His
Daughters* 1840–1841
oil on canvas 72.6 x 58.7
1912.61

Brown, Ford Madox 1821–1893
Manfred on the Jungfrau 1841–1861
oil on canvas 140.2 x 115
1916.13

Brown, Ford Madox 1821–1893
The Prisoner of Chillon 1843
oil on canvas 53.2 x 64.9
1911.107

Brown, Ford Madox 1821–1893
Out of Town 1843–1858
oil on board 23.2 x 14.4
1947.94

Facing page: Bryce, Alexander Joshua Caleb, 1868–1940, *The Last Days of Censorship: Prisoners of War Mails*, 1919
Manchester City Galleries (p. 49)

Brown, Ford Madox 1821–1893
The Bromley Family 1844
oil on canvas 145 x 81.1
1947.142

Brown, Ford Madox 1821–1893
Wilhelmus Conquistador (The Body of Harold)
1844–1861
oil on canvas 105 x 123.1
1907.9

Brown, Ford Madox 1821–1893
Study for 'Courtier in Yellow Hood' (Sir John Froissart) 1847
oil on millboard 60.9 x 46.6
1931.21

Brown, Ford Madox 1821–1893
Two Studies of a Little Girl's Head 1847
oil on linen 35.6 x 45.8
1947.7

Brown, Ford Madox 1821–1893
William Shakespeare (c.1564–1616) 1849
oil on canvas 135 x 87.5
1900.16

Brown, Ford Madox 1821–1893
Heath Street, Hampstead (Study for Work)
1852–1856
oil on canvas 22.8 x 30.8
1924.3

Brown, Ford Madox 1821–1893
Work 1852–1865
oil on canvas 137 x 197.3
1885.1

Brown, Ford Madox 1821–1893
Stages of Cruelty 1856–1890
oil on canvas 73.3 x 59.9
1911.104

Brown, Ford Madox 1821–1893
The English Boy 1860
oil on canvas 39.6 x 33.3
1932.1

Brown, Ford Madox 1821–1893
The Traveller 1868–1884
oil on panel 31.6 x 48.6
1925.83

Brown, Ford Madox 1821–1893
Byron's Dream 1874
oil on canvas 71.5 x 54.8
1947.82

Brown, Ford Madox 1821–1893
Cromwell, Protector of the Vaudois 1877
oil on canvas 86 x 107
1901.12

Brown, Ford Madox 1821–1893
Crabtree Watching the Transit of Venus, 1639
1881–1888
tempera on panel 26.4 x 55.9
1947.87

Brown, Ford Madox 1821–1893
Madeline Scott 1883
oil on canvas 122.1 x 78.5
1932.14

Brown, Ford Madox 1821–1893
The Establishment of the Flemish Weavers in Manchester, 1363 1888
tempera on panel 49 x 79
1947.86

Brown, Ford Madox 1821–1893
Unfinished Sketch for 'John Kay, Inventor of the Fly Shuttle, 1753' 1888
tempera on panel 35.4 x 78.8
1947.81

Brown, Ford Madox 1821–1893
The Proclamation Regarding Weights and Measures, 1556 1889
tempera on panel 26.2 x 56.9
1947.85

Brown, Frederick 1851–1941
Marketing 1887
oil on canvas 137.4 x 103
1968.16

Brown, John Alfred Arnesby 1866–1955
The Drinking Pool 1895
oil on canvas 128.5 x 165.5
1895.5

Brown, Reginald Victor 1897–1940
The Wye River 1927–1931
oil on canvas 46 x 56.2
1930.145

Browning, Amy Katherine 1881–1978
Seascape 1892–1970
oil on canvas 38.4 x 45.6
1935.181

Brown-Morison, Guy Edward 1868–1949
The Harbour, Pont Aven
oil on panel 25.4 x 35.6
1979.604

Brueghel the elder, Jan (follower of)
1568–1625
*Landscape with Figures on a Path in the
Foreground and a Castle on a River* 1600–1625
oil on copper 17 x 22.9
1979.452

Brueghel the elder, Jan (follower of)
1568–1625
Landscape with Windmills
oil on copper 30 x 38
1908.34

Bryce, Alexander Joshua Caleb 1868–1940
*The Last Days of Censorship: Prisoners of War
Mails* 1919
oil on canvas 45.5 x 60.6
1920.15

Bryce, Alexander Joshua Caleb 1868–1940
*A Room in the Censor's Office: Neutral Trade
Mails* c.1919
oil on canvas 50.5 x 76
1920.135

Bunce, William Harold S. 1920–1995
Park Farm 1941–1959
oil on board 65.7 x 118.8
1959.2

Burn, Rodney Joseph 1899–1984
Snow Scene 1929–1940
oil on canvas 74 x 107
1940.307

Burne-Jones, Edward 1833–1898
Sibylla Delphica c.1886
oil on panel 152.8 x 60.3
1886.5

Burr, John 1831–1893
The Incorrigible 1879
oil on canvas 91.3 x 71.2
1910.19

Butler, Arthur Stanley George 1888–1965
The Church, Briancon 1920–1939
oil on plywood 35.9 x 30.6
1939.25

Butler, Arthur Stanley George 1888–1965
Flamingoes 1955
acrylic on canvas 61.1 x 76.4
1955.131

Butler, Elizabeth Southerden Thompson
1846–1933
Balaclava 1876
oil on canvas 103.4 x 187.5
1898.13

Butterworth, Alice active 1936–1946
Miss M. B. Moorcroft 1936
oil on canvas 55.9 x 48.3
1986.458

Byrne, John b.1940
Self Portrait 1986
oil on board 76.4 x 76.3
1987.101

Cadell, Francis Campbell Boileau 1883–1937
Interior with Figure 1914–1915
oil on canvas 63.6 x 76.5
1930.2

Cadell, Francis Campbell Boileau 1883–1937
Lady in a Black Hat (Miss Don Wauchope of Edinburgh) 1929
oil on canvas 73.6 x 63.4
1955.113

Caille, Léon Émile 1836–1907
Chiding 1854–1907
oil on panel 16.1 x 10.9
1918.422

Caille, Léon Émile 1836–1907
Prayer 1872
oil on panel 16.2 x 10.7
1918.423

Caldecott, Randolph 1846–1886
May Day
oil on millboard 14.1 x 22.9
1884.12

Caldecott, Randolph 1846–1886
The Girl I Left Behind Me
oil on canvas 20.9 x 30.3
1886.3

Calderon, Philip Hermogenes 1833–1898
Study of a Historical Scene Showing Henry VIII and His Courtiers 1868–1872
oil & gum arabic on paper 24.1 x 36
1983.128

Calderon, Philip Hermogenes 1833–1898
Margaret 1876
oil on canvas 50.9 x 46.3
1917.214

Callcott, Augustus Wall 1779–1844
View of Ghent 1779–1844
oil on canvas 74 x 104.5
1905.3

Callcott, Augustus Wall 1779–1844
Landscape with Water Mill c.1803
oil on canvas 71 x 91
1898.6

Callow, William 1812–1908
The Wartburg; The Place of Luther's Captivity in 1521 1855
oil on panel 35.5 x 30.1
1903.12

Cambier, Juliette 1879–1963
Flowers, Harmony in Rose 1938
oil on canvas 46.3 x 38.5
1938.513

Cameron, David Young 1865–1945
Dark Angers 1903
oil on canvas 68.6 x 129.4
1904.4

Cameron, David Young 1865–1945
The Hills of Arran 1903
oil on canvas 89.3 x 152.3
1913.9

Canaletto 1697–1768
The Church of San Giorgio Maggiore, Venice c.1740
oil on canvas 60.5 x 95.1
1984.3

Canaletto 1697–1768
The Church of the Redentore, Venice c.1740
oil on canvas 61 x 94.5
1984.31

Cappelle, Jan van de 1626–1679
Winter Scene with Thatched Cottages and a Frozen River Spanned by a Wooden Bridge c.1650
oil on panel 33.4 x 42.3
1979.455

Cappelle, Jan van de 1626–1679
Shipping Anchored in a Calm Sea 1650s
oil on panel 26.2 x 23.3
1979.453

Cappelle, Jan van de 1626–1679 & **Dubbels, Hendrik Jacobsz. (follower of)** 1621–1707
Shipping at Anchor off the Shore in a Calm Sea 17th C
oil on panel 53.4 x 65.9
1979.454

Carabain, Jacques François 1834–1933
Coast Scene
oil on canvas 50.1 x 77.1
1918.401

Carline, Nancy 1909–2004
VE Night 1946
oil on canvas 76.8 x 61.6
1986.1

Carline, Sydney William 1888–1929
The Walnut Tree 1928
oil on canvas 60 x 62.5
1929.43

Carline, Sydney William 1888–1929
The Eiderdown
oil on canvas 108.2 x 88.6
1929.4

Carlone, Carlo Innocenzo (attributed to)
1686–1775
A Soldier Entering the Tent of a Queen
oil on canvas 17.5 x 22
1966.18

Carmichael, John Wilson 1799–1868
Shipping on the Thames 1863
oil on canvas 61.8 x 99.5
1918.413

Caroselli, Angelo 1585–1652
Madonna and Child with the Infant Baptist
1600–1652
oil on panel 55.9 x 45.2
1931.127

Carpenter, Dora active 1870–1883
Mare and Foal
oil on canvas 26.1 x 31.1
1918.412

Carr, Thomas James 1909–1999
The Window 1924–1945
oil on canvas 60.9 x 40.4
1945.197

Facing page: Waterhouse, John William, 1849–1917, *Hylas and the Nymphs,* 1896, Manchester City Galleries (p. 257)

Caulfield, Patrick 1936–2005
Inside a Weekend Cabin 1969
oil & acrylic on canvas 274.4 x 183
1972.36

Cavaillès, Jules 1901–1977
Interior, Music Room 1919–1930s
oil on canvas 81.1 x 65
1974.91

Cave, William Wilfred 1879–1962(?)
Girl's Head (Phyllis Sachs) c.1906–1910
oil on canvas 45.7 x 30.5
1925.299

Cazin, Jean-Charles 1841–1901
The Barleyfield
oil on canvas 45.8 x 55.4
1930.29

Chaigneau, Jean Ferdinand 1830–1906
Flock of Sheep
oil on panel 23.9 x 33.1
1944.47

Chaigneau, Jean Ferdinand 1830–1906
Sheep
oil on panel 27.1 x 21.8
1917.226

Challié, Jean Laurent 1880–1943
Snow in Sunshine
oil on canvas 38.1 x 61.1
1928.122

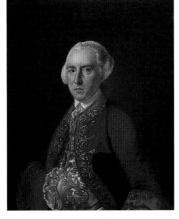

Chalmers, George c.1720–c.1791
Colonel Archibald Grant 1762
oil on canvas 75.5 x 62.5
1986.268

Chalmers, George c.1720–c.1791
Mrs Anne Grant 1762
oil on canvas 73 x 63
1986.269

Charles, James 1851–1906
Christening Sunday (South Harting, Sussex)
1887
oil on canvas 159.6 x 126.7
1908.41

Charles, James 1851–1906
The Knifegrinder 1887
oil on canvas 49.1 x 38.4
1908.42

Cheston, Evelyn 1875–1929
Creech Barrow, Dorset
oil on canvas 84.4 x 110.5
1925.95

Chettle, James Patchell 1871–1944
The Grain Warehouse 1931
oil on canvas 50.8 x 61
1932.18

Chettle, James Patchell 1871–1944
Sharpness 1934
oil on canvas 55.8 x 76.2
1935.5

Chettle, James Patchell 1871–1944
Early Morning, Poole Harbour 1937
oil on canvas 63.6 x 76.3
1938.45

Chettle, James Patchell 1871–1944
Pulteney Bridge, Bath 1938
oil on canvas 71 x 91.2
1979.605

Chettle, James Patchell 1871–1944
Bloody but Unbowed (Portland Street, Manchester) 1941
oil on canvas 45.7 x 61
1941.68

Chettle, James Patchell 1871–1944
Derbyshire Farm 1941
oil on canvas 40.7 x 51.1
1957.6

Chettle, James Patchell 1871–1944
War Memorial, Manchester 1941
oil on canvas 63.5 x 76.5
1941.67

Chowne, Gerard 1875–1917
Polyanthus 1904
oil on canvas 28 x 35.8
1917.238

Chowne, Gerard 1875–1917
Stocks 1906
oil on canvas 31.9 x 39.8
1925.271

Christopherson, John 1921–1996
Jardin de Luxembourg, Paris
oil on paper
1954.106

Chubb, Ralph Nicholas 1892–1960
A Berkshire Farm 1926
oil on canvas 51.1 x 61.3
1954.893

Citti Ferreira, Lucy b.1914
Still Life with Lamp
oil on canvas 64 x 81
1949.257

Clause, William Lionel 1887–1946
Marcel and His Sister 1923
oil on canvas 50.5 x 65.3
1928.4

Clause, William Lionel 1887–1946
Portrait of a Man's Head 1926
oil on canvas 61.3 x 51
1932.7

Clausen, George 1852–1944
Portrait of a Girl's Head 1886
oil on canvas 56.7 x 44.5
1922.4

Clausen, George 1852–1944
Portrait of a Village Woman 1904
oil on canvas 46 x 35.5
1906.104

Clausen, George 1852–1944
Winter Morning 1906
oil on canvas 64.3 x 76.8
1907.36

Clausen, George 1852–1944
The Old Reaper 1909
oil on canvas 76.7 x 63.7
1947.135

Clough, Prunella 1919–1999
The Dead Bird 1946
oil on canvas 48.3 x 34.2
1951.386

Clough, Prunella 1919–1999
Cave 1990
oil on canvas 198.5 x 214
1994.104

Clover, Chris b.1948
*Your Memory Is Your Bible, Your Imagination
Your Future* 1967
oil on hardboard 58.8 x 59.5
1968.14

Coates, George James 1869–1930
Memories 1926
oil on panel 50.4 x 37.9
1935.284

Codrington, Isabel 1874–1943
Evening 1925
oil on canvas 127 x 102
1927.3

Cole, Chisholm 1871–1902
An Anglesey Common
oil on canvas 61 x 101.2
1902.7

Cole, George 1810–1883
Showery Weather 1877
oil on canvas 50.8 x 76.5
1917.184

Cole, George Vicat 1833–1893
Springtime 1865
oil on canvas 66.1 x 101.7
1917.232

Cole, George Vicat 1833–1893
The Heart of Surrey 1874
oil on canvas 142.2 x 214.5
1895.1

Cole, John Vicat 1903–1975
In Church Street, Kensington 1936
oil on canvas 63.4 x 76.2
1936.128

Cole, Leslie 1910–1976
10 H. A. A., Zeebug, Malta 1942–1944
oil on canvas 71.5 x 91.8
1947.396

Colkett, Samuel David 1806–1863
Farmhouse with Pond
oil on panel 25.5 x 34.6
1934.437

Colles, Elizabeth Orme 1869–1943
Miss M. C. Murray 1926
oil on canvas 61.5 x 50.4
1954.1062

Collins, Cecil 1908–1989
Landscape of the Unknown God 1960
oil on hardboard 91.4 x 122
1966.2

Collins, Charles Allston 1828–1873
The Pedlar 1850
oil on canvas 101.2 x 106.7
1896.1

Collins, William 1788–1847
The Cottage Door 1825
oil on panel 25.4 x 33.1
1934.392

Collinson, James 1825–1881
Answering the Emigrant's Letter 1850
oil on panel 70.1 x 91.2
1966.179

Collinson, James 1825–1881
A Son of the Soil 1856
oil on canvas 30.5 x 25
2003.31

Colquhoun, Robert 1914–1962
Mater Dolorosa 1958
oil on canvas 122 x 91.2
1962.47 🐝

Colquhoun, Robert 1914–1962 & **MacBryde, Robert** 1913–1966
Costume for Donald (in a Palace Scene)
1948–1952
oil on paper 36.9 x 26.6
1952.4 🐝

Colquhoun, Robert 1914–1962 & **MacBryde, Robert** 1913–1966
The Goatmen (…) 1948–1952
oil on paper 37.6 x 55.7
1952.3 🐝

Colquhoun, Robert 1914–1962 & **MacBryde, Robert** 1913–1966
The Sword Dancer 1948–1952
oil on paper 56.6 x 38.5, 56.6 x 38.5
1952.5 🐝

Compard, Émile 1900–1977
Portrait of a Woman (L'étudiante) 1932
oil on canvas 72.8 x 60
1936.278

Compton, Edward Theodore 1849–1921
The Jungfrau 1890
oil on canvas 125.8 x 180.3
1927.57

Conca, Sebastiano 1680–1764
The Blessings of Good Government
oil on canvas 44.6 x 91.1
1966.297

Conca, Sebastiano 1680–1764
The Government of Pope Benedict XIV
oil on canvas 44.5 x 91
1966.296

Conder, Charles 1868–1909
Smoke and Chrysanthemum Flowers 1890
oil on canvas 54.6 x 38.4
1925.264

Conder, Charles 1868–1909
The Moulin Rouge 1890
oil on panel 25.6 x 34.1
1925.27

Conder, Charles 1868–1909
Dieppe 1895
oil on canvas 33.2 x 46.5
1925.268

Conder, Charles 1868–1909
Self Portrait c.1895–1900
oil on millboard 47.5 x 35
1925.291

Conder, Charles 1868–1909
On the Beach, Swanage 1901
oil on canvas 40.6 x 60.7
1925.278

Conder, Charles 1868–1909
The Gardener's Daughter 1902–1903
oil on canvas 49.2 x 76
1923.53

Conder, Charles 1868–1909
The Red Kimono
oil on panel 27.4 x 37.4
1932.11

Connard, Philip 1875–1958
Lady in Pink c.1900–1930
oil on canvas 56 x 45.8
1968.207

Connard, Philip 1875–1958
The River Tang 1913
oil on canvas 76.2 x 101.9
1914.62

Connard, Philip 1875–1958
British Warships at Constantinople 1914–1920
oil on canvas 50.9 x 61.1
1920.6

Constable, John 1776–1837
*View from Hampstead Heath, Looking
Towards Harrow* 1821
oil on canvas & paper 25 x 29.8
1917.176

Constable, John (after) 1776–1837
London from Hampstead Heath
oil on canvas 45 x 60.7
1939.105

Constable, John (attributed to) 1776–1837
Early Morning c.1809
oil on panel 23.8 x 30.4
1909.13

Constable, John (attributed to) 1776–1837
Cottage in a Cornfield c.1815–1817
oil on canvas 30.3 x 35.2
1917.171

Constable, John (attributed to) 1776–1837
Moonlight at Brighton 1824–1825
oil on panel 25 x 30.1
1909.12

Constable, John (follower of) 1776–1837
A Windy Day
oil on panel 15.3 x 23.4
1947.68

Constable, John (follower of) 1776–1837
Landscape with a Fisherman on a Bridge
oil on canvas 30.4 x 40.8
1917.253

Constable, John (follower of) 1776–1837
South Downs
oil on millboard 25.7 x 34.3
1931.22

Conti, Francesco 1681–1760
The Assumption of the Virgin
oil on canvas 86 x 105
1983.58

Cook, Francis Ferdinand Maurice 1907–1978
Cornish Flooded Claypit 1936
oil on board 31.5 x 40.6
1944.1

Cook, Francis Ferdinand Maurice 1907–1978
Falls of Inversnaid, Scotland 1937
oil on panel 43.2 x 33
1944.11

Cook, Francis Ferdinand Maurice 1907–1978
Trees, Richmond Park, Surrey 1938
oil on panel 43.3 x 33.1
1943.43

Cooke, Edward William 1811–1880
Venetian Lagoons – Sunset 1862
oil on canvas 19.6 x 28.2
1917.206

Cooke, Edward William 1811–1880
On the Shore at Scheveling – Low Water 1872
oil on millboard 23.2 x 31.5
1917.202

Cooper, Byron 1850–1933
Godrevy Light, Cornwall
oil on canvas 102.5 x 153.6
1905.24

Facing page: Cadell, Francis Campbell Boileau, 1883–1937, *Lady in a Black Hat (Miss Don Wauchope of Edinburgh)*, 1929, Manchester City Galleries(p. 52)

Cooper, John Albert 1894–1943
Alpine Love 1930
oil on canvas 50.7 x 60.8
1931.3

Cooper, Thomas Sidney 1803–1902
Heat Showers in August 1857
oil on panel 50 x 71
1921.16

Cooper, Thomas Sidney 1803–1902
Cattle by the River Side 1871
oil on panel 45.7 x 60.9
1934.41

Cooper, Thomas Sidney 1803–1902
Sheep on the Common 1873
oil on panel 45.5 x 61.1
1934.411

Cooper, Thomas Sidney 1803–1902
O'er the Braes of Balquhidder (Perthshire)
1896–1897
oil on canvas 121.9 x 180.3
1908.16

Cooper, Thomas Sidney 1803–1902
Cattle Crossing a Stream
oil on canvas 39.9 x 53.7
1896.9

Cooper, Thomas Sidney 1803–1902
Cattle Crossing a Stream and a Man Fishing
oil on canvas 85.5 x 131
1896.14

Copley, John 1875–1950
Men and Mountains 1934
oil on panel 71.3 x 44.8
1935.8

Copley, John 1875–1950
A Maiden
oil on canvas 42.3 x 18.9
1940.74

Copley, John 1875–1950
Chamber Music
oil on canvas 73.5 x 91.5
1938.9

Corot, Jean-Baptiste-Camille 1796–1875
Rider in the Water
oil on canvas 60 x 81.9
1947.14

Corot, Jean-Baptiste-Camille 1796–1875
Sunset: Figures under Trees
oil on canvas 33.8 x 43.8
1908.7

Corsi, Nicolas de 1882–1956
Morning Mists in Venice
oil on canvas 45.4 x 51.1
1930.79

Cortona, Pietro da (follower of) 1596–1669
The Finding of Moses
oil on canvas 34 x 54.5
1928.12

Cotman, John Sell 1782–1842
An Old House at St Albans c.1806
oil on millboard laid on panel 42 x 33.2
1981.297

Courbet, Gustave 1819–1877
Le ruisseau du puits noir
oil on panel 55.5 x 46
1955.104

Cox the elder, David 1783–1859
Boys Fishing 1849
oil on panel 22.4 x 35.7
1937.127

Cox the elder, David 1783–1859
Crossing the Ford 1849
oil on canvas 35.8 x 45.7
1917.163

Cox the elder, David 1783–1859
Landscape with Man on a Horse 1849
oil on panel 16.1 x 31.7
1947.6

Cox the elder, David 1783–1859
Crossing the Moor 1851
oil on panel 30 x 40.5
1917.167

Cox the elder, David 1783–1859
Haymaking near Conway 1852–1853
oil on canvas 47.5 x 72.8
1948.49

Cox the elder, David 1783–1859
Dudley Castle 1853
oil on canvas 30.1 x 65.5
1900.22

Cox the elder, David 1783–1859
Rhyl Sands 1853–1855
oil on canvas 45.8 x 63.5
1917.17

Cox the elder, David 1783–1859
The Gathering of the Flocks
oil on canvas 93.8 x 142
1902.1

Coxon, Raymond James 1896–1997
Henry Moore (1898–1986) 1924
oil on canvas 61.8 x 51.3
1925.593

Coxon, Raymond James 1896–1997
Landscape with Barn 1928
oil on canvas 60.9 x 50.9
1929.3

Coxon, Raymond James 1896–1997
Knitting
oil on canvas 92.2 x 73
1934.17

Coxon, Raymond James 1896–1997
Linton Village
oil on canvas 65.5 x 81.7
1946.3

Coxon, Raymond James 1896–1997
Model Resting
oil on canvas 89 x 66
1931.42

Coxon, Raymond James 1896–1997
Muker Village, Swaledale
oil on canvas 45.9 x 54.8
1946.31

Coxon, Raymond James 1896–1997
Penrhyndeudraeth
oil on canvas 73 x 92.2
1936.126

Craig-Martin, Michael b.1941
Inhale (Yellow) 2002
acrylic on canvas 243.8 x 182
2003.153

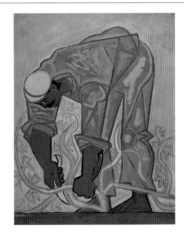

Craxton, John 1922–2009
Vine Pruner 1953
oil on paper 58.9 x 46.5
1954.1059

Crespi, Giuseppe Maria 1665–1747
A Singer with a Donkey
oil on canvas 57.7 x 45
1963.147

Creswick, Thomas 1811–1869
The Mouth of a River 1855
oil on panel 20.4 x 25.6
1917.16

Creswick, Thomas 1811–1869
The River Tees at Rokeby, Yorkshire c.1860
oil on canvas 48.2 x 66.3
1904.7

Creswick, Thomas 1811–1869
Coast Scene with Figures
oil on panel 17.8 x 28
1940.8

Creswick, Thomas 1811–1869
The Weald, Surrey
oil on canvas 101.2 x 127
1917.264

Crome, John 1768–1821
View near Norwich with Harvesters 1810–1821
oil on panel 39 x 53.8
1900.1

Crome, John 1768–1821
Woodland Scene with Sheep (Chapel Fields)
c.1810–1812
oil on canvas 64 x 76
1979.547

Crome, John 1768–1821
The Steam Packet c.1813–1817
oil on panel 51.5 x 42.4
1905.5

Crome, William Henry 1806–1873
Wooded Landscape with Windmill 1843
oil on panel 67.1 x 94.2
1914.84

Crome, William Henry 1806–1873
Wooded Landscape with Cottage
oil on panel 67.3 x 94.6
1914.83

Crowe, Eyre 1824–1910
The Dinner Hour, Wigan 1874
oil on canvas 76.3 x 107
1922.48 A

Crozier, Robert 1815–1891
The Patriot (John Sheldon) 1846
oil on canvas 91 x 71
1909.2

Culbert, Bill b.1935
Journey through Landscape, Lacoste to Bonnieux 1963
oil on wood 90.7 x 121.8
1964.48

Cundall, Charles Ernest 1890–1971
The Arena, Assisi 1922
oil on panel 35.7 x 46.1
1925.296

Cundall, Charles Ernest 1890–1971
A Chelsea Cup-Tie 1923
oil on plywood 37.7 x 46.1
1924.58

Cundall, Charles Ernest 1890–1971
Temeside, Ludlow 1923
oil on panel 37.8 x 46
1923.22

Cundall, Charles Ernest 1890–1971
Surrey Hills 1924
oil on panel 24.2 x 34.9
1947.8

Cundall, Charles Ernest 1890–1971
Pont Neuf, Paris 1925
oil on canvas 50.2 x 65.4
1926.1

Cundall, Charles Ernest 1890–1971
The Demolition of Devonshire House 1925
oil on panel 49.9 x 60.9
1931.3

Cundall, Charles Ernest 1890–1971
Quai des Grands Augustins, Paris 1927
oil on canvas 46 x 55
1927.16

Cundall, Charles Ernest 1890–1971
William Burton, MA, FCS 1932
oil on canvas 96.5 x 76.2
1964.134

Cundall, Charles Ernest 1890–1971
Liverpool from the Mersey 1938
oil on canvas 45.1 x 76.7
1939.147 🐝

Cundall, Charles Ernest 1890–1971
Avro Lancaster Bombers at Woodford 1944
oil on canvas 76.5 x 119.4
1945.268 🐝

Cundall, Charles Ernest 1890–1971
Metropolitan-Vickers Works, Trafford Park
1945
oil on canvas 71.9 x 112.4
1945.252 🐝

Cundall, Charles Ernest 1890–1971
Fête at St Cloud
oil on panel 64.7 x 51.1
1925.132 🐝

Cunningham, Vera 1897–1955
Exhuberant Flower 1954
oil on canvas 74.3 x 50.8
1968.144

Currie, Ken b.1960
On the Edge of a City 1987
oil on canvas 214 x 366
1988.19

Cuyp, Aelbert 1620–1691
River Scene with a View of Dordrecht and a
Windmill
oil on panel 19 x 32.2
1979.456

Cuyp, Aelbert (follower of) 1620–1691
Poultry with a Distant View of Dordrecht
oil on canvas 64.7 x 77.8
1908.23

Dacre, Susan Isabel 1844–1933
Lydia Becker 1860s–1910
oil on canvas 66.5 x 52.3
1920.1

Facing page: Leighton, Frederic, 1830–1896, *The Isle of Chios*, c.1867, Manchester City Galleries (p. 149)

Dacre, Susan Isabel 1844–1933
Colonel Volbert 1865–1870
oil on panel 23.7 x 21.1
1932.17

Dacre, Susan Isabel 1844–1933
Louise c.1879
oil on canvas 35.6 x 25.6
1923.6

Dacre, Susan Isabel 1844–1933
A View in Venice 1880
oil on panel 34.6 x 27
1928.5

Dacre, Susan Isabel 1844–1933
The Artist's Mother 1880–1888
oil on canvas 91.3 x 73.7
1932.16

Dacre, Susan Isabel 1844–1933
Alderman Sir Thomas Baker 1886
oil on canvas 63.9 x 49.1
1911.26

Dacre, Susan Isabel 1844–1933
Little Annie Rooney 1898
oil on canvas 71.4 x 53.6
1911.3

Dacre, Susan Isabel 1844–1933
Assisi from Perugia c.1899
oil on canvas 30.6 x 38.1
1932.13

Dacre, Susan Isabel 1844–1933
A Girl (Bertha Edgar)
oil on canvas 50.7 x 33
1931.46

Dacre, Susan Isabel 1844–1933
Assisi
oil on canvas 43.8 x 58.7
1932.12

Dacre, Susan Isabel 1844–1933
Assisi from the City Walls
oil on canvas 53.8 x 64.8
1943.67

Dacre, Susan Isabel 1844–1933
Gateway at Siena
oil on canvas 31.7 x 23.6
1942.74

Dacre, Susan Isabel 1844–1933
Italian Child
oil on panel 32.1 x 23.9
1884.15

Dacre, Susan Isabel 1844–1933
Italian Girl with Necklace
oil on canvas 38.7 x 27.5
1884.16

Dacre, Susan Isabel 1844–1933
Italian Women in Church
oil on canvas 76 x 61
1927.14

Dacre, Susan Isabel 1844–1933
Swans
oil on canvas 30.5 x 40.5
1927.55

Dacre, Susan Isabel 1844–1933
The Walls of Siena
oil on canvas 23.1 x 28
1942.73

Daddi, Bernardo (style of) c.1280–1348
Virgin and Child with the Goldfinch
tempera on panel 62 x 32.2
1959.29

Daintrey, Adrian Maurice 1902–1988
Augustus John (1878–1961)
oil on canvas 76.3 x 63.7
1928.47

Daintrey, Adrian Maurice 1902–1988
Miss Ann Knox
oil on canvas 61.2 x 51.1
1928.45

Daintrey, Adrian Maurice 1902–1988
Still Life
oil on canvas 35.7 x 45.8
1928.46

Daintrey, Adrian Maurice 1902–1988
Wallflowers
oil on canvas 45.5 x 35.5
1953.109

Dance-Holland, Nathaniel 1735–1811
Thomas Dawson, Lord Cremorne 1790–1811
oil on canvas 51.4 x 42
1905.27

Dance-Holland, Nathaniel (attributed to)
1735–1811
A Country Gentleman (Charles Burney)
c.1770
oil on canvas 91.7 x 71.3
1934.489

Dandridge, Bartholomew 1691–c.1754
The Ladies Noel c.1740
oil on canvas 118 x 156.7
1957.161

Daniels, Leonard 1909–1998
Kirkstall Forge (Steam Hammer) 1944
oil on canvas 60.9 x 76.1
1947.365

Danson, George 1799–1881
Manchester from Belle Vue 1861
oil on panel 15 x 33.8
1947.328

Darwin, Robin 1910–1974
T. A. Brocklebank 1938
oil on canvas 61 x 50.8
1938.364

Darwin, Robin 1910–1974
Watchmaker's Shop, Downe 1946
oil on canvas 63.7 x 76.2
1946.71

Daubigny, Charles-François 1817–1878
Avant et après le vote
oil on panel 43.5 x 51.6
1995.38

Daumier, Honoré 1808–1879
Le wagon de troisième classe c.1865
oil on panel 29.6 x 33.6
1995.36

Davie, Alan b.1920
Red's New Ball Game No.1 1960
oil on paper 42.2 x 53.7
1961.307

Davies, Austin 1926–2012
Forms on a Horizontal Surface
oil on hardboard 46.1 x 63.3
1960.128

Davies, James Hey 1844–1930
Young Poachers 1878–1888
oil on canvas 71.3 x 107.4
1888.1

Davies, James Hey 1844–1930
Study of an Ash Tree in Summer 1883
oil on canvas 55.2 x 39.7
1918.415/2b

Davies, James Hey 1844–1930
Study of an Ash Tree in Winter 1883
oil on canvas 55.2 x 39.2
1918.415/2a

Davies, James Hey 1844–1930
Late Autumn: Irlam Hall, near Manchester
1909
oil on canvas 50.8 x 76.5
1928.4

Davies, James Hey 1844–1930
Flint's Farm, Moss Side, Manchester
oil on canvas 20.5 x 30.5
1934.439

Davies, James Hey 1844–1930
Stiggins Lock
oil on canvas 60.8 x 50.8
1917.277

Davies, Norman Prescott 1862–1915
Love's Whispers 1896
oil on canvas 45.8 x 45.8
1917.194

Davis, Henry William Banks 1833–1914
Noonday Rest 1863
oil on canvas 28 x 50.9
1917.23

Davis, Henry William Banks 1833–1914
Afternoon on the Cliffs 1878
oil on canvas 50.9 x 76.2
1917.222

Davis, Joseph Barnard 1861–1943
A Cotswold Farm
oil on canvas 45.9 x 61.2
1943.52

Dawson, Charles Frederick b.1864
Accrington from My Window 1932
oil on canvas 51 x 61
1934.25

Dawson, Henry 1811–1878
On the Trent near Nottingham 1872
oil on canvas 81.2 x 126.7
1891.4

de Grey, Roger 1918–1995
Gasometer, Long Benton
oil on canvas 63.5 x 76.7
1955.133

De Karlowska, Stanislawa 1876–1952
Adamson Road, NW3 c.1918
oil on canvas 55.7 x 48.3
1968.91 🐝

De Karlowska, Stanislawa 1876–1952
At Woodnesborough, Kent
oil on canvas 45.9 x 37.8
1936.262 🐝

**de Maistre, Leroy Leveson Laurent
Joseph** 1894–1968
Interior 1930
oil on canvas 61.2 x 50.8
1934.52

De Wint, Peter 1784–1849
Landscape with Willow Tree 1810
oil on millboard on panel 27.5 x 43.3
1946.164

De Wint, Peter 1784–1849
View over Flat Country c.1812
oil on canvas 21.2 x 35.2
1947.67

Deane, Frederick b.1924
Edward John Stanley
oil on canvas 152 x 112
1958.196

Degas, Edgar (style of) 1834–1917
Woman in a Café 1880–1917
oil on canvas 49.7 x 35
1947.163

Derain, André 1880–1954
Head of a Girl
oil on canvas 46 x 38
1947.189

Destrée, Johannes Joseph 1827–1888
Haarlem from the Dunes 1851–1888
oil on canvas 88.5 x 113
1935.212

Detmold, Henry Edward 1854–1924
Spearing
oil on canvas 152.6 x 203.5
1927.24

Devas, Anthony 1911–1958
Mrs Creswick Atkinson 1947
oil on canvas 53.4 x 30.1
1947.401

Devas, Nicolette Macnamara 1911–1987
Juanita in the Morning 1940
oil on canvas 60.5 x 73
1940.146

Devis, Arthur 1712–1787
A Young Gentleman at a Drawing Table 1761
oil on canvas 63.5 x 50.9
1928.89

Devis, Arthur 1712–1787
Two Children and a Dog in a Park
oil on canvas 62.5 x 75.3
1947.1

Dewhurst, Wynford 1864–1941
The Blue Valley 1908
oil on canvas 81.3 x 100.3
1918.1

Dewhurst, Wynford 1864–1941
The Picnic 1908
oil on canvas 82 x 100.7
1909.29

**Dickey, Edward Montgomery
O'Rorke** 1894–1977
Monte Scalambra from San Vito Romano 1923
oil on canvas 76.7 x 102.5
1924.33

Dicksee, Frank 1853–1928
The Funeral of a Viking 1893
oil on canvas 186.4 x 305.5
1928.13

Dicksee, Frank 1853–1928
My Lady Fair 1903
oil on canvas 125.9 x 76.4
1917.192

Dodd, Francis 1874–1949
Miss Caroline Herford (Mrs Robert Blake)
1904
oil on canvas 81.4 x 66
1928.116

Dodd, Francis 1874–1949
Henry Lamb (1883–1960) 1905
oil on canvas 71.7 x 53.2
1940.639

Dodd, Francis 1874–1949
Signora Lotto 1906
oil on canvas 81.6 x 66.1
1910.38

Dodd, Francis 1874–1949
High Street, Greenwich 1908
oil on canvas 46.1 x 56
1919.4

Dodd, Francis 1874–1949
Charles Prestwich Scott (1846–1932) 1916
oil on canvas 76.2 x 63.5
1978.18

Dodd, Francis 1874–1949
Willow in Winter c.1925–1928
oil on canvas 55.7 x 68.4
1929.12

Dodson, Sarah Paxton Ball 1847–1906
Budding Elms in April, Mayfield 1901
oil on canvas 61 x 45.5
1920.2

Dods-Withers, Isobelle Ann 1876–1939
Old Houses at Espalion 1900–1910
oil on canvas 46 x 56.2
1911.53

Dou, Gerrit 1613–1675
Portrait of a Girl 1630s
oil on panel 21.2 x 17.6
1979.457

Dow, Thomas Millie 1848–1919
A Vision of Spring
oil on canvas 137.5 x 183
1902.15

Draper, Herbert James 1864–1920
Calypso's Isle c.1897
oil on canvas 84 x 147.3
1919.25

Draper, Herbert James 1864–1920
A Water Baby c.1900
oil on canvas 68.5 x 68.5
1900.12

Du Plessis, Enslin 1894–1978
Boats, La Rochelle
oil on panel 30.5 x 40.7
1933.57

Du Plessis, Enslin 1894–1978
Flower Piece
oil on canvas 60.5 x 50.9
1945.272

Dubufe, Claude Marie 1790–1864
*Mrs Hervey Francis de Montmorency and Her
Daughter Frances* 1835
oil on canvas 145.8 x 113.3
1955.123

Duccio (school of) c.1255–before 1319
The Crucifixion c.1315–1330
tempera on panel 59.7 x 38
1984.53

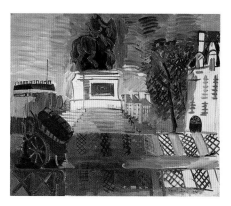

Dufy, Raoul 1877–1953
Equestrian Statue of Henri IV, Paris 1921
oil on canvas 54.2 x 65
1974.9

Facing page: Daintrey, Adrian Maurice, 1902–1988, *Augustus John (1878–1961)*, Manchester City Galleries (p. 75)

Dugdale, Thomas Cantrell 1880–1952
*Allenby's White Mice: Feeding the Pack
Donkeys: Desert Corps HQ* 1918
oil on canvas 24.7 x 34.8
1920.65

Dugdale, Thomas Cantrell 1880–1952
Night 1926
oil on canvas 63.3 x 76
1927.4

Dugdale, Thomas Cantrell 1880–1952
William Temple 1929
oil on canvas 127 x 102
1930.23

Dugdale, Thomas Cantrell 1880–1952
A. S. Mitchell 1934
oil on canvas 178.3 x 112.8
1957.11

Dugdale, Thomas Cantrell 1880–1952
Boy with Boats 1935–1941
oil on canvas 76.4 x 63.8
1941.4

Dugdale, Thomas Cantrell 1880–1952
A Boy
oil on canvas 61.5 x 51.2
1957.3

Dugdale, Thomas Cantrell 1880–1952
Cecil Rowntree
oil on canvas 112 x 86.5
1942.21

Dugdale, Thomas Cantrell 1880–1952
Posies
oil on canvas 76.7 x 63.4
1912.38

Dughet, Gaspard 1615–1675
Landscape with Shepherds c.1660
oil on canvas 46.5 x 3.2
1950.63

Dunbar, Evelyn Mary 1906–1960
The Cerebrant 1948
oil on canvas 76.5 x 66.4
2005.51

Dunbar, Evelyn Mary 1906–1960
A 1944 Pastoral: Land Girls Pruning at East Malling
oil on canvas 91.3 x 121.8
1947.393

Dunbar, Evelyn Mary 1906–1960
Potato Sorting, Berwick
oil on canvas 30.7 x 76.2
1947.363

Dunbar, Evelyn Mary 1906–1960
Sprout Picking, Monmouthshire
oil on canvas 22.8 x 23
1947.428

Dunington, Albert 1860–1941
Barton Aqueduct 1893
oil on canvas 51.6 x 76.5
1936.119

Dunlop, Ronald Ossory 1894–1973
Tom Balston (1883–1967) 1931
oil on canvas 40.5 x 30.5
1950.47

Dunlop, Ronald Ossory 1894–1973
Still Life
oil on paper 35.6 x 43.2
1946.53

Durden, James 1878–1964
Summer in Cumberland 1925
oil on canvas 101.5 x 101.5
1926.72

Dutch School
A Female Saint
oil on panel 58.9 x 47
1917.168

Dutton, John Frederick Harrison 1872–1909
Robert Henry Grenville Tatton (Young Man Seated with a Dog) 1904
oil on canvas 127 x 101.5
1984.33

Dyck, Anthony van (after) 1599–1641
Charles I (1600–1649) 1700–1800
oil on canvas 157.9 x 128.2
1902.1

Dyck, Anthony van (attributed to) 1599–1641
The Holy Family
oil on canvas 122 x 97.9
1947.137

Dyck, Anthony van (studio of) 1599–1641
Saint Sebastian
oil on canvas 195.6 x 135.4
1882.43

East, Alfred 1844/1849–1913
Autumn 1887
oil on canvas 120 x 172
1888.6

East, Alfred 1844/1849–1913
The Sleepy River Somme 1897
oil on canvas 101.9 x 153.2
1898.1

Eastlake, Charles Lock 1793–1865
Christ Blessing Little Children 1839
oil on canvas 79 x 103.2
1886.1

Edgar, James H. active 1857–1870
Thomas Grosvenor Egerton, 2nd Earl of Wilton 1857
oil on millboard 38.2 x 32.3
1973.27

Edgar, James H. active 1857–1870
The Mushroom Gatherer
oil on canvas 38.2 x 32.3
1971.4

Edwards, Arthur Sherwood 1887–1960
Mr and Mrs Robinson at St Ives 1938
oil on panel 71.2 x 71.5
1938.492

Egg, Augustus Leopold 1816–1863
A Walk on the Beach c.1855–1860
oil on panel 35.5 x 24.5
1947.446

Eisler, Georg 1928–1998
London Road Station I 1987
oil on canvas 151.8 x 132.2
1988.135

Ekels the younger, Jan 1759–1793
Interior with Man Reading 1784
oil on canvas 57.4 x 46.6
1935.286

Eldridge, Mildred E. 1909–1991
Poplars, Chirk Valley
oil on canvas 84.1 x 68.9
1939.28

Ellis, Edwin 1842–1895
The Haven under the Hill (Anglesey) 1885–1895
oil on canvas 91.3 x 183.2
1885.26

Elmslie, Essil R. 1880–1952
Emma, Covent Garden 1909
oil on canvas 76.8 x 64.2
1953.31

Emslie, Alfred Edward 1848–1918
Henry Dunckley 1889
oil on canvas 139 x 78
1905.1

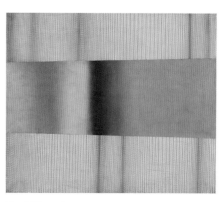

Erni, Hans b.1909
Composition No.36 1935
oil on canvas 61 x 50
1956.406

Ernst, Max 1891–1976
La ville pétrifiée (The Petrified City) 1933
oil on paper 50.5 x 60.9
1955.112

Espagnat, Georges d' 1870–1950
Woman Reading
oil on canvas 50.1 x 60.9
1908.4

Estall, William Charles 1857–1897
The Sheepfold
oil on canvas 33.3 x 51
1907.3

Etty, William 1787–1849
The Destroying Angel and Daemons of Evil Interrupting the Orgies of the Vicious and Intemperate 1822–1832
oil on canvas 101.9 x 127.8
1882.146

Etty, William 1787–1849
Self Portrait 1825
oil on canvas 66 x 56
1882.147

Etty, William 1787–1849
The Storm 1829–1830
oil on canvas 91 x 104.5
1882.4

Etty, William 1787–1849
The Warrior Arming (Godfrey de Bouillon) 1833–1834
oil on canvas 89 x 74.4
1882.145

Etty, William 1787–1849
Venus and Her Doves 1836
oil on canvas 64.9 x 61
1920.528

Etty, William 1787–1849
The Bather 'At the Doubtful Breeze Alarmed' 1839–1849
oil on canvas 53.5 x 44.5
1917.261

Etty, William 1787–1849
Andromeda and Perseus c.1840
oil on canvas 76 x 63.5
1894.4

Etty, William 1787–1849
The Honourable Mrs Caroline Norton and Her Sisters c.1847
oil on canvas 52 x 62.2
1947.74

Etty, William 1787–1849
'An Israelite Indeed'
oil on millboard 66.7 x 50.3
1947.99

Etty, William 1787–1849
Seated Male Model
oil on millboard 106.4 x 78.7
1940.3

Etty, William 1787–1849
Study of a Peacock
oil on millboard 59.5 x 82.1
1882.148

Etty, William 1787–1849
The Sirens and Ulysses
oil on canvas 297 x 442.5
1882.3

Etty, William (follower of) 1787–1849
Reclining Model
oil on panel 66 x 78
1928.117

Eurich, Richard Ernst 1903–1992
Lyme Regis 1930
oil on canvas 60.5 x 50.8
1939.3 ✳

Eurich, Richard Ernst 1903–1992
From the Old Walls, Lyme Regis 1932
oil on hardboard 57.1 x 73.6
1933.35 ✳

Eurich, Richard Ernst 1903–1992
The Blue Barge 1934
oil on canvas 86.5 x 131.2
1938.158 🐝

Eurich, Richard Ernst 1903–1992
Collier Brig, Falmouth 1936
oil on canvas 40.6 x 50.5
1936.261 🐝

Eurich, Richard Ernst 1903–1992
Flowers in a Glass 1937
oil on canvas 25 x 20
1940.713 🐝

Eurich, Richard Ernst 1903–1992
The Boats Were Machine-Gunned 1941
oil on canvas 92.3 x 117.5
1947.394 🐝

Evans, Edmund 1826–1905
Folkstone
oil on paper 10.2 x 16.5
1947.286/21a

Evans, Edmund 1826–1905
Landscape with Cottage and Farmcart
oil on paper
1947.286/43b

Evans, Edmund 1826–1905
Landscape with Cottage at Sunset
oil on paper 13.7 x 20.8
1947.286/42

Ewald, Clara 1859–1948
Lake Scene 1926
oil on board 51 x 36.2
1939.13

Faed, Thomas 1826–1900
Evangeline
oil on canvas 59.4 x 52.6
1917.256

Facing page: Rossetti, Dante Gabriel, 1828–1882, *The Bower Meadow,* 1850–1872, Manchester City Galleries (p. 210)

Faithfull, Leila 1896–1994
Rosette 1938
oil on canvas 46 x 38
1954.1053

Faithfull, Leila 1896–1994
In the Luxembourg Gardens
oil on canvas 27.1 x 22.1
1940.147

Fantin-Latour, Henri 1836–1904
Self Portrait 1867
oil on canvas 64 x 55.2
1919.8

Fantin-Latour, Henri 1836–1904
Grapes and an Apple 1870
oil on canvas 36.7 x 42.1
1920.541

Fantin-Latour, Henri 1836–1904
La source 1871
oil on canvas 42 x 33.6
1920.538

Fantin-Latour, Henri 1836–1904
L'amour vainqueur 1871–1874
oil on canvas 81 x 60
1934.527

Fantin-Latour, Henri 1836–1904
Cupid and Venus c.1871–1874
oil on canvas 37 x 32.1
1920.54

Fantin-Latour, Henri 1836–1904
The Bathers c.1871–1874
oil on canvas 46.4 x 50.3
1920.56

Fantin-Latour, Henri 1836–1904
Flowers 1872
oil on canvas 58 x 68.2
1882.11

Fantin-Latour, Henri 1836–1904
A Woodland Glade c.1872
oil on canvas 47.4 x 52.1
1920.557

Fantin-Latour, Henri 1836–1904
Flowers in a Vase 1873
oil on canvas 52.7 x 44.8
1920.559

Fantin-Latour, Henri 1836–1904
Peaches and Grapes 1874
oil on canvas 45.7 x 55.9
1920.539

Fantin-Latour, Henri 1836–1904
Still Life: Roses in a Glass Vase 1879
oil on canvas 63 x 58
1979.532

Farleigh, John F. W. C 1900–1965
Hillmorton Locks 1924
oil on canvas 50.4 x 67
1925.59

Farquharson, David 1839–1907
Summer's Eve 1895
oil on canvas 152.9 x 229.2
1895.4

Farquharson, Joseph 1846–1935
Market on the Nile c.1893
oil on canvas 43.3 x 69.1
1924.27

Farquharson, Joseph 1846–1935
When the West with Evening Glows 1901
oil on canvas 81.2 x 121.3
1934.394

Farquharson, Joseph 1846–1935
'The Sun Had Closed the Winter Day'
oil on canvas 43.3 x 33.7
1917.205

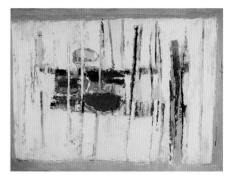

Farquharson, Joseph 1846–1935
'The Weary Waste of Snow'
oil on canvas 122 x 183
1898.8

Faulkner, Benjamin Rawlinson 1787–1849
Robert Hindley 1827
oil on canvas 76.5 x 63.8
1882.21

Feiler, Paul b.1918
Gwavas Verticals 1956
oil on hardboard 55.6 x 76.1
1956.405 🐝

Fellowes, James c.1690–c.1760
Arabelle Pennant 1735
oil on canvas 76.2 x 63
1947.134

Fergusson, John Duncan 1874–1961
Le quartier, Paris c.1906
oil on millboard 54.1 x 37.5
1966.83

Feyen, Jacques Eugène 1815–1908
On the Shore
oil on panel 16 x 22.1
1917.221

Fielding, Anthony V. C. 1787–1855
Herstmonceux Castle, Sussex c.1835
oil on panel 20.3 x 25.8
1917.153

Fielding, Anthony V. C. (attributed to)
1787–1855
Durham Cathedral
oil on canvas 71.1 x 91.4
1947.141

Fildes, Luke 1843–1927
Venetians 1885
oil on canvas 231.5 x 166.1
1885.23

Fildes, Luke 1843–1927
A Devotee c.1908
oil on canvas 63.8 x 48.5
1917.2

Fildes, Luke 1843–1927
Carina 1910
oil on canvas 63.2 x 47.9
1917.208

Finlayson, A. S. active from 1940
Multi-Spindle Drilling Machines on Aero-Engine Work 1944
oil on canvas 56.4 x 76.5
1945.6

Fisher, Mark 1841–1923
Horses by a Lock 1851–1920
oil on canvas 80 x 131.8
1920.533

Fisher, Mark 1841–1923
Fen Meadows with Cattle 1877
oil on canvas 124 x 183.6
1906.102

Fisher, Mark 1841–1923
On the Road to Newport 1895
oil on canvas 77.2 x 92.2
1942.72

Fisher, Mark 1841–1923
Pond and Willows (Widdington, Essex) c.1898
oil on canvas 86 x 119.4
1924.7

Fisher, Mark 1841–1923
Cattle
oil on canvas 62.1 x 77.8
1925.58

Fisher, Mark 1841–1923
Cattle in a Meadow
oil on canvas 35.5 x 41.4
1920.531

Fisher, Mark 1841–1923
Landscape with River and Cattle
oil on canvas 45.2 x 65.6
1947.128

Fisher, Mark 1841–1923
Under the Olives
oil on canvas 60.3 x 82.1
1947.136

Fitton, James 1899–1982
Les Girls c.1952–1954
oil on canvas 55.9 x 89.2
1953.23

Flemish (Antwerp) School
The Judgement of Solomon 1526
oil on panel 110.2 x 95.3
1960.331

Fletcher, Blandford 1858–1936
The Old Beech Tree 1910
oil on canvas 91.5 x 70.7
1988.95

Fleuss, Henry Joseph 1811–1888
Thomas Grosvenor Egerton, 2nd Earl of Wilton
1872
oil on millboard 18.9 x 13.6
1972.46

Forain, Jean Louis 1852–1931
Dancers in the Wings c.1904
oil on canvas 87.5 x 72.8
1938.366

Forbes, Elizabeth Adela Stanhope 1859–1912
Jean, Jeanne and Jeannette 1892
oil on canvas 55.6 x 45.4
1913.12

Forbes, Stanhope Alexander 1857–1947
Farmyard 1937
oil on canvas 76.5 x 61
1979.133 ✻

Forbes, Stanhope Alexander 1857–1947
The Lighthouse (Newlyn, Cornwall)
oil on canvas 228.5 x 173.2
1892.3 🐝

Forbes, Vivian 1891–1937
German Landscape 1933–1937
oil on canvas 40.6 x 34
1943.8

Foster, Myles Birket 1825–1899
The Brook 1874
oil on canvas 77.5 x 62.4
1934.4

Foster, William Gilbert 1855–1906
Whispering Eve 1897
oil on canvas 122.4 x 183.7
1916.7

Fragonard, Jean-Honoré (attributed to)
1732–1806
Tristano Martinelli (actor)
oil on canvas 45.3 x 37.5
1930.171

Francis, Mark b.1962
Release 1994
oil on canvas 186 x 217
1995.184

Francken II, Frans 1581–1642
The Seven Works of Mercy 1606–1616
oil on panel 50.2 x 89
1912.51

Francken II, Hieronymus (attributed to)
1578–1623
The Adoration of the Shepherds
oil on copper 36.1 x 28.1
1912.52

Fraser, Donald Hamilton 1929–2009
Composition
oil on paper 45.6 x 29.7
1962.48

Fraye, André 1888–1963
Old Harbour and Cathedral, Marseilles 1920
oil on canvas 65 x 81.2
1935.179

French School
Classical Landscape with a Sphinx c.1700
oil on canvas 67.6 x 84.2
1988.139

French School
Classical Landscape with an Urn c.1700
oil on canvas 49 x 65.5
1988.138

Frere, E. J. active c.1860–c.1870
Landscape 1864
oil on canvas 27 x 40
1968.212

Frère, Pierre Edouard 1819–1886
Roasting Chestnuts
oil on panel 26.9 x 21.3
1920.546

Freud, Lucian 1922–2011
Girl with Beret 1951
oil on canvas 35.5 x 25.6
1952.278

Freyse, Albert d.1652
Allegory of Virtue 1640–1649
oil on panel 65.2 x 56.6
1953.113

Frith, William Powell 1819–1909
Claude Duval 1859–1860
oil on canvas 108.8 x 153
1917.27

Frith, William Powell 1819–1909
The Squire's Boxing Lesson 1860
oil on canvas 24.3 x 40
1920.534

Frith, William Powell 1819–1909
The Derby Day 1893–1894
oil on canvas 102.3 x 234.4
1896.4

Frith, William Powell 1819–1909
Elizabeth I and Courtiers
oil on canvas 38.2 x 51.6 (E)
1920.548

Frith, William Powell 1819–1909
*Mme Jourdain Discovers Her Husband at the
Dinner Which He Gave to the Belle Marquise
and the Count Dorante*
oil on millboard 18.4 x 23.8
1920.535

Fry, Roger Eliot 1866–1934
The Church at Ramatuelle 1922
oil on canvas 96.9 x 128.9
1940.1

Fry, Roger Eliot 1866–1934
Chiswick House
oil on canvas 62.8 x 78.8
1958.192

Fry, Roger Eliot 1866–1934
Excavations at St Rémy
oil on canvas 78.3 x 98
1935.161

Gabain, Ethel Leontine 1883–1950
Miss Flora Robson as Lady Audley 1933
oil on canvas 76.3 x 63.7
1934.446

Gabain, Ethel Leontine 1883–1950
The Little Bride 1934
oil on canvas 50.7 x 40.7
1935.4

Gabain, Ethel Leontine 1883–1950
The Airman 1937
oil on canvas 50.8 x 61.2
1940.11

Gabain, Ethel Leontine 1883–1950
Sybilla
oil on canvas 35.7 x 25.3
1968.206

Gabain, Ethel Leontine 1883–1950
The Little Hat
oil on canvas 51.2 x 61.2
1950.103

Gainsborough, Thomas 1727–1788
Mrs Prudence Rix c.1756
oil on canvas 75.7 x 63.5
1950.61

Gainsborough, Thomas 1727–1788
Portrait of a Young Gentleman c.1760–1765
oil on canvas 76.5 x 63.5
1900.14

Gainsborough, Thomas 1727–1788
Sir Richard Perryn (1723–1803) 1779
oil on canvas 270 x 110.7
1981.38

Gainsborough, Thomas 1727–1788
A Peasant Girl Gathering Faggots in a Wood
1782
oil on canvas 169 x 123
1978.138

Gainsborough, Thomas 1727–1788
Landscape with Figures 1784–1785
oil on canvas 62.5 x 76.2
1950.66

Gainsborough, Thomas 1727–1788
Landscape with Sheep
oil on canvas 30.1 x 35.2
1948.48

Gardini, Theophile
Spring at Nayland, Suffolk 1938
oil on panel 40.7 x 51.1
1939.36

Facing page: Garstin, Norman 1847–1926, *The Card Players*, 1908, Manchester City Galleries (p. 102)

Garstin, Norman 1847–1926
The Card Players 1908
oil on canvas 78.1 x 92.3
1927.48

Gauffier, Louis 1761–1801
Pygmalion and Galatea 1797
oil on canvas 67 x 51.2
1979.546

Gauguin, Paul 1848–1903
Harbour Scene, Dieppe c.1881–1885
oil on canvas 60.2 x 72.3
1944.46

Gaulli, Giovanni Battista 1639–1709
Saint John the Baptist
oil on canvas 183.5 x 118.5
1968.104

Gear, William 1915–1997
Study with Blue and Orange 1951
oil on canvas 46 x 55.4
1960.118

Gere, Charles March 1869–1957
Vintage in Northern Italy 1913
tempera on canvas 37.8 x 71
1925.287

Gere, Margaret 1878–1965
Mrs Alfred Thornton 1916–1925
tempera on canvas 30 x 19
1925.279

German School
The Bath of Diana
oil on copper 23 x 28
1917.154

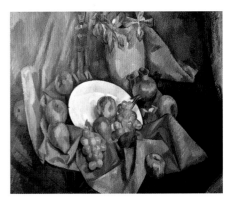

Gertler, Mark 1891–1939
Still Life 1917
oil on canvas 64 x 76.2
1928.91

Gertler, Mark 1891–1939
Fruit 1922
oil on cardboard 17.6 x 35.2
1925.267

Gertler, Mark 1891–1939
After Bathing 1924
oil on canvas 101.6 x 63.8
1924.22

Gheyn II, Jaques de 1565–1629
Master and Pupil 1620
oil on panel 58 x 69.5
1949.224

Ghirlandaio, Ridolfo (attributed to)
1483–1561
The Adoration of the Shepherds 1504–1508
oil on panel 114 x 114
1947.188

Gibbon, James active 1860–1865
William Forbes Gibbon
oil on canvas 44.5 x 34.3
1965.55

Gibbon, James active 1900–1927
William Forbes Gibbon 1900
oil on canvas 103 x 87.9
1966.268

Gibbon, James active 1900–1927
Mrs W. C. A. Gibbon 1906
oil on canvas 33 x 25.4
1965.54

Gibbon, James active 1900–1927
Edna Forbes Gibbon (1902–1974) 1908–1909
oil on canvas 17.8 x 12.7
1966.27

Gibbon, James active 1900–1927
Mrs W. C. A. Gibbon 1924
oil on canvas 49.5 x 39.4
1966.272

Gibbon, James active 1900–1927
Edna Forbes Gibbon (1902–1974) 1927
oil on canvas 38.1 x 33
1966.273

Gibbon, James active 1900–1927
William Charles Alexander Gibbon 1927
oil on canvas 38.1 x 33
1966.274

Gilbert, John 1817–1897
Don Sancho Panza, Governor of Barataria
1875
oil on canvas 30.5 x 25.6
1893.8

Gilbert, John 1817–1897
Gipsies 1882–1884
oil on canvas 52 x 64.8
1893.9

Gilbert, John 1817–1897
Breaking up the Encampment 1887–1888
oil on canvas 122 x 152.6
1893.6

Gilbert, John 1817–1897
'Onward' 1890
oil on canvas 152.8 x 122.1
1893.7

Gilbert, John 1817–1897
A Venetian Council of War 1891–1892
oil on canvas 87 x 112
1893.5

Gilchrist, Philip Thomson 1865–1956
Loch-an-Eilan 1902–1912
oil on canvas 50.8 x 91.4
1961.277

Gilchrist, Philip Thomson 1865–1956
A Forgotten Lancashire Port (Sunderland on the Lune) 1905
oil on canvas 76.3 x 132.3
1926.38

Giles, Catherina Dawson 1878–1955
Snow Scene, Étaples
oil on canvas 47.8 x 58.9
1911.105

Gill, Basil 1876–1955
Buildings by a Stream
oil on canvas 50.8 x 80
1952.53

Gill, Colin Unwin 1892–1940
Catherine 1902–1940
oil on canvas 45 x 37
1952.52

Gilman, Harold 1876–1919
Interior with Artist's Mother 1917–1918
oil on canvas 51.2 x 61.4
1931.32

Gilman, Harold 1876–1919
Portrait of a Lady (Miss Fletcher)
oil on canvas 61.5 x 51.5
1929.5

Ginesi, Edna 1902–2000
The Thames at Hammersmith 1922–1946
oil on canvas 51 x 61
1946.33

Ginesi, Edna 1902–2000
Cross Roads in the Village 1928
oil on canvas 50.8 x 61
1929.4

Ginesi, Edna 1902–2000
Grassington 1929
oil on panel 49.8 x 61
1946.34

Ginesi, Edna 1902–2000
Farm Buildings, Burnsall
oil on canvas 38.2 x 49.2
1946.32

Ginner, Charles 1878–1952
Flask Walk, Hampstead 1922
oil on canvas 61 x 45.7
1922.5

Ginner, Charles 1878–1952
Bethnal Green Allotment 1943
oil on canvas 55.9 x 76
1947.399

Ginner, Charles 1878–1952
Landscape with Farmhouses
oil on canvas 51.2 x 68.7
1929.6

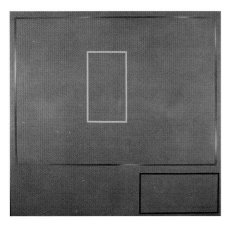

Ginsborg, Michael b.1943
Her Day at Sneaker's Creek 1967
acrylic on canvas 183.2 x 198.2
1980.388

Giordano, Luca 1634–1705
The Cave of Eternity 1685–1705
oil on canvas 69 x 84.5
1964.284

Glehn, Wilfrid Gabriel de 1870–1951
A Study 1929
oil on canvas 61.2 x 49.5
1930.174

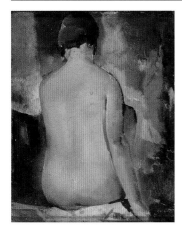

Gluckmann, Grigory 1898–1973
Female Nude 1918
oil on panel 20.7 x 16.5
1946.35

Gluckstein, Hannah 1895–1978
Lilac and Guelder Rose
oil on canvas 109.2 x 109.3
1937.732

Godward, John William 1861–1922
On the Balcony 1898
oil on canvas 50.5 x 76
1917.191

Godward, John William 1861–1922
Expectation 1900
oil on canvas 46 x 91.5
1917.243

Godward, John William 1861–1922
Nude Study
oil on canvas 95.6 x 45.5
1917.243 a

Goodall, Frederick 1822–1904
Poultry 1842
oil on millboard 25.4 x 34.9
1896.1

Goodall, Frederick 1822–1904
The Water of the Nile 1893
oil on canvas 131.5 x 305
1893.22

Gordon, John Watson 1788–1864
Sir Walter Scott (1771–1832)
oil on canvas 76.2 x 63.7
1903.1

Gordon, John Watson (after) 1788–1864
Primaticcio (1504–1570)
oil on canvas 277 x 100
1907.41

Gore, Frederick John Pym 1913–2009
Teesdale
oil on canvas 50.9 x 61.3
1938.261

Gore, Spencer 1878–1914
Richmond: Winter 1913–1914
oil on canvas 50.8 x 60.9
1928.78

Gosse, Laura Sylvia 1881–1968
Lilies and Fruit 1933
oil on canvas 61.2 x 51
1933.2

Goubau, Laureys c.1640–after 1670
A Girl at a Kitchen Window Slicing a Lemon
c.1651–1669
oil on panel 37.6 x 30.7
1979.477

Gower, George c.1540–1596
Mary Cornwallis c.1580–1585
oil on panel 117.2 x 94
1953.112

Gowing, Lawrence 1918–1991
Miss R. of Dinnington Village 1951
oil on canvas 76.1 x 63.7
1955.114

Goyen, Jan van 1596–1656
Landscape with a Cottage and a Barn 1632
oil on panel 24.7 x 34.6
1979.458

Goyen, Jan van 1596–1656
*Winter Scene with a Sledge in the Foreground
and Figures Gathering Round a Tent on the Ice*
1653
oil on panel 27.9 x 43.1
1979.459

Graham, Fergus 1900–1968
Landscape with Farm
oil on canvas 91.5 x 71.2
1931.11

Graham, Fergus 1900–1968
The Far Journey
oil on canvas 53.3 x 76.3
1935.133

Graham, Peter 1836–1921
A Spate in the Highlands 1866
oil on canvas 120 x 176.8
1901.3

Graham, Peter 1836–1921
Highland Cattle, Perthshire 1866
oil on canvas 60.9 x 91.4
1917.207

Facing page: Armstrong, John, 1893–1973, *September, 1940*, 1941, Manchester City Galleries (p. 20)

Graham, Peter 1836–1921
The Seabirds' Domain 1902
oil on canvas 76.5 x 63.5
1917.216

Graham Bell, Frank 1910–1943
The Café (Café Conte, London) 1937–1938
oil on canvas 121.9 x 91.7
1944.49

Grant, Duncan 1885–1978
Caryatid c.1912
oil & collage on canvas 140.5 x 45.6
1964.286

Grant, Duncan 1885–1978
Window, South of France 1928
oil on canvas 100 x 81.1
1930.179

Grant, Duncan 1885–1978
Boats, St Tropez
oil on canvas 63.5 x 76.2
1928.87

Grant, Duncan 1885–1978
Red Hot Pokers
oil on canvas 81.5 x 65
1925.313

Grant, Francis (attributed to) 1803–1878
Lord Wilton of the Leicestershire Hunt
1850–1878
oil on canvas 26.5 x 27
1992.44

Grant, Ian 1904–1993
Cheshire Mill 1939
oil on canvas 60.5 x 50.5
1947.4

Grant, Ian 1904–1993
Self Portrait 1939
oil on canvas 63.5 x 48.2
1940.9

Grant, Ian 1904–1993
Margo Ingham 1951
oil on canvas 91.6 x 70.7
1979.654

Greaves, Walter 1846–1930
Chelsea Regatta 1863–1868
oil on canvas 91.8 x 191.7
1922.8

Grebber, Pieter Fransz. de c.1600–c.1653
The Nativity 1634
oil on canvas 164.2 x 200.5
1926.34

Green, Dora active 1900–1926
Grapes 1908
oil on canvas 91 x 71
1926.37

Green, Madeline 1884–1947
The Future 1925
oil on canvas 92 x 61.1
1927.27

Greenwood, Orlando 1892–1989
The Keeper 1922
oil on canvas 101.5 x 86.5
1925.96

Gresty, Hugh 1899–1958
Spanish City
oil on canvas 80 x 94
1965.31

Gresty, Kenneth Harry 1928–2002
Bolton Landscape 1954
oil on hardboard 45.5 x 60.5
1955.3

Gribble, Kenneth 1925–1995
Park Parade, Ashton 1958
oil on canvas 71.3 x 91.8
1959.19

Gribbon, Charles Edward 1898–1939
Stormy Afternoon near Cannes
oil on canvas 45.1 x 64.1
1928.44

Grundy, Cuthbert Cartwright 1846–1946
Old Skelwith Bridge, Ambleside
oil on canvas 45.7 x 61
1912.46

Guardi, Francesco (attributed to) 1712–1793
An Island in the Lagoon
oil on panel 11.9 x 18.6
1979.522

Guardi, Francesco (attributed to) 1712–1793
Capriccio with a Church Seen through a Portico
oil on panel 13.9 x 10.2
1979.527

Guardi, Francesco (attributed to) 1712–1793
Lagoon Capriccio with a Church
oil on panel 6.8 x 14.3
1979.525

Guardi, Francesco (attributed to) 1712–1793
Lagoon Capriccio with a Church and a Bridge
oil on panel 6.8 x 14.3
1979.524

Guardi, Francesco (attributed to) 1712–1793
Lagoon Capriccio with a Peasant and Cattle
oil on panel 6.7 x 14.3
1979.526

Guardi, Francesco (attributed to) 1712–1793
Lagoon Capriccio with a Ruined Arch
oil on panel 6 x 14.3
1979.523

Guardi, Francesco (attributed to) 1712–1793
Piazza San Marco, Venice
oil on panel 18.2 x 32.1
1979.518

Guardi, Francesco (attributed to) 1712–1793
Storm at Sea
oil on panel 12 x 18.6
1979.521

Guardi, Francesco (attributed to) 1712–1793
The Bridge over the Brenta at Dolo (the Porta del Dolo)
oil on panel 20 x 24.7
1979.52

Guardi, Francesco (attributed to) 1712–1793
The Piazzetta, Venice
oil on panel 18.1 x 31.8
1979.519

Guercino (after) 1591–1666
The Death of Dido 1650–1666
oil on canvas 107 x 145
1981.307

Guerrieri, Giovanni Francesco (attributed to)
1589–1656
Lot and His Daughters
oil on canvas 136.3 x 99.3
1882.45

Guevara, Alvaro 1894–1951
The Hunter
oil on canvas 88.8 x 65
1939.14

Gumuchian, Margaret 1928–1996
Peel Park, Salford
oil on cardboard 50.6 x 76.1
1962.27

Guthrie, Robin 1902–1971
Late Snowfall 1932
oil on canvas 90.6 x 84.2
1938.259

Guthrie, Robin 1902–1971
Wild Wales 1941
oil on canvas 51.3 x 76.6
1968.208

Gwynne-Jones, Allan 1892–1982
Field near Ruan Minor 1919
oil on panel 25 x 35.5
1925.281

Hacker, Arthur 1858–1919
Syrinx 1892
oil on canvas 193.4 x 61.4
1892.1

Hacker, Arthur 1858–1919
Buttercup Meadow
oil on panel 26 x 35.3
1938.52

Hacker, Arthur 1858–1919
Peonies
oil on canvas 25.6 x 35.9
1921.15

Hagedorn, Karl 1889–1969
Clerkenwell Green 1933
oil on canvas 76 x 63.5
1933.18

Hagedorn, Karl 1889–1969
The Aloe Farm 1935
oil on canvas 50 x 60.9
1936.4

Hagedorn, Karl 1889–1969
Harbour Scene 1938
oil on canvas 51 x 61
1957.4

Hague, Joshua Anderson 1850–1916
June 1898
oil on canvas 127 x 192.5
1898.1

Hague, Joshua Anderson 1850–1916
Landscape in North Wales
oil on canvas 97 x 127.5
1919.26

Hague, Joshua Anderson 1850–1916
Springtime
oil on canvas 49.8 x 74.9
1885.27

Hague, Joshua Anderson 1850–1916
The Mill Pool
oil on canvas 127.3 x 95.3
1931.55

Haile, Samuel 1909–1948
Woman and Suspended Man 1939
oil on canvas 53 x 79
1968.173

Hakim-Dowek, Leslie b.1960
Flowers of the Mediterranean No.13 1989
oil & wax on wood 45.6 x 19.8
1991.68

Hakim-Dowek, Leslie b.1960
Flowers of the Mediterranean No.2 1989
oil & wax on wood 45.5 x 24.7
1991.67

Hakim-Dowek, Leslie b.1960
Vulnerables 1991
oil & wax on wood 126.5 x 95.3
1991.66

Hall, Kenneth 1913–1946
Two Figures
oil on canvas 50.7 x 40.7
1951.391

Hals, Frans (follower of) c.1581–1585–1666
A Fisher Boy
oil on panel 28.6 x 21.9
1979.460

Hammersley, James Astbury 1815–1869
*Mountains and Clouds – A Scene from the Top
of Loughrigg, Westmoreland* 1850
oil on canvas 131.1 x 183.5
1882.23

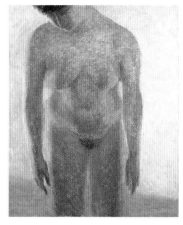

Hannot, Johannes (attributed to) 1633–1685
Still Life: Fruit and Oysters on a Table
oil on panel 33.6 x 49.8
1979.461

Hardie, Gwen b.1962
Me in Sea 1984
oil on canvas 182.8 x 152.4
1989.124

Hardy, Heywood 1842–1933
The Disputed Toll c.1875
oil on canvas 88 x 140.4
1991.58

Harlow, George Henry 1787–1819
The Sisters
oil on canvas 86 x 68
1917.186

Harmar, Fairlie 1876–1945
Sarson Farm, Early Spring
oil on canvas 63.9 x 77
1923.34

Harmar, Fairlie 1876–1945
St Giles, Oxford
oil on canvas 51 x 61.1
1957.5

Harpignies, Henri-Joseph 1819–1916
The Winding River 1882
oil on canvas 32.4 x 51.5
1920.132

Harpignies, Henri-Joseph 1819–1916
The Castle of Clisson 1895
oil on canvas 106.7 x 117.5
1930.82

Harris, Albert
Barton Old Aqueduct and Bridge 1894
oil on canvas 50.3 x 75.3
1963.189

Haughton, Benjamin 1865–1924
A Summer Morning 1902
oil on canvas 41.9 x 45.6
1927.31

Hawkins, Dennis 1925–2001
Bus Pier, Putney 1950
oil on board 54.8 x 73.6
1968.92

Hawthorne, Elwin 1905–1954
Church near Blackheath
oil on canvas 62.2 x 75
1939.1

Hayden, Henri 1883–1970
Pot a Tabac, Fond Bleu 1965
acrylic on paper 51.9 x 63.5
1995.57

Hayes, Frederick William 1848–1918
Cnicht, Caernarvonshire 1880
oil on millboard 59 x 42.9
1921.18

Hayes, Frederick William 1848–1918
On the Glaslyn River 1883
oil on paper 44 x 59.5
1921.17

Hayes, George c.1823–1895
*The Visit of Queen Victoria and Prince Albert
to Manchester in 1851* 1876
oil on canvas 43.2 x 60
1957.171

Haynes-Williams, John 1836–1908
Spanish Dancer 1873
oil on canvas 70.5 x 91
1918.1154

Heck, Claes Jacobsz. van der (studio of)
1575/1581–1652
Egmond-ann-Zee 1600–1652
oil on panel 27.5 x 70.6
1979.515

Heemskerck, Maerten van 1498–1574
Margaretha Banken 1540–1542
oil on panel 89.5 x 72.3
1958.55

Heeremans, Thomas c.1640–1697
*River Scene with a Ruined Tower on the Bank
and Figures in Rowing Boats* 1664–1697
oil on panel 20.5 x 26.7
1979.462

Hemy, Charles Napier 1841–1917
God's Houses, Maestricht 1870
oil on canvas 59 x 89.3
1919.11

Hemy, Charles Napier 1841–1917
Old Putney Bridge 1882
oil on canvas 126 x 171.8
1883.28

Henderson, Keith 1883–1982
Loading Gantry for Pluto 1945
oil on canvas 76.6 x 101.6
1945.232

Henderson, Keith 1883–1982
A Garden in Cyprus
oil on cardboard 66 x 55.8
1971.1

Henderson, Keith 1883–1982
Cock of the North
oil on canvas 102.1 x 152.5
1932.53

Henderson, Keith 1883–1982
Gas Practice in a Hangar
oil on canvas 101.4 x 152.3
1947.391

Henriques, Ethel Quixano 1868–1936
February 1929
oil on canvas 61.5 x 51.3
1930.17

Facing page: Flemish (Antwerp) School, *The Judgement of Solomon*, 1526, Manchester City Galleries (p. 96)

Henriques, Ethel Quixano 1868–1936
Field Flowers
oil on panel 35 x 25.7
1928.7

Henry, George 1858–1943
Landscape with Rainbow
oil on canvas 71.6 x 91.9
1945.256

Henry, James Levin 1855–1929
Wensleydale 1905
oil on canvas 61.3 x 72.3
1908.28

Hepworth, Barbara 1903–1975
Theatre Group No.3 1947
oil & crayon on board 34.5 x 49.5
1948.135

Herkomer, Hubert von 1849–1914
Hard Times 1885
oil on canvas 86.5 x 112
1885.24

Herman, Josef 1911–2000
Man Kneeling
oil (?) on cardboard 22.5 x 17.2
1968.141

Herman, Josef 1911–2000
Potato Diggers
oil on board 38 x 54.3
1954.1061

Herring I, John Frederick 1795–1865
The Ascot Cup 1829
oil on canvas 20.6 x 30.2
1979.531

Herring I, John Frederick 1795–1865
Seed Time 1856
oil on canvas 66.7 x 112.4
1947.139

Herring I, John Frederick 1795–1865
Ducks by a Stream 1863
oil on panel 25.1 x 30.4
1934.404

Hervier, Louis Adolphe 1818–1879
A Farmyard 1874
oil on canvas 47.1 x 39.4
1919.5

Hewit, Forrest 1870–1956
Whangpoo River, Shanghai 1937
oil on canvas 71 x 91.4
1938.46

Hewit, Forrest 1870–1956
Beech Trees in the New Forest
oil on canvas 61.3 x 51
1930.177

Hewit, Forrest 1870–1956
Boats at Menaggio
oil on canvas 50.8 x 61.5
1930.178

Hewland, Elsie Dalton 1901–1979
Assembling a Hawker Hurricane 1940–1947
oil on canvas 45.7 x 60.9
1947.402

Heyden, Jan van der 1637–1712
*A Street in Cologne with the Unfinished
Cathedral in the Centre* 1694
oil on panel 31.7 x 40.5
1979.463

Hicks, George Elgar 1824–1914
Mother and Child 1873
oil on canvas 91.5 x 71.3
1920.526

Highmore, Joseph 1692–1780
John Sidney, 6th Earl of Leicester 1728
oil on canvas 76.2 x 63.5
1963.268

Highmore, Joseph 1692–1780
Miss Taylor 1760–1780
oil on canvas 60.5 x 50.5
1947.83

Hilder, Richard H. 1813–1852
Okehampton, Devon
oil on panel 53.3 x 41.9
1948.5

Hill, James Stevens 1854–1921
The Thames at Southwark
oil on canvas 93.3 x 140.2
1905.4

Hillier, Tristram Paul 1905–1983
Le Havre de Grace 1939
oil on canvas 70.4 x 84.2
1946.76

Hillier, Tristram Paul 1905–1983
The War in Somerset 1943
oil on panel 25.5 x 40.6
1943.69

Hilton, Arthur Cyril 1897–1960
Torsos in a Landscape 1945
oil on pulpboard 60.6 x 50.5
1947.878

Hilton, Roger 1911–1975
Untitled 1966
oil & chalk on wood 34 x 85.5
1967.242

Hilton II, William 1786–1839
Phaeton c.1820
oil on canvas 63.5 x 76.2
1882.18

Hitchens, Ivon 1893–1979
Spring Woodland 1910–1945
oil on canvas 49.8 x 63.7
1977.84

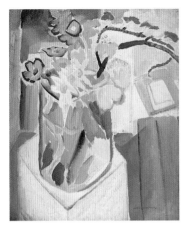

Hitchens, Ivon 1893–1979
Flowers in a Vase 1934–1936
oil on strawboard on canvas 60.7 x 50.4
1944.94

Hitchens, Ivon 1893–1979
Lavington Common 1938
oil on canvas 50.9 x 76.2
1940.145

Hoare, William (attributed to) 1707–1792
Frances Rix 1735–1737
oil on canvas 76.3 x 64.2
1950.62

Hobbema, Meindert (style of) 1638–1709
*Figures Halted at the Outskirts of a Wood, a
Pool at the Right*
oil on panel 46.8 x 63.1
1979.464

Hockney, David b.1937
Peter.C 1961
oil on canvas 111.7 x 40.6
1985.22

Hodges, William 1744–1797
View of Calcutta 1789–1791
oil on canvas 62.9 x 94.8
1949.104

Hodgkin, Howard b.1932
The Hopes at Home 1973–1977
oil on plywood 91.3 x 106.7
1978.71

Hodgkins, Frances 1869–1947
Cheviot Farm 1938–1940
oil on canvas 65.2 x 81
1947.445

Hodgson, Louisa 1905–1980
In Search of Peace 1935–1936
tempera on panel 91.4 x 213.5
1936.253

Hogarth, William 1697–1764
The Pool of Bethesda 1734–1736
oil on canvas 62 x 74.5
1955.126

Hogarth, William 1697–1764
Portrait of a Gentleman 1739
oil on canvas 76.4 x 69.9
1928.119

Hoggatt, William 1879–1961
Cregneish 1933
oil on canvas 51 x 61.1
1937.4

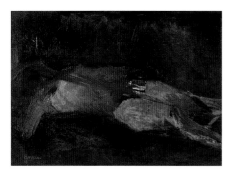

Holden, Cliff b.1919
Reclining Form 1 1948
oil on canvas 62 x 91
1963.26

Holland, James 1799–1870
Lisbon from Porto Brandas 1845
oil on millboard 26.6 x 33.7
1906.3

Holland, James 1799–1870
Venice 1845–1855
oil on canvas 57.5 x 101.1
1917.155

Holland, James 1799–1870
Herne Bay, Kent 1855
oil on millboard 19.6 x 36.6
1917.157

Holmes, Charles John 1868–1936
The Mythen, Switzerland 1903
oil on canvas 45.8 x 81.2
1925.3

Holmes, Charles John 1868–1936
Biasca 1908
oil on canvas 45.7 x 81.6
1909.22

Holmes, Charles John 1868–1936
Keswick Mountains 1921
oil on canvas 46 x 81.7
1928.2

Holt, Edwin Frederick 1830–1912
Clayton Hall 1897
oil on canvas 40.8 x 51
1972.84

Hondecoeter, Melchior de (style of)
1636–1695
Domestic Fowls and a Man
oil on canvas 120 x 188.5
1910.41

Hone I, Nathaniel 1718–1784
Self Portrait 1778
oil on canvas 75 x 62.6
1928.75

Hooch, Pieter de 1629–1684
*Interior with a Gentleman and Two Ladies
Conversing* 1661–1684
oil on canvas 70 x 61.8
1979.465

Hooch, Pieter de (follower of) 1629–1684
Interior with a Lady Seated, a Dog on Her Lap
1647–1684
oil on canvas 35.5 x 28.3
1979.466

Hoogstraten, Samuel van 1627–1678
A Young Man Reaching for His Cap
oil on canvas 114.1 x 108.2
1973.29

Hook, James Clarke 1819–1907
The Defeat of Shylock 1850
oil on panel 80 x 100.3
1896.11

Hook, James Clarke 1819–1907
From under the Sea 1864
oil on canvas 108.2 x 82.6
1891.8

Hook, James Clarke 1819–1907
Crabbers 1876
oil on canvas 77.2 x 132.4
1904.6

Hooper, John Horace 1851–1906
Early Morning Scene in Surrey 1877–1899
oil on canvas 101.3 x 152.4
1930.146

Hornel, Edward Atkinson 1864–1933
Tom-Tom Players, Ceylon 1908
oil on canvas 122.1 x 152.9
1908.3

Horsley, John Callcott 1817–1903
Coming Down to Dinner 1876
oil on canvas 124.1 x 163
1905.22

Houbraken, Arnold 1660–1719
Susannah and the Elders
oil on copper 36.5 x 27.3
1931.128

How, Julia Beatrice 1867–1932
L'ombrelle bleu
oil & charcoal on canvas 46.1 x 38.4
1977.55

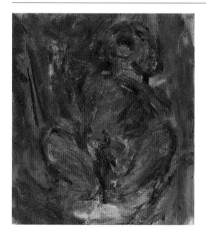

Howard, Ghislaine b.1953
Newly Born Babe 1993
oil on canvas 51 x 43
1993.141

Hoyland, Henry George 1895–1948
Interval 1938
oil & pencil on canvas 40.5 x 50.6
1939.206

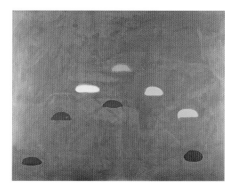

Hoyland, John 1934–2011
14.6.64 1964
acrylic resin on canvas 213.3 x 274.4
1964.287

Facing page: Watts, George Frederic, 1817–1904, *Paolo and Francesca*, 1870, Manchester City Galleries (p. 258)

Hudson, Thomas 1701–1779
John Sharp, Archdeacon of Durham 1757
oil on canvas 124.2 x 100.7
1901.8

Hughes, Arthur 1832–1915
Ophelia 1852
oil on canvas 68.7 x 123.8
1955.105

Hughes, Malcolm Edward 1920–1997
Performers 1950
oil on canvas 40.6 x 51
1950.295

Hughes-Stanton, Herbert Edwin Pelham
1870–1937
Mons 1918
oil on canvas 102 x 127.1
1919.29

Hunt, William Holman 1827–1910
The Hireling Shepherd 1851
oil on canvas 76.4 x 109.5
1896.29

Hunt, William Holman 1827–1910
The Light of the World 1851–1856
oil on canvas 49.8 x 26.1
1912.53

Hunt, William Holman 1827–1910
The Scapegoat 1854–1855
oil on canvas 33.7 x 45.9
1906.2

Hunt, William Holman 1827–1910
The Lantern-Maker's Courtship c.1854–1860
oil on panel 29.4 x 18.8
1917.266

Hunt, William Holman 1827–1910
The Shadow of Death 1870–1873
oil on canvas 214.2 x 168.2
1883.21

Hunt, William Holman 1827–1910
Study of a Head 1884
oil on panel 33.5 x 30.7
1920.6

Hunt, William Holman 1827–1910
The Lady of Shalott c.1886–1905
oil on panel 44.4 x 34.1
1934.401

Hunter, Colin 1841–1904
The Herring Market at Sea (on Loch Fyne, Argyll) 1884
oil on canvas 108.3 x 183.5
1884.1

Hunter, George Leslie 1879–1931
Still Life
oil on canvas 56.1 x 45.8
1936.133

Hunter, Robert c.1715/1720–c.1803
Mrs Margaret Bolton 1756
oil on canvas 90.5 x 78
1986.266

Hunter, Robert c.1715/1720–c.1803
Theophilus Bolton 1765
oil on canvas 90.5 x 77.8
1986.265

Hunter, Robert c.1715/1720–c.1803
Mrs Anna Maria Neynoe
oil on canvas 96 x 86
1986.27

Hunter, Robert c.1715/1720–c.1803
Mrs Laetitia Christina Sheridan
oil on canvas 73 x 62.5
1986.271

Hurt, Louis Bosworth 1856–1929
Scotch Cattle and Mist 1896
oil on canvas 61.5 x 102
1917.236

Huysum, Jan van 1682–1749
Still Life: Flowers and Fruit 1690s–1720s
oil on panel 88.9 x 67.5
1979.467

Ibbetson, Julius Caesar 1759–1817
Ludlow Castle from Whitcliffe, Shropshire
1792
oil on canvas 33 x 46
1928.118

Ibbetson, Julius Caesar 1759–1817
Cave in St Catherine's Rock, Tenby,
Pembrokeshire
oil on canvas 32.7 x 24
1902.4

Ibbetson, Julius Caesar 1759–1817
The Gathering Storm
oil on panel 29.5 x 38
1934.204

Ibbetson, Julius Caesar 1759–1817
View of Llantrisant, Glamorganshire, from the
Westward
oil on canvas 66.6 x 92.4
1903.4

Ihlee, Rudolf 1883–1968
The Well 1913
oil on canvas 50.9 x 61
1925.258

Innes, James Dickson 1887–1914
Bala Lake c.1911
oil on panel 32.7 x 40.9
1934.194

Innes, James Dickson 1887–1914
The Ring c.1912
oil on canvas 33.5 x 43.3
1934.528

Isabey, Eugène 1803–1886
The Smithy
oil on panel 32.9 x 21.8
1913.15

Italian School
Classical Landscape with a River c.1675–1700
oil on canvas 50 x 66.8
1971.108

Italian School
Landscape with Abraham and Isaac c.1695–1705
oil on canvas 58.6 x 86.6
1931.64

Jackson, Frederick William 1859–1918
A Flowery Bank 1869
oil on canvas 25.2 x 35.3
1979.573

Jackson, Frederick William 1859–1918
Bread and Cheese 1913
oil on canvas 50.8 x 60
1918.9

Jackson, Frederick William 1859–1918
Poplars, Montreuil-sur-Mer
oil on millboard 50.7 x 40.3
1918.8

Jackson, Frederick William 1859–1918
Runswick Bay
oil on canvas 50.9 x 61.1
1947.78

Jackson, Frederick William 1859–1918
Shadows on the Snow
oil on canvas 37.6 x 45.5
1918.7

Jackson, Frederick William 1859–1918
The Back of Hinderwell
oil on canvas 41.6 x 49.1
1918.6

Jackson, Frederick William 1859–1918
The Path to Ellerby
oil on canvas 64.7 x 80.8
1918.1

Jackson, Frederick William 1859–1918
The Stream
oil on canvas 45.3 x 65.5
1947.98

Jackson, John 1778–1831
Thomas Stothard (1755–1834), RA 1829
oil on panel 71.7 x 59.7
1909.3

Jacomb-Hood, George Percy 1857–1929
Victor Cavendish Bentinck c.1914
oil on canvas 63.8 x 51.2
1935.482

Jacquet, Gustave Jean 1846–1909
Head of a Girl
oil on panel 33 x 23.7
1934.406

Jacquet, Gustave Jean 1846–1909
Meditation
oil on canvas 32.6 x 24.8
1917.224

James, David 1834–1892
*The Tide Coming in, Gurnard's Head,
Cornwall* 1889
oil on canvas 64 x 127.8
1979.6

Jamesone, George c.1588–1644
*James Hamilton, 2nd Marquess of Hamilton
(after Daniel Mytens)* 1620–1625
oil on panel 39.6 x 30.7
1947.84

Janes, Norman 1892–1980
Hampstead Ponds 1938
oil on canvas 51 x 61.1
1939.148

Janssens van Ceulen, Cornelis 1593–1661
Portrait of a Man (believed to be Robert
Tatton) 1620–1630
oil on canvas
2001.133

Jarman, Derek 1942–1994
Queer 1992
oil on canvas 251.5 x 179
1992.114

John, Augustus Edwin 1878–1961
Signorina Estella c.1900
oil on canvas 90.1 x 69.9
1923.24

John, Augustus Edwin 1878–1961
Merikli 1902
oil on canvas 76.2 x 63.7
1925.292

John, Augustus Edwin 1878–1961
Ardor 1904
oil on canvas 46 x 35.6
1925.289

John, Augustus Edwin 1878–1961
William Butler Yeats 1907
oil on canvas 76.2 x 51.2
1928.79

John, Augustus Edwin 1878–1961
Dorelia in a Landscape 1910
oil on panel 40.5 x 30.3
1934.531

John, Augustus Edwin 1878–1961
A Boy c.1915
oil on canvas 61 x 40.7
1922.9

John, Augustus Edwin 1878–1961
Head of a Spanish Gypsy
oil on canvas 41 x 33
1973.3

John, Augustus Edwin 1878–1961
Lady with a Mantilla
oil on canvas 61.6 x 40.9
1947.95

John, Gwen 1876–1939
The Student 1903
oil on canvas 56.1 x 33.1
1925.295

John, Gwen 1876–1939
Interior 1924
oil on canvas 22.2 x 27.1
1925.262

John, Gwen 1876–1939
The Letter 1924
oil on canvas 41.1 x 33.2
1925.255

John, Gwen 1876–1939
Flowers
oil on canvas 35.2 x 27.2
1928.43

Jones, Charles 1836–1902
Sheep in Snow 1876
oil on canvas 51 x 96.8
1918.403

Jones, David 1895–1974
Out Tide c.1931
oil on panel 50.6 x 60.9
1949.36

Jongkind, Johan Barthold 1819–1891
Le Boulevard Jourdan, Paris 1865
oil on canvas 19 x 37.4
1995.41

Jopling, Louise 1843–1933
Self Portrait 1877
oil on panel 20.3 x 15
1934.2

Jopling, Louise 1843–1933
The Painter's Son
oil on panel 55.8 x 42.8
1935.18

Kalf, Willem 1619–1693
Still Life: Fruit, Goblet and Salver 1660s
oil on canvas 58.9 x 50.7
1979.468

Kauffmann, Angelica 1741–1807
Ellis Cornelia Knight 1793
oil on canvas 96 x 80
1901.9

Kelly, Gerald Festus 1879–1972
Bishop James Edward Cowell Welldon 1921
oil on canvas 127 x 103.2
1921.26

Kennedy, Charles Napier 1852–1898
A Fair-Haired Slave Who Made Himself a King 1888
oil on canvas 214.6 x 142.7
1888.4

Key, Geoffrey b.1941
Albert Square, Manchester 1965
oil on hardboard 34.7 x 49.9
1979.5

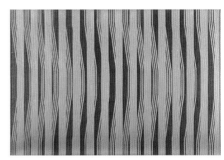

Kidner, Michael 1917–2009
Red, Yellow and Blue 1960
acrylic on canvas 103 x 152.3
1965.136

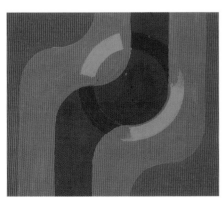

Kidner, Michael 1917–2009
Untitled Sketch 1962–1965
oil on paper 25.2 x 30
1965.217

Kiesel, Conrad 1846–1921
Marguerites
oil on canvas 119.7 x 78.4
1917.242

Kilburne, George Goodwin 1839–1924
On the Staircase
oil on panel 25.3 x 17.7
1917.197

King, Henry John Yeend 1855–1924
Landscape 1932
oil on canvas 51 x 76.3
1932.198

King-Farlow, Hazel 1903–1995
Unicorn 1936–1937
oil on canvas 50.5 x 61
1937.182

King-Farlow, Hazel 1903–1995
The Harbour 1936–1939
oil on canvas 50 x 61.2
1939.274

King-Farlow, Hazel 1903–1995
Powder Mill House 1938
oil on canvas 76.5 x 63.6
1939.204

Kingsley, Harry 1914–1998
The Green Fence, Hulme 1960
oil on hardboard 45.6 x 55.2
1965.267

Kirk, Eve 1900–1969
Aix-en-Provence 1938
oil on canvas 50.4 x 73.1
1938.365

Kirk, Janet 1884–1966
Cranes 1937
oil on canvas 45.6 x 55.8
1937.41

Klinghoffer, Clara 1900–1970
Giuseppina 1934
oil on canvas 70.4 x 50.4
1934.529

Kneller, Godfrey (follower of) 1646–1723
James II (1633–1701) 1961
oil on canvas 231.5 x 141.8
1961.251

Facing page: Wright of Derby, Joseph, 1734–1797, *Thomas Day,* 1770, Manchester City Galleries (p. 270))

Knight, Harold 1874–1961
Sewing c.1924
oil on canvas 61.2 x 50.1
1925.46

Knight, John William Buxton
1842/1843–1908
Hop Garden 1852
oil on canvas 88.6 x 124
1947.138

Knight, John William Buxton
1842/1843–1908
The Hoppers 1888
oil on canvas 76.5 x 152.4
1931.59

Knight, John William Buxton
1842/1843–1908
Midday 1891
oil on canvas 102 x 128
1908.14

Knight, John William Buxton
1842/1843–1908
Evening 1902–1906
oil on canvas 50.8 x 76.3
1979.606

Knight, John William Buxton
1842/1843–1908
The Mill, Basingstoke, Hampshire
oil on canvas 30.7 x 40.7
1979.607

Knight, John William Buxton
1842/1843–1908
Tidal Breeze, Gosport, Hampshire
oil on canvas 61.5 x 92
1909.6

Knight, Joseph 1837–1909
Lifting Mist 1883
oil on canvas 137.5 x 91.8
1884.9

Knight, Joseph 1870–1952
Chinese Pottery 1931
oil on canvas 40.6 x 50.2
1932.19

Knight, Joseph 1837–1909
A Welsh Hillside, 1883 1936
oil on canvas 117 x 159 (E)
1936.27

Knight, Laura 1877–1970
Carnaval 1920
oil on canvas 101.6 x 132.6
1922.3

Knox, Jack b.1936
Studio 11.1.64 1964
oil & chalk on canvas 160.2 x 126.5
1965.308

Knüpfer, Benes 1848–1910
Arthur Wasse
oil on canvas 50.8 x 66.7
1983.821

Kohn, Elias active 1916–1968
French Landscape
oil on hardboard 32.3 x 47.2
1968.155

Kohn, Elias active 1916–1968
Israeli Landscape
oil on canvas 81.3 x 100.5
1968.154

Kondracki, Henry b.1953
Easter Evening 1991
oil on canvas 191.2 x 218
1992.117

Kondracki, Henry b.1953
*Sunday Night at the London Palladium (The
Silent Ventriloquist)* 1991
oil on canvas 213.7 x 152.7
1993.179

Koninck, Philips de 1619–1688
Flat Landscape with a View to Distant Hills
1648
oil on panel 29.8 x 40.8
1979.469

Koninck, Philips de 1619–1688
A Woman with a Glass of Wine and a Man Looking at Her 1649
oil on panel 33 x 24.8
1979.47

Kramer, Jacob 1892–1962
Mrs Florence Moser 1916
oil on canvas 76.2 x 63.8
1925.259

Kynaston, Arthur 1876–1919
A Moonlight Idyll 1913
oil on panel 40.6 x 45.7
1928.11

La Fosse, Charles de 1636–1716
Apollo and Phaeton with the Seasons
oil on canvas 143 x 110
1964.4

La Thangue, Henry Herbert 1859–1929
Gathering Plums 1901
oil on canvas 110.4 x 92.4
1901.7

La Thangue, Henry Herbert 1859–1929
A Provençal Fountain
oil on canvas 80.4 x 89.4
1941.119

Lake, Gertrude 1858–1928
Market Day, Concarneau
oil on canvas 33.1 x 55.8
1923.31

Lamb, Henry 1883–1960
The Lady with Lizards c.1900–1933
oil on canvas 51.5 x 40.9
1954.1054

Lamb, Henry 1883–1960
Francis Jones 1920
oil on canvas 95 x 77.2
1961.84

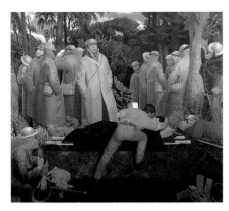

Lamb, Henry 1883–1960
Advance Dressing Station on the Struma, 1916
1921
oil on canvas 183.6 x 212.3
1921.4

Lamb, Henry 1883–1960
David John 1922
oil on canvas 51 x 40.8
1947.194

Lamb, Henry 1883–1960
Darsie Japp and Family 1926–1928
oil on canvas 183.2 x 146.7
1928.98

Lamb, Henry 1883–1960
The Yellow Jumper 1931
oil on canvas 120.3 x 94.7 (E)
1931.61

Lamb, Henry 1883–1960
An Officer of the Foreign Legion 1941
oil on canvas 86.5 x 68.8
1947.397

Lamb, Henry 1883–1960
Lawrence Haward (1878–1957) 1945
oil on canvas 86.6 x 71.8
1945.288

Lamb, Henry 1883–1960
Teas 1947
oil on canvas 114.5 x 91.8
1947.367

Lamb, Henry 1883–1960
Margaret Ashton
oil on canvas 112 x 86.3
1979.601

Lambert, George c.1700–1765
Classical Landscape 1747
oil on canvas 73.6 x 99.4
1960.33

Lander, John Saint-Helier 1869–1944
HRH Edward, Prince of Wales 1923
oil on canvas 238.6 x 147.5
1924.1

Landseer, Edwin Henry 1802–1873
On the Tilt, Perthshire 1826
oil on millboard 25.8 x 35.5
1920.554

Landseer, Edwin Henry 1802–1873
Bolton Abbey, Yorkshire c.1830–1835
oil on millboard 25.3 x 35.5
1920.543

Landseer, Edwin Henry 1802–1873
The Desert 1849
oil on canvas 177.5 x 270
1902.2

Lanyon, Peter 1918–1964
Silent Coast 1957
oil on Masonite 122 x 93.6
1978.263

Lanyon, Peter 1918–1964
Built up Coast 1960
oil & mixed media on Masonite 60.4 x 41.3
1978.89

Larcher, Dorothy 1884–1952
White Centaureas 1939
oil on canvas 45.5 x 34.7
1945.13

Larcher, Dorothy 1884–1952
Black and White Pansies 1941
oil on canvas 40.2 x 30.3
1941.75

Lascaux, Elie 1888–1969
Les vignes sous la neige 1929
oil on canvas 54.1 x 65.1
1974.92

142

László, Philip Alexius de 1869–1937
Sir Thomas Gardner Horridge (1857–1938)
1917
oil on canvas 140 x 114.9
1942.56

Lavery, Hazel 1880–1935
George Bernard Shaw (1856–1950) 1925
oil on panel 60.6 x 45.4
1942.105

Lavery, John 1856–1941
Violet and Gold (L'Entente Cordiale)
1905–1906
oil on canvas 127.2 x 101.8
1906.1

Lavery, John 1856–1941
The Lady in White
oil on panel 34.2 x 26
1947.77

Lawrence, Thomas 1769–1830
James Curtis 1804
oil on canvas 128.7 x 102.7
1953.441

Lawrence, Thomas (after) 1769–1830
Sir Robert Peel (1750–1830), 1st Bt 19th C
oil on canvas 92 x 71.3
1968.240

Lawrence, Thomas (follower of) 1769–1830
Colonel Thomas Stanley 1779–1810
oil on canvas 283.5 x 181
1968.243

Lawson, Cecil Gordon 1851–1882
'Twixt Sun and Moon 1878
oil on canvas 61 x 66.1
1907.6

Lawson, Cecil Gordon 1851–1882
The Minister's Garden 1878–1882
oil on canvas 184.2 x 275
1883.6

Lawson, Cecil Gordon 1851–1882
Landscape
oil on canvas 63.4 x 76.1
1948.73

Le Jeune, Henry 1819–1904
Children with a Toy Boat 1865
oil on panel 29.9 x 40.6
1896.12

Le Jeune, Henry 1819–1904
The Timid Bather 1872
oil on panel 30.6 x 25.4
1934.395

Le Sidaner, Henri Eugène 1862–1939
Courtyard from a Window 1904–1910
oil on canvas 80.7 x 99.9
1929.27

Leader, Benjamin Williams 1831–1923
Stepping Stones 1863
oil on canvas 91.7 x 137.5
1934.407

Leader, Benjamin Williams 1831–1923
February Fill Dyke 1881
oil on canvas 76.6 x 122.6
1934.398

Leader, Benjamin Williams 1831–1923
Stratford-on-Avon Church and Lock 1883
oil on canvas 142.5 x 102.7
1913.14

Leader, Benjamin Williams 1831–1923
The Building of the Manchester Ship Canal
1891
oil on board 27 x 35.5
1991.59

Leader, Benjamin Williams 1831–1923
Shere Church, Surrey 1892
oil on canvas 76.2 x 162.6
1934.415

Facing page: Bissill, George William, 1896–1973, *Winter Landscape*, Manchester City Galleries (p. 29)

Leader, Benjamin Williams 1831–1923
Green Pastures and Still Waters 1896
oil on canvas 50.1 x 76.4
1917.215

Leader, Benjamin Williams 1831–1923
Sunset on the Severn 1896–1917
oil on canvas 57.5 x 72.9 (E)
1917.217

Leader, Benjamin Williams 1831–1923
At Evening Time It Shall Be Light 1897
oil on canvas 76.5 x 127.3
1934.397

Leader, Benjamin Williams 1831–1923
On the Severn below Worcester 1897
oil on canvas 30.5 x 46
1917.234

Leader, Benjamin Williams 1831–1923
The Breezy Morn 1897
oil on canvas 122.1 x 183.2
1935.481

Leader, Benjamin Williams 1831–1923
Goring Church on the Thames 1898
oil on canvas 45.9 x 66
1917.233

Leader, Benjamin Williams 1831–1923
Evening's Last Gleam 1899
oil on canvas 30.6 x 46.2
1917.213

Leapman, Edwina b.1931
Untitled 1989 1989
acrylic on canvas 188 x 102
1992.125

Lear, Edward 1812–1888
View in the Campagna, Rome (with a River)
1861
oil on canvas 30 x 96.6
1988.137

Lear, Edward 1812–1888
View in the Campagna, Rome (with Ruins)
1861
oil on canvas 30 x 74
1988.136

Lee, Sydney 1866–1949
Malham Cove 1919
oil on canvas 263 x 341.6
1929.379

Lee, Sydney 1866–1949
The Top of the Pass 1923–1924
oil on canvas 88.8 x 131.7
1924.29

Leech, Beatrice Mary Seccombe 1880–1945
Rome, from The Pincio, Piazza Del Popolo,
1933 1933
oil on canvas 29 x 44.5
1934.26

Lee-Hankey, William 1869–1952
Fish Market, Dieppe
oil on canvas 104.6 x 124.4
1944.25

Leeming, Matthew Rodway 1875–1956
William Batho 1936
oil on canvas 86.4 x 81.3
1985.17

Lees, Derwent 1885–1931
The Blue Pool 1911
oil on panel 40 x 50.7
1930.77

Lees, Derwent 1885–1931
Lyndra by the Pool 1914
oil on panel 50.9 x 40
1937.731

Lees, Derwent 1885–1931
A Woodland Idyll
oil on panel 50.9 x 39.5
1933.11

Léger, Fernand 1881–1955
Painting 1926
oil on canvas 65.1 x 46
1949.102

Legros, Alphonse 1837–1911
Study of a Head 1870–1885
oil on canvas 91.5 x 81
1884.2

Legros, Alphonse 1837–1911
Study of a Head 1879
oil on canvas 51 x 40.8
1882.8

Legros, Alphonse 1837–1911
Head of an Old Man 1881
oil on canvas 61.3 x 50.7
1933.68

Legros, Alphonse 1837–1911
Saint Jerome 1881
oil on canvas 176.4 x 107.6
1882.1

Legros, Alphonse 1837–1911
Study of a Head
oil on canvas 58.3 x 45.2
1882.9

Leighton, Edmund Blair 1852–1922
Waiting for the Coach 1895
oil on canvas 33.2 x 48.4
1917.201

Leighton, Edmund Blair 1852–1922
'Off' 1899
oil on panel 32.7 x 24.8
1917.244

Leighton, Edmund Blair 1852–1922
On the Threshold 1900
oil on canvas 35.6 x 25.5
1917.239

Leighton, Edmund Blair 1852–1922
Adieu 1901
oil on canvas 86.1 x 49.4
1917.193

Leighton, Frederic 1830–1896
A Roman Peasant Girl 1840
oil on canvas 42.8 x 32.3
1917.245

Leighton, Frederic 1830–1896
The Isle of Chios c.1867
oil on canvas 26.5 x 41.5
1933.32

Leighton, Frederic 1830–1896
The Temple of Philae 1868
oil on canvas 18.7 x 29.3
1934.416

Leighton, Frederic 1830–1896
The Last Watch of Hero 1887
oil on canvas 160.3 x 91.7
1887.9

Leighton, Frederic 1830–1896
Captive Andromache c.1888
oil on canvas 197 x 407
1889.2

Lely, Peter 1618–1680
Sir John Cotton and His Family 1660
oil on canvas 157.4 x 225.3
1966.344

Lely, Peter (attributed to) 1618–1680
Lady Whitmore 1670–1680
oil on canvas 99.8 x 52.4
1901.4

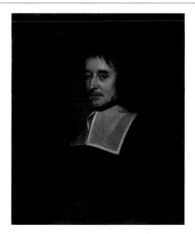

Lely, Peter (follower of) 1618–1680
Raphe Worsley of Platt Hall, Manchester
1650–1660
oil on canvas 76 x 64
1976.83

Lely, Peter (follower of) 1618–1680
Sir William Godolphin 1660–1670
oil on canvas 78.5 x 65.7
1917.172

Lely, Peter (follower of) 1618–1680
A Lady Holding a Rose 1660–1680
oil on canvas 113.5 x 92
1952.1

Leslie, George Dunlop 1835–1921
The Language of Flowers 1885
oil on canvas 112.3 x 145
1900.9

Lessore, Thérèse 1884–1945
Victoria Park – 'Let's Go Home Sis!' 1929
oil on canvas 91.4 x 70.9
1946.125

Lessore, Thérèse 1884–1945
My Little Piccaninny 1936
oil on canvas 50.9 x 61.2
1977.85

Levy, Emmanuel 1900–1986
Ursula in a Red Scarf 1953
oil on canvas 61.6 x 51.5
1953.208

Lewis, Edward Morland 1903–1943
Beach Scene 1937
oil on canvas 40 x 50.2
1938.157

Lewis, John active 1736–1776
Miss Anne Bolton
oil on canvas 89.5 x 78
1986.267

Lewis, John Frederick 1804–1876
The Coffee Bearer 1857
oil on panel 30.4 x 19
1977.2

Lewis, Neville 1895–1972
A Barotse Woman 1928
oil on panel 40.8 x 30.4
1929.25

Lewis, Wyndham 1882–1957
Self Portrait 1921
oil on canvas over hardboard 76.3 x 68.6
1925.579

Lhermitte, Léon-Augustin 1844–1925
A Flood 1876
oil on canvas 42.8 x 64.8
1947.92

Liedts, Abraham c.1604–1668
A Lady with Gloves 1650–1655
oil on canvas 101.3 x 81.5
1947.143

Lingelbach, Johannes 1622–1674
A Party of Falconers outside the Gates of a Château
oil on canvas 35.1 x 42.2
1979.471

Linnell, John 1792–1882
Hampstead Heath c.1855–1856
oil on canvas 45.8 x 61.1
1917.151

Linnell, John 1792–1882
Mid-Day Rest 1863
oil on canvas 71.3 x 99.4
1934.418

Linnell, John 1792–1882
Leith Hill, Surrey 1864
oil on panel 34 x 46
1900.21

Liverseege, Henry 1803–1832
The Betrothed 1830
oil on canvas 63 x 34.8
1912.58

Liverseege, Henry 1803–1832
Sir Piercie Shafton and Mysie Happer 1831
oil on canvas 42.1 x 34.8
1912.59

Liverseege, Henry 1803–1832
The Grave Diggers 1831
oil on canvas 28.5 x 22.3
1903.3

Liverseege, Henry 1803–1832
A Touch of the Spasms
oil on canvas 39.7 x 31.6
1912.6

Liverseege, Henry 1803–1832
Shakespearian Scene
oil on panel 24.5 x 15.8
1983.808

Liverseege, Henry 1803–1832
The Conversation (sketch for 'The Story of My Life')
oil & pencil on panel 25.4 x 20.1
1983.807

Loiseau, Gustave 1865–1935
The Seine near Port-Marly 1903
oil on canvas 50.2 x 61
1908.3

Lomax, John Arthur 1857–1923
News of the Army
oil on panel 30.5 x 25.1
1917.246

Lomax, John Arthur 1857–1923
'Old birds are not caught by chaff'
oil on panel 30.4 x 40.9
1917.241

Lorrain, Claude 1604–1682
The Adoration of the Golden Calf 1660
oil on canvas 112.8 x 156.6
1981.3

Lowry, Laurence Stephen 1887–1976
An Accident 1926
oil on panel 36.3 x 61
1930.153

Lowry, Laurence Stephen 1887–1976
Coming Home from the Mill 1928
oil on panel 43 x 53.3
1962.26

Lowry, Laurence Stephen 1887–1976
An Organ Grinder 1934
oil on canvas 53.5 x 39.5
1936.1

Lowry, Laurence Stephen 1887–1976
Laying a Foundation Stone 1936
oil on canvas 45.7 x 61
1940.73

Lowry, Laurence Stephen 1887–1976
St John's Church, Manchester 1938
oil on board 31 x 30.3
1987.78

Lowry, Laurence Stephen 1887–1976
An Island 1942
oil on canvas 45.6 x 60.9
1948.268

Lowry, Laurence Stephen 1887–1976
Waiting for the Shop to Open 1943
oil on canvas 43.3 x 53.3
1948.269

Lowry, Laurence Stephen 1887–1976
St Augustine's Church, Manchester 1945
oil on canvas 46 x 61.3
1947.404

Lowry, Laurence Stephen 1887–1976
Street in Pendelbury 1948
oil on canvas 61 x 46
1995.4

Lowry, Laurence Stephen 1887–1976
The Mid-Day Studios 1952
oil on board 14 x 25.3
2005.2

Lowry, Laurence Stephen 1887–1976
Piccadilly Gardens 1954
oil on canvas 76.2 x 101.6
1956.45

Lucas, Caroline Byng c.1886–1967
A Bouquet of Wild Flowers 1937
oil on canvas 55.1 x 45.8
1939.208

Luxmoore, Myra E. 1851–1919
The Very Reverend Edward C. Maclure 1895
oil on canvas 142.6 x 112
1906.97

Luyten-Behnisch, Jadwiga 1873–1963
Plums
oil on canvas 40.7 x 51
1928.103

Lynch, Albert 1851–1912
Head of a Girl
oil on canvas 27 x 21.8
1917.21

Macallum, John Thomas Hamilton 1841–1896
Dipping for Sprats 1893
oil on canvas 122.5 x 215.5
1899.3

Macbeth, Robert Walker 1848–1910
Osier Peeling on the Cam 1875
oil on canvas 51.6 x 40.8
1940.79

MacBryde, Robert 1913–1966
Woman with Cantaloupe c.1945
oil on canvas 126 x 62
1950.7

Facing page: Gabain, Ethel Leontine, 1883–1950, *The Little Hat*, Manchester City Galleries (p. 101)

155

MacBryde, Robert 1913–1966
Still Life with Fish Head 1947
oil on canvas 30.5 x 46
1947.444

MacCallum, Andrew 1821–1902
The River of Life: Birth 1850
oil on canvas 44 x 62
1933.2 A

MacCallum, Andrew 1821–1902
The River of Life: Death 1850
oil on canvas 44 x 61
1933.2 E

MacCallum, Andrew 1821–1902
The River of Life: Decline 1850
oil on canvas 66 x 45.5
1933.2 D

MacCallum, Andrew 1821–1902
The River of Life: Manhood 1850
oil on canvas 66 x 58
1933.2 C

MacCallum, Andrew 1821–1902
The River of Life: Youth 1850
oil on canvas 65.5 x 45.5
1933.2 B

MacCallum, Andrew 1821–1902
Oak Trees in Sherwood Forest 1877
oil on canvas 78.5 x 119
1918.418

MacColl, Dugald Sutherland 1859–1948
Augustus John at Ambleteuse, 1907 1907
oil on panel 25.4 x 17.6
1943.76

MacDougall, William Brown 1869–1936
Water Frolic, Barton Broad 1922
oil on panel 63.9 x 76.2
1936.244

MacKinnon, Sine 1901–1996
The 'Concepcion' in the Harbour, St Tropez
1936
oil on canvas 53.9 x 65
1946.129

MacKinnon, Sine 1901–1996
Flowers against the Sea 1939
oil on canvas 55 x 46
1940.191

MacKinnon, Sine 1901–1996
Fishing Boat
oil on board 33 x 41
1937.673

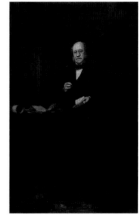

Maclise, Daniel 1806–1870
The Origin of the Harp 1842
oil on canvas 110.4 x 85
1917.269

Maclise, Daniel 1806–1870
A Winter Night's Tale c.1867
oil on canvas 101.3 x 126.3
1908.18

Macnee, Daniel 1806–1882
William Gibb, JP 1871
oil on canvas 231.8 x 147.4
1968.244

MacWhirter, John 1839–1911
*Constantinople and the Golden Horn from
Eyoub* 1869–1889
oil on canvas 154.2 x 245
1908.9

MacWhirter, John 1839–1911
The Lady of the Woods 1876
oil on canvas 152.7 x 105
1937.126

MacWhirter, John 1839–1911
Autumn in the Highlands
oil on canvas 102.7 x 150.8
1934.408

Magnus, Emma 1856–1936
Refreshments
oil on canvas 36.7 x 47.1
1926.7

Magnus, Rose 1859–1900
A Bunch of Thistles 1896
oil on canvas 57.6 x 45
1936.241

Maidment, Thomas 1871–1952
The Old Harbour, St Ives 1936–1937
oil on canvas 71 x 92
1937.646

Major, Theodore 1908–1999
Head Study 1946
oil on canvas 45.8 x 40.4
1948.56

Manson, James Bolivar 1879–1945
Summer Flowers 1923
oil on canvas 60.8 x 50.8
1925.315

Manson, James Bolivar 1879–1945
Antibes 1928
oil on panel 34.9 x 45.8
1929.26

Manson, James Bolivar 1879–1945
Lucien Pissarro 1939
oil on canvas 60 x 72.6
1941.66

Marchand, Jean Hippolyte 1883–1941
French Village
oil on canvas 60.5 x 73.3
1940.4

Marchand, Jean Hippolyte 1883–1941
Olive Trees, Vence
oil on canvas 65.1 x 92.1
1925.317

Marchand, Jean Hippolyte 1883–1941
Portrait of a Lady
oil on canvas 65.4 x 53.3
1937.676

Marchand, Jean Hippolyte 1883–1941
The Lady in Brown
oil on canvas 65.3 x 54.7
1925.583

Marcoussis, Louis 1878/1883–1941
Still Life 1927
oil on canvas 80.9 x 100.2
1951.59

Maris, Jacob Henricus 1837–1899
In the Garden
oil on panel 29 x 19.6
1911.77

Maris, Jacob Henricus 1837–1899
The Gathering Storm
oil on canvas 48.1 x 90.5
1927.39

Maris, Willem 1844–1910
Cows at Pasture 1900–1910
oil on canvas 25 x 42.5
1947.93

Marks, Edmund active 1837–1875
Deal Beach 1860
oil on canvas 35.4 x 61
1907.11

Marks, Edmund active 1837–1875
On Brighton Beach 1860
oil on canvas 73.5 x 122
1907.1

Marks, Henry Stacy 1829–1898
South African Crowned Cranes
oil on canvas 63.5 x 122
1920.1347

Marlow, William 1740–1813
Matlock, Derbyshire
oil on canvas 38.3 x 53
1938.263

Marlow, William 1740–1813
View in Lyons
oil on canvas 50 x 65.5
1932.21

Martin, Benito Quinquela 1890–1977
Morning Sun, Buenos Aires 1930
oil on canvas 201.2 x 165.1
1931.4

Martineau, Robert Braithwaite 1826–1869
A Lady with a Gold Chain and Earrings 1861
oil on panel 35.6 x 25.4
1985.13

Martineau, Robert Braithwaite 1826–1869
Study for a Woman of San Germano c.1864
oil on canvas 44.7 x 37.4
1951.9

Martineau, Robert Braithwaite 1826–1869
The Artist's Wife in a Red Cape
oil on canvas 35.5 x 27.9
1951.1

Mason, Arnold 1885–1963
Head of a Girl
oil on canvas 45.5 x 38
1940.143

Mason, Bateson 1910–1977
Landscape 1936
oil on canvas 61 x 76.5
1936.265

Mason, Bateson 1910–1977
Great Gable and Wastwater 1937
oil on canvas 66.3 x 91.5
1938.42

Mason, George Heming 1818–1872
Landscape – Derbyshire 1870
oil on canvas 46 x 94.4
1908.13

Mason, George Heming 1818–1872
Only a Shower
oil on canvas 45.9 x 91.7
1911.18

Master of Frankfurt 1460–c.1533
Saint Catherine and Saint Barbara with Donors (diptych) c.1500
oil on panel 89.9 x 26
1957.51

Master of the Magdalen Legend c.1483–c.1530
Virgin and Child
oil on panel 25.2 x 15.4
1911.27

Matteo di Giovanni (school of) c.1430–1495
The Crucifixion 1484–1490
tempera on panel 31.4 x 71.1
1951.2

Maufra, Maxime 1861–1918
Springtime at Lavardin (Touraine) 1907
oil on canvas 65 x 80.6
1908.6

Mayer, William Edgar 1910–2002
Square Forms
oil on pulpboard 34.5 x 41
1959.21

Mayor, William Frederick 1865–1916
Paris Plage 1914
oil on canvas 79.4 x 115.1
1934.487

Maze, Paul Lucien 1887–1979
Villefranche 1924
oil on canvas 45.9 x 38.2
1939.27

McCannell, Ursula Vivian b.1923
Self Portrait 1940
oil on plywood 45.8 x 35.4
1942.76

McEvoy, Ambrose 1878–1927
Silver and Grey 1915
oil on canvas 85.8 x 73.4
1925.71

McEvoy, Ambrose 1878–1927
Miss Teddy Gerrard 1921
oil on canvas 76.4 x 63.8
1947.96

McEvoy, Ambrose 1878–1927
Head of a Girl
oil on canvas 30.9 x 24.5
1947.88

McFadyen, Jock b.1950
Waiting for the Cortina Boys 1985
oil on canvas 213.4 x 213.4
1986.231

McFadyen, Jock b.1950
New York, New York 1986
oil & collage on canvas 262.5 x 173
2002.65

McFadyen, Jock b.1950
Canal (diptych, left panel) 1990
oil on canvas 207.4 x 149.9
1991.64.1

McFadyen, Jock b.1950
Canal (diptych, right panel) 1990
oil on canvas 207.4 x 149.9
1991.64.2

McGlynn, Terry 1903–1973
Ponte Tresa, Lugano, Switzerland 1930–1954
oil, watercolour, pen & black ink on
paper 36 x 48.5
1954.1124

Facing page: Hicks, George Elgar, 1824–1914, *Mother and Child*, 1873, Manchester City Galleries (p. 121)

McGlynn, Terry 1903–1973
Interior with Two Figures, No.2, 1966 1966
oil, ink & pencil on paper 74.9 x 51
1966.194

McGlynn, Terry 1903–1973
Chartres
oil & ink on paper 36.4 x 49
1954.1125

McGlynn, Terry 1903–1973
Place de Furstenberg, Paris
oil & chalk on paper 48.9 x 62.2
1956.404

McKenna, Stephen b.1939
Still Life of the Sea 1980
oil on canvas 70 x 100
1986.228

Measham, Henry 1844–1922
The Artist's Mother 1870
oil on canvas 61.5 x 51.2
1907.4

Medley, Robert 1905–1994
An ARP Demonstration
oil on canvas 35.5 x 45.5
1947.427

Medley, Robert 1905–1994
Gate Duty
oil on canvas 33 x 22.9
1947.368

Meissonier, Jean Louis Ernest 1815–1891
A General Officer
oil on panel 12.9 x 9.4
1979.533

Meissonier, Jean Louis Ernest 1815–1891
Advance Guard of an Army
oil on panel 11.5 x 20.5
1979.534

Melcarth, Edward 1914–1973
Dinner Time 1937
oil on canvas 40.6 x 96.5
1938.43

Melland, Sylvia 1906–1993
Outpatients, Manchester Royal Infirmary
1934–1937
oil on canvas 51 x 61
1997.2

Melland, Sylvia 1906–1993
Back Street, Manchester 1935
oil on canvas 51 x 41
1997.21

Melland, Sylvia 1906–1993
Martello Tower 1950–1951
oil on canvas 52 x 60.7
1997.22

Melland, Sylvia 1906–1993
Military Canal 1951–1952
oil on canvas 40.5 x 51
1997.23

Mengin, Auguste Charles 1853–1933
Sappho 1877
oil on canvas 230.7 x 151.1
1884.5

Mengs, Anton Raphael 1728–1779
Saint Eusebius Carried to Heaven c.1757
oil on canvas 73.3 x 36.5
1966.49

Meredith, William 1851–1916
Homewards, Conway Marsh 1881
oil on canvas 65.5 x 122
1884.13

Messent, Charles 1911–1977
Road through a French Village
oil on hardboard 40 x 59.8
1976.4

Methuen, Paul Ayshford 1886–1974
Helford River, 1944, with Training Ship 1944
oil on millboard 39.3 x 53.3
1947.362

Metsu, Gabriel (after) 1629–1667
A Woman Seated Smoking a Pipe (copy of an original)
oil on panel 19.8 x 16.6
1979.472

Michau, Theobald 1676–1765
Farmyard Scene: Reaping
oil on panel 18.3 x 28.2
1979.473

Michau, Theobald 1676–1765
Farmyard Scene: The Vintage
oil on panel 18.6 x 28
1979.474

Michel, Georges 1763–1843
Landscape
oil on canvas 63.8 x 80
1958.14

Middleditch, Edward 1923–1987
Sheffield Weir
oil on hardboard 122.2 x 152
1955.134

Miereveld, Michiel Jansz. van 1567–1641
Portrait of a Lady, Aged 58 1636
oil on panel 69.2 x 59
1947.144

Miereveld, Michiel Jansz. van (after)
1567–1641
Lubbert Gerritsz.
oil on canvas 68.4 x 52.2
1914.3

Mieris, Willem van 1662–1747
A Lady Seated Holding a Small Dog 1680–1700
oil on panel 16 x 12.5
1979.475

Mieris, Willem van 1662–1747
Interior with a Cavalier and Lady 1685
oil on panel 24.7 x 20.6
1979.476

Millais, John Everett 1829–1896
The Death of Romeo and Juliet c.1848
oil on millboard 16.1 x 26.9
1947.89

Millais, John Everett 1829–1896
Wandering Thoughts c.1855
oil on canvas 35.2 x 24.9
1913.28

Millais, John Everett 1829–1896
Autumn Leaves 1856
oil on canvas 104.3 x 74
1892.4

Millais, John Everett 1829–1896
Only a Lock of Hair 1857–1858
oil on panel 35.3 x 25
1917.268

Millais, John Everett 1829–1896
Stella 1868
oil on canvas 112.7 x 92.1
1908.12

Millais, John Everett 1829–1896
A Flood 1870
oil on canvas 99.3 x 144.9
1891.7

Millais, John Everett 1829–1896
Victory O Lord 1871
oil on canvas 194.7 x 141.3
1894.1

Millais, John Everett 1829–1896
Winter Fuel 1873
oil on canvas 194.5 x 149.5
1897.4

Millais, John Everett 1829–1896
Mrs Leopold Reiss 1876
oil on canvas 122 x 95
1932.1

Millais, John Everett 1829–1896
James Fraser 1880
oil on canvas 128 x 93.6
1979.134

Millais, John Everett 1829–1896
Glen Birnam 1891
oil on canvas 145.2 x 101.1
1908.15

Miller, William Ongley 1883–1960
The Artist's Daughter 1929
oil on canvas 86.4 x 59.2
1930.19

Millet, Jean-François (style of) 1814–1875
Peasant Girl 1850–1875
oil on canvas 30.3 x 21.9
1919.7

Milne, Malcolm Midwood 1887–1954
Autumn Flowers 1935–1936
oil on millboard 71 x 57.1
1937.42

Milne, Malcolm Midwood 1887–1954
The Hundred Flowers 1938
oil on canvas 73.8 x 60.4
1938.505

Mitchell, John Campbell 1862–1922
At the Close of Day 1903
oil on canvas 51 x 62
1979.608

Modigliani, Amedeo 1884–1920
Portrait of an Unknown Model c.1918
oil on canvas 64 x 68
1995.35

Molenaer, Jan Miense c.1610–1668
Interior with Peasants and School Children
oil on panel 33.8 x 42.7
1979.478

Molenaer, Klaes c.1630–1676
Skating Scene: Figures on the Ice near the Walls of a Town
oil on panel 33.3 x 41.5
1979.479

Monks, John Christopher b.1954
The Chandelier 1991
oil on canvas 154 x 113
1991.78

Monnington, Walter Thomas 1902–1976
The Holy Family (unfinished) 1929
tempera on canvas 45.5 x 35.5
1954.1051

Monnington, Walter Thomas 1902–1976
Battle Area, 15,000ft 1943
oil on canvas 50.8 x 61.2
1947.403

Monti, Francesco 1685–1768
Moses and the Daughters of Jethro 1720–1768
oil on canvas 62.7 x 104.5
1928.39

Monticelli, Adolphe Joseph Thomas
1824–1886
A Woodland Glade
oil on panel 48.2 x 79.3
1910.1

Monticelli, Adolphe Joseph Thomas
1824–1886
Ladies on a Terrace
oil on panel 47.2 x 69.4
1931.1

Mooney, Edward Hartley 1877–1938
Still Life 1916
oil on canvas 71.6 x 61.4
2010.146

Mooney, Edward Hartley 1877–1938
Still Life 1918
oil on canvas 51 x 61
1920.5

Mooney, Edward Hartley 1877–1938
Anemones 1925
oil on canvas 38 x 45.6
1925.64

Moore, Albert Joseph 1841–1893
A Reader c.1877
oil on canvas 87.2 x 32
1934.413

Moore, Albert Joseph 1841–1893
Birds of the Air c.1879
oil on canvas 86.7 x 36.2
1934.414

Moore, Albert Joseph 1841–1893
A Garland 1887–1888
oil on canvas 49.3 x 25.1
1917.255

Moore, Albert Joseph 1841–1893
A Footpath 1888
oil on canvas 44.2 x 16.2
1917.227

Moore, Albert Joseph 1841–1893
An Idyll 1893
oil on canvas 86.5 x 78.9
1917.223

Moore, Alfred Harvey 1843–1905
The Thames off Yantlett Creek, Kent 1874–1903
oil on canvas 35.7 x 58.6
1907.12

Moore, Henry 1831–1895
Cattle Fording a Stream 1862
oil on canvas 71.5 x 111.8
1918.419

Moore, Henry 1831–1895
Mount's Bay: Early Morning – Summer 1886
oil on canvas 122.2 x 213.5
1886.7

Moore, Henry 1831–1895
Arran (Across Kilbrannan Sound) 1894
oil on canvas 30.5 x 54.7
1940.78

Moret, Henry 1856–1913
Fishing Boats at Douelan 1880–1900
oil on canvas 60.3 x 73
1908.5

**Morgenstern, Christian Ernst
Bernhard** 1805–1867
Bavarian Highlands
oil on canvas 92.5 x 140.2
1927.2

Morland, George 1763–1804
A Farrier's Shop 1793
oil on canvas 71.1 x 91.5
1882.1

Morland, Henry Robert c.1716–1797
Portrait of an Officer of the Foot Guards
1750–1770
oil on canvas 43.7 x 35.1
1928.9

Morris, Cedric Lockwood 1889–1982
(George) Loraine Conran (1912–1986)
1930–1934
oil on canvas 73 x 60.3
1976.9

Morris, Charles Greville 1861–1922
Marshland 1874–1894
oil on canvas 108.5 x 165.5
1909.8

Morris, Philip Richard 1836–1902
Daniel Adamson
oil on canvas 223.5 x 127
1900.15

Morris, Philip Richard 1836–1902
The 'Nancy Lee' of Great Yarmouth
oil on canvas 91.9 x 153.2
1883.27

Morris, William Bright 1844–1912
Near the Village of Crécy, France
oil on canvas 86.4 x 127.6
1890.62

Morris, William Bright 1844–1912
Spanish Beggars
oil on canvas 120.8 x 96.5
1898.2

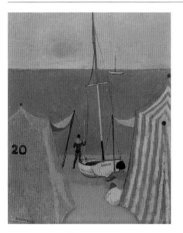

Morrocco, Alberto 1917–1998
Bathing Tent and Boat 1976
oil on canvas 34.2 x 25.4
2003.43

Mostyn, Thomas Edwin 1864–1930
James Thomas Blair (1863–1917) 1917
oil on canvas 127 x 101.7
1918.4

Mostyn, Thomas Edwin 1864–1930
J. K. Bythell
oil on canvas 127.3 x 101.7
1916.11

Mostyn, Thomas Edwin 1864–1930
Peace
oil on canvas 51 x 61
1911.51

Mostyn, Thomas Edwin 1864–1930
Romance
oil on canvas 127 x 101.7
1911.5

Motesiczky, Marie-Louise von 1906–1996
Henriette M. 1961
oil on canvas 76 x 81
1995.139

Facing page: MacBryde, Robert, 1913–1966, *Woman with Cantaloupe*, c.1945, Manchester City Galleries (p. 155)

Moynihan, Rodrigo 1910–1990
The Garden Wall 1940
oil on canvas 61.2 x 71.2
1941.73

Moynihan, Rodrigo 1910–1990
The Artist's Mother
oil on canvas 45.6 x 35.6
1977.86

Muckley, William Jabez 1829–1905
Grapes 1875
oil on canvas 40.7 x 49.7
1936.12

Muckley, William Jabez 1829–1905
Roses 1883
oil on canvas 69.1 x 50.8
1888.2

Mudd, James 1821–1906
Mountainous Landscape
oil on board 36.8 x 54.6
2007.73

Mudd, James 1821–1906
River Scene
oil on canvas 25.4 x 35.5
2007.74

Muirhead, David 1867–1930
Night Shadows
oil on canvas 108 x 91.5
1925.273

Müller, Adèle Rose Bertha c.1868–1948
The Annunciation (after Lippo Lippi) 1893
oil on canvas 27 x 64
1918.416

Müller, Adèle Rose Bertha c.1868–1948
Angels (after Fra Angelico)
oil on canvas 34 x 34
1918.429

Müller, William James 1812–1845
*Landscape: Cottage, Trees, a Stream and
Distant Hills* 1837
oil on panel 67 x 99
1964.253

Müller, William James 1812–1845
A Rock Tomb, Lycia 1843–1844
oil on canvas 41.4 x 53.4
1896.3

Müller, William James 1812–1845
An Encampment in the Desert 1844–1845
oil on canvas 101.7 x 210.3
1897.3

Müller, William James 1812–1845
Burial Ground, Smyrna 1845
oil on canvas 32.7 x 51.1
1907.8

Müller, William James 1812–1845
The Approaching Storm 1845
oil on panel 39.8 x 28.2
1917.162

Müller, William James 1812–1845
Hauling Timber
oil on canvas 78.4 x 126.8
1927.26

Mulready, William 1786–1863
Study for 'The Careless Messenger Detected'
1821
oil on canvas 26 x 20.7
1920.524

Munsch, Josef 1832–1896
The Antiquaries
oil on panel 41 x 30.5
1918.411

Mura, Francesco de 1696–1782
The Death of Virginia 1750–1760
oil on canvas 90.5 x 144
1971.52

Mura, Frank 1863–1913
In West Mersea: Essex 1880
oil on panel 63.9 x 77
1924.34

Mura, Frank 1863–1913
Hayricks 1880–1900
oil on canvas 54.5 x 85.1
1914.63

Mura, Frank 1863–1913
Village Scene 1890–1913
oil on canvas 61.1 x 50.5
1919.6

Murray, David 1849–1933
'Britannia's' Anchor (on the River Dart) 1887
oil on canvas 101.7 x 154
1888.5

Murray, David 1849–1933
Old Shoreham 1898
oil on canvas 121.3 x 182.4
1939.228

Murray, George b.c.1935
Robot, 1966 1966
oil on canvas 69 x 50.7
1967.67

Murry, Richard 1902–1984
Crater 1941
oil on canvas 40.7 x 51
1947.4

Myers, William H. 1890–1924
The Model
oil on canvas 60.9 x 50.5
1924.61

Nash, John Northcote 1893–1977
Winter Scene, Buckinghamshire 1920
oil on canvas 47 x 77.6
1925.316

Nash, John Northcote 1893–1977
Jug of Flowers 1930
oil on canvas 76.3 x 61.1
1930.16 ✤

Nash, John Northcote 1893–1977
The Road up to Whiteleaf, Buckinghamshire
oil on canvas 51.1 x 76.4
1937.675 ✤

Nash, Paul 1889–1946
Sandling Park, Kent 1924
oil on canvas 91.9 x 71
1925.318

Nash, Paul 1889–1946
Nocturnal Landscape 1938
oil on canvas 76.5 x 101.5
1948.134

Nash, Paul 1889–1946
Wounded, Passchendaele
oil on canvas 45.9 x 50.7
1920.79

Nash, Thomas Saunders 1891–1968
Bathers, 1926 1926
oil & pencil on paper 27.7 x 28
1950.44

Nash, Thomas Saunders 1891–1968
Oranges and Lemons 1928
oil on paper 38 x 56
1939.22

Nash, Thomas Saunders 1891–1968
The Farmyard 1928
oil (?) on paper 38.3 x 56
1950.45

Nash, Thomas Saunders 1891–1968
Fowls 1929
oil on paper 35.4 x 25.5
1939.53

Nash, Thomas Saunders 1891–1968
The Woodgatherers 1929
oil on canvas 38.3 x 28
1950.46

Nash, Thomas Saunders 1891–1968
The Sermon on the Mount
oil on canvas 127.2 x 102.2
1939.23

Nasmyth, Alexander 1758–1840
View of the Ponte Molle, on the Sylvan Side of Rome 1800–1820
oil on canvas 81.9 x 116
1902.12

Nasmyth, Alexander 1758–1840
River Landscape with Ruined Castle
oil on canvas 45.9 x 61
1884.7

Nasmyth, Patrick 1787–1831
Wooded Landscape with Distant View
1820–1829
oil on panel 23.4 x 31.6
1934.436

Nasmyth, Patrick 1787–1831
Near Dulwich 1826
oil on panel 24.7 x 39.3
1917.263

Nasmyth, Patrick 1787–1831
Landscape with Haystacks 1827
oil on panel 29.6 x 40.7
1934.393

Nasmyth, Patrick 1787–1831
Landscape with Sheep and a Shepherd
1898–1811
oil on panel 28.7 x 41.9
1947.9

Nasmyth, Patrick 1787–1831
Sonning on the Thames
oil on panel 31.6 x 48.7
1953.439

Naylor, Martin b.1944
Fortress 8 1975
acrylic & collage on canvas 101.6 x 68.6
1975.75

Naylor, Martin b.1944
Lover Variation 3
oil on cotton duck 183 x 188
1992.126

Neer, Aert van der (imitator of) 1603–1677
*Skating Scene: Figures on a River Flowing
through a Village*
oil on canvas 52.3 x 73
1979.480

Neiland, Brendan b.1941
Juxtaposed Buildings 1974
acrylic on paper on board 55.9 x 81.3
1974.101

Neiland, Brendan b.1941
Quadrate 1987 1987
acrylic on canvas 24 x 53.5
1989.125

Nelson, Geoffrey C. b.1887
The Church, Port Vendres 1929
oil on canvas 60 x 73.5
1929.45

Netherlandish School
A Lady Seated Holding a Small Dog 1649–1684
oil on canvas 25.3 x 21.7
1979.481

Nevinson, Christopher 1889–1946
The Railway Bridge, Charenton 1911–1912
oil on canvas 40.9 x 51.5
1912.35

Nevinson, Christopher 1889–1946
Searchlights 1916
oil on canvas 76.4 x 56
1920.149

Nevinson, Christopher 1889–1946
A Front Line near St Quentin 1918
oil on canvas 45.9 x 61.2
1925.314

Nevinson, Christopher 1889–1946
Any Wintry Afternoon in England 1930
oil on canvas 61.1 x 76.3
1934.49

Nevinson, Christopher 1889–1946
Barges on the Thames
oil on canvas 76.2 x 46.1
1931.29

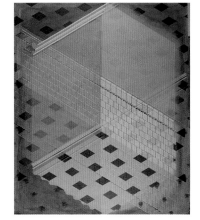

Nevinson, Christopher 1889–1946
Motor Lorries
oil on canvas 50.8 x 60.8
1925.322

Newsome, Victor b.1935
A Corner of the Bathroom 1973
acrylic on panel 122 x 106.4
1975.195

Newton, Herbert H. 1881–1959
Track of Forest Brook 1938
oil on canvas 63.5 x 79
1953.127

Nicholls, Bertram 1883–1974
Picturesque Steyning 1914
oil on canvas 54 x 65
1917.249

Nicholls, Bertram 1883–1974
Villeneuve-les-Avignons 1925
oil on canvas 50.6 x 60.8
1926.9

Nicholls, Bertram 1883–1974
Maidstone Revisited 1948
oil on canvas 61 x 91.5
1974.95

Facing page: Caulfield, Patrick, 1936–2005, *Inside a Weekend Cabin*, 1969, Manchester City Galleries (p. 56)

Nicholls, Margaret S. active 1908–1932
Flower Piece 1927
oil on board 61.2 x 50.7
1930.1

Nicholson, Ben 1894–1982
1931 (St Ives Bay: sea with boats) 1931
oil & pencil on canvas 40.9 x 56
1950.6

Nicholson, Ben 1894–1982
1932 (Au Chat Botté) 1932
oil & pencil on canvas 92.3 x 122
1948.316

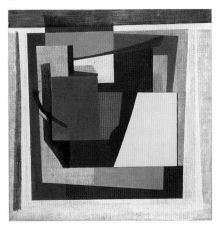

Nicholson, Ben 1894–1982
1946 (composition, still life) 1946
oil & pencil on canvas 43.3 x 43.3
1947.19

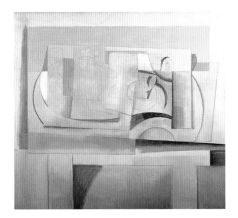

Nicholson, Ben 1894–1982
1950 (still life) 1950
oil on canvas 203.9 x 228.5
1951.463

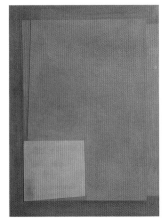

Nicholson, Ben 1894–1982
1971 (Piero) 1971
oil on board 116.5 x 87.5
1986.461

Nicholson, William 1872–1949
The Landlord 1895–1905
oil on canvas 76.1 x 76.1
1919.2

Nicholson, William 1872–1949
Walter Greaves (1846–1930) 1917
oil on canvas 190.5 x 143
1925.68

Nicholson, Winifred 1893–1981
Primulas 1921–1922
oil on hardboard 53.1 x 57.7
1928.48

Nicholson, Winifred 1893–1981
Boothby Bank c.1940
oil on canvas 61.1 x 61
1946.64

Nixon, Job 1891–1938
Place Saint-André des Arts, Paris 1930
oil on canvas 46 x 61.1
1930.175

North, John William 1842–1924
The Flower and the Leaf 1890–1901
oil on canvas 66.5 x 99.8
1901.2

North, John William 1842–1924
Springtime 1890–1908
oil on canvas 66.2 x 98.9
1908.1

Northcote, James 1746–1831
Othello, the Moor of Venice 1826
oil on canvas 76.2 x 63.5
1882.2

Oakes, John Wright 1820–1887
Glen Muick, Aberdeenshire 1872
oil on canvas 122.8 x 168.7
1887.14

Ochtervelt, Jacob 1634–1682
The Doctor's Visit 1655–1675
oil on canvas 65 x 51.8
1979.536

Ochtervelt, Jacob 1634–1682
The Sleeping Cavalier 1660–1665
oil on panel 46 x 37.7
1979.483

Ochtervelt, Jacob 1634–1682
The Embracing Cavalier c.1660–1663
oil on panel 44.6 x 35.6
1979.482

Ochtervelt, Jacob 1634–1682
Merry Company c.1663–1665
oil on canvas 52.2 x 42
1926.11

Oguiss, Takanori 1901–1986
Paris Landscape 1928
oil on canvas 50 x 61
1946.36

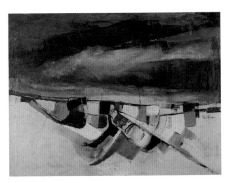

Oliver, Peter 1927–2006
Blue Beach 1957–1965
oil on canvas 108 x 138.5
1965.26

Oliver, William 1823–1901
The Duenna 1877
oil on canvas 50.7 x 40.6
1917.19

Oliver, William (attributed to) 1804–1853
At the Opera
oil on canvas 45.6 x 35.9
1939.145

Ollivary, Annette b.1926
Après l'école 1957
oil on canvas 38 x 46.5
1995.53

Ollivary, Annette b.1926
Scène de famille 1995
oil on canvas 40.7 x 52
1995.54

O'Malley, Tony 1913–2003
Graffiti, 1963 1963
oil on millboard
1973.166

Ommeganck, Balthazar Paul 1755–1826
Pastoral Landscape 1797
oil on canvas 44.8 x 38.5
1971.107

Oppenheimer, Charles 1875–1961
Kirkcudbright: Evening 1914
oil on canvas 120.9 x 151.7
1923.13

Oppenheimer, Charles 1875–1961
Evening: Lake of Lucerne 1922
oil on canvas 63.5 x 76.3
1923.14

Oppenheimer, Charles 1875–1961
The Old Tolbooth, Kirkcudbright 1931
oil on panel 35.5 x 45.6
1941.3

Oppenheimer, Charles 1875–1961
Last of the Snow
oil on canvas 51 x 61
1947.75

Orchardson, William Quiller 1832–1910
Mrs John Pettie 1865
oil on canvas 99.9 x 79.5
1926.12

Orchardson, William Quiller 1832–1910
Mrs Robert Mackay c.1868
oil on canvas 91.4 x 71.3
1935.18

Orchardson, William Quiller 1832–1910
Her Idol c.1869
oil on canvas 75.2 x 95.9
1910.39

Orpen, William 1878–1931
James Staats Forbes 1900
oil on canvas 94.1 x 85.1
1926.17

Orpen, William 1878–1931
Homage to Manet 1909
oil on canvas 162.9 x 130
1910.9

Os, Jan van 1744–1808
Still Life: Flowers and Fruit
oil on panel 72.3 x 55.5
1979.484

Os, Jan van 1744–1808
Still Life: Flowers and Fruit
oil on panel 72.1 x 55.6
1979.485

Oss, Tom W. Van 1901–1941
Foggy Afternoon, Boulevard St Michel, Paris
1926
oil on canvas 51.3 x 40.9
1940.220

Ostade, Adriaen van 1610–1685
Two Peasants Smoking 1650–1660
oil on panel 18.1 x 15.4
1979.486

Ostade, Adriaen van (follower of) 1610–1685
Interior of a Barn with Two Peasants Fighting
oil on canvas 22.4 x 27.2
1979.488

Ostade, Adriaen van (follower of) 1610–1685
An Itinerant Musician Playing the Hurdy-Gurdy to a Group of Children Outside an Inn Door 1660–1685
oil on panel 33 x 23.2
1979.487

Ostade, Isack van 1621–1649
Winter Scene, with Figures on a Frozen River in front of a Walled Town 1642
oil on panel 39.9 x 61
1979.489

Ostade, Isack van 1621–1649
Interior of a Barn with an Old Woman at a Distaff
oil on panel 41.6 x 53.2
1979.49

Ostade, Isack van 1621–1649
Scene on the Shore at Scheveningen
oil on panel 74.2 x 110.1
1908.2

Ouless, Walter William 1848–1933
Alderman Philip Goldschmidt 1887
oil on canvas 127.7 x 102.7
1888.8

Owen, Joseph active 1926–1933
At Bettws-y-Coed, North Wales 1926
oil on canvas 45.7 x 61
1927.8

Palmer, Jean b.1961
Head
oil on canvas 24.5 x 20
1992.184

Palmer, Jean b.1961
Self Portrait
oil on canvas 30.2 x 25
1992.183

Palmer, Samuel 1805–1881
The Bright Cloud c.1833–1834
tempera on mahogany 23.3 x 32
1976.82

Panini, Giovanni Paolo (follower of)
1691–1765
Roman Ruins with Figures
oil on canvas 118.7 x 160.8
1903.18

Park, John Anthony 1880–1962
Shipping, Venice 1934
oil on canvas 60.7 x 73.6
1935.6

Park, John Anthony 1880–1962
Spring in Mallorca 1934
oil on canvas 50.3 x 60.9
1937.39

Park, John Anthony 1880–1962
Snowfalls in Essex 1938
oil on plywood 63.2 x 76.5
1939.153

Park, John Anthony 1880–1962
This England
oil on canvas 64 x 76.5
1957.1

Parker, Brynhild 1907–1987
The White Hat 1934
oil on canvas 60.9 x 50.1
1935.16

Parlby, Samuel
The Bridgewater Canal from Dr White's Bridge, Looking towards Manchester 1857
oil on canvas 34.9 x 46
1928.76

Parry, Joseph 1756–1826
Eccles Wakes: Racing for the Smock 1808
oil on canvas 71.7 x 91.8
1927.12

Parry, Joseph 1756–1826
The Village Fair 1819
oil on panel 26.9 x 34.9
1927.1

Parry, Joseph 1756–1826
Eccles Wakes
oil on panel 30.3 x 30.7
1927.11

Parry, Joseph 1756–1826
Eccles Wakes: Ale-House Interior
oil on canvas 71.3 x 71.3
1927.13

Partington, John Herbert Evelyn 1843–1899
Dr Joseph Gouge Greenwood 1883
oil on canvas 60.9 x 51
1912.69

Partington, John Herbert Evelyn 1843–1899
William Alfred Turner 1886
oil on canvas 127.2 x 101.7
1886.4

Pasini, Alberto 1826–1899
A Cavalcade of Arabs 1869
oil on canvas 55.6 x 46.4
1918.407

Pasmore, Victor 1908–1998
Parisian Café 1936–1937
oil on canvas 71.2 x 91.6
1941.72

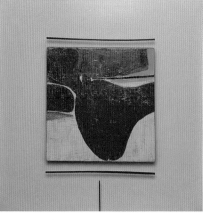

Pasmore, Victor 1908–1998
Red Development No.5 1964
oil on canvas 79.2 x 79.1
1964.288

Passarotti, Bartolomeo (attributed to)
1529–1592
Domenico Giuliani and His Servant 1579
oil on canvas 121 x 92.2
1959.114

Paterson, Emily Murray 1855–1934
Still Life
oil on canvas 34.3 x 42.5
1934.486

Paterson, James 1854–1932
Honfleur
oil on canvas 25.6 x 17.3
1941.69

Patrick, James McIntosh 1907–1998
The Ettrick Shepherd 1936
oil on canvas 76.5 x 101.6
1937.212 🐝

Peake, Mervyn 1911–1968
The Glassblower 1944
oil on canvas 205.4 x 118
1947.39

Peake, Robert (after) c.1551–1619
A Procession of Elizabeth I c.1800–1840
oil on panel 38.4 x 53.3
1947.145

Pearce, Charles Maresco 1874–1964
Conspiracy, Café Verrey 1920
oil on panel 40.6 x 32.4
1925.261

Pearce, Charles Maresco 1874–1964
Corner of Café Verrey 1920
oil on hardboard 40.3 x 31.1
1925.266

Pears, Charles 1873–1958
Camouflaged Merchant Steamer Aground
1918
oil on paper 41.6 x 62.2
1920.8

Peeters I, Bonaventura 1614–1652
A Yacht in a Choppy Sea
oil on panel 40.7 x 36.2
1979.491

Penteshin, Ivan Milyevich b.1927
February Blue 1981
oil on canvas 69.7 x 49.6
1981.91

Peploe, Samuel John 1871–1935
The Aloe Tree 1925
oil on canvas 61 x 50.9
1929.376

Peploe, Samuel John 1871–1935
Rocks at Iona
oil on panel 32 x 39.8
1944.14

Peppercorn, Arthur Douglas 1847–1924
Corn Ricks 1898
oil on canvas 40 x 66.3
1898.11

Peppercorn, Arthur Douglas 1847–1924
Path by the River Ripley
oil on canvas 39.5 x 67.4
1925.6

Facing page: Ansaldo, Giovanni Andrea, 1584–1638, *Allegory of the Arts*, 1590s–1638, Manchester City Galleries (p. 18)

Peppercorn, Arthur Douglas 1847–1924
Seascape
oil on canvas 45.8 x 81.3
1925.61

Peppercorn, Arthur Douglas 1847–1924
The Yacht
oil on canvas 62.2 x 92.6
1913.1

Percy, William 1820–1893
Edwin Waugh 1882
oil on canvas 91.4 x 71.2
1884.49

Perrault, Léon Bazile 1832–1908
Meditation 1870
oil on canvas 92.4 x 73.4
1911.29

Perugini, Charles Edward 1839–1918
Girl Reading 1878
oil on canvas 97.9 x 73
1917.237

Perugino (follower of) c.1450–1523
The Adoration of the Magi c.1510
tempera on panel 22.5 x 59.3
1947.186

Perugino (follower of) c.1450–1523
The Annunciation c.1510
tempera on panel 23.6 x 57.6
1947.184

Perugino (follower of) c.1450–1523
The Nativity with Saint Bridget c.1510
tempera on panel 23.1 x 59.8
1947.185

Perugino (follower of) c.1450–1523
The Presentation in the Temple c.1510
tempera on panel 22.4 x 59.1
1947.187

Peters, Matthew William 1742–1814
Portrait of a Child 1752–1814
oil on canvas 61.3 x 51.5
1947.133

Pether, Abraham 1756–1812
St Albans Abbey, Hertfordshire 1796
oil on canvas 38 x 48
1947.73

Pether, Abraham 1756–1812
Thirlmere, Cumberland 1801
oil on canvas 61.4 x 92
1909.11

Pettie, John 1839–1893
A Song without Words 1859–1888
oil on canvas 60.8 x 43.2
1904.9

Pettie, John 1839–1893
The Duke of Monmouth's Interview with James II
c.1882
oil on canvas 93.4 x 130.5
1899.2

Philippeau, Karel Frans 1825–1897
Playing Cards 1860–1897
oil on panel 33.7 x 46.3
1918.409

Philippeau, Karel Frans 1825–1897
Spinning: Italian Scene 1860–1897
oil on panel 29.5 x 40.1
1918.42

Philpot, Glyn Warren 1884–1937
A Street Accident 1925
oil on canvas 72 x 54.2
1925.69

Pickersgill, Frederick Richard 1820–1900
Mercury Instructing the Nymphs in Dancing
1848
oil on panel 58.3 x 91.7
1896.8

Pickersgill, Frederick Richard 1820–1900
Samson Betrayed 1850
oil on canvas 243.8 x 306
1882.19

Pickersgill, Frederick Richard 1820–1900
A Little Gondelay
oil on millboard 48.3 x 61.1
1909.16

Piot, Antoine 1869–1934
An Italian Lady 19th C
oil on canvas 89.5 x 65.4
1918.408

Piper, John 1903–1992
Autumn at Stourhead 1939
oil on board 63.3 x 76.2
1948.331

Piper, John 1903–1992
Coventry Cathedral, 15 November, 1940 1940
oil on plywood 76.2 x 63.4
1947.42

Piper, John 1903–1992
Ruined Cottage, Tomen y Mur, North Wales
1943
oil on canvas 51.3 x 61.6
1950.67

Pissarro, Camille 1830–1903
Rue de Voisins 1871
oil on canvas 46 x 55.5
1969.67

Pissarro, Camille 1830–1903
Pont de la Clef in Bruges, Belgium 1903
oil on canvas 46.4 x 55.2
1946.69

Pissarro, Félix 1874–1897
The Bonfire
oil on canvas 46.2 x 55.1
1951.62

Pissarro, Lucien 1863–1944
The Hills from Cadborough, Sunset 1913
oil on canvas 54 x 65
1925.309

Pissarro, Lucien 1863–1944
Wild Boar Fell, Brough 1914
oil on canvas 59.6 x 75
1925.306

Pissarro, Lucien 1863–1944
Fishpond Bottom 1915
oil on canvas 40.2 x 59.7
1928.97

Pissarro, Lucien 1863–1944
Willows, Fishpond, Dorset 1915
oil on panel 34.8 x 45.7
1916.9

Pissarro, Lucien 1863–1944
Crockers Lane, Coldharbour 1916
oil on canvas 64.9 x 53.2
1925.302

Pissarro, Lucien 1863–1944
The Dorking Road, Coldharbour, in Snow
1916
oil on canvas 35.5 x 45.7
1925.298

Pissarro, Lucien 1863–1944
November Sunset on the Thames, Kew 1919
oil on canvas 43.4 x 53.2
1925.305

Pissarro, Lucien 1863–1944
Dartmouth 1922
oil on canvas 53.3 x 64.3
1946.19

Pissarro, Lucien 1863–1944
Kingswear through the Mist 1922
oil on canvas 64.8 x 53.3
1925.312

Pissarro, Lucien 1863–1944
On the Dart 1922
oil on canvas 64.8 x 50.5
1939.15

Pissarro, Lucien 1863–1944
The Dart from Week's Hill 1922
oil on canvas 53.3 x 64.7
1951.61

Pissarro, Lucien 1863–1944
La Pierre d'Avignon, Le Lavandou 1923
oil on canvas 60.2 x 73.3
1925.308

Pissarro, Lucien 1863–1944
Quai de Seine 1924
oil on panel 23.4 x 32.9
1944.113

Pissarro, Lucien 1863–1944
Rue Jean Aicard, Bormes 1926
oil on canvas 73 x 60.1
1951.6

Pissarro, Orovida Camille 1893–1968
Zebras Drinking 1937
tempera on canvas 74.2 x 49
1970.1

Pitchforth, Roland Vivian 1895–1982
Burnsall 1925
oil on canvas 51.3 x 61.3
1946.38

Pitchforth, Roland Vivian 1895–1982
Old Stone Waller 1925
oil on canvas 45.6 x 36
1946.42

Pitchforth, Roland Vivian 1895–1982
Bainbridge 1928
oil on canvas 50.6 x 60.9
1946.39

Pitchforth, Roland Vivian 1895–1982
Cottage, Bainbridge 1928
oil on canvas 50.6 x 60.9
1946.37

Pitchforth, Roland Vivian 1895–1982
Still Life 1930
oil on canvas 53.7 x 64.8
1946.41

Pitchforth, Roland Vivian 1895–1982
Still Life 1931
oil on canvas 54 x 65
1946.4

Pitchforth, Roland Vivian 1895–1982
Little Ships on Patrol 1944
oil on canvas 86.5 x 127
1947.366

Pitchforth, Roland Vivian 1895–1982
Hebden, Yorkshire
oil on canvas 63.8 x 76.6
1934.18

Poel, Egbert Lievensz. van der 1621–1664
Skating Scene with a Tent and Numerous Figures on a Wide River 1661
oil on panel 39 x 51.1
1979.492

Polunin, Elizabeth Violet 1878–1950
Anna Pavlova
oil on canvas 50.2 x 38.2
1939.213

Poole, Paul Falconer 1807–1879
Rustic Scene 1849
oil on canvas 50 x 41.1
1896.7

Poole, Paul Falconer 1807–1879
The Goths in Italy 1851–1853
oil on canvas 142 x 209.5
1891.9

Porter, Frederick James 1883–1944
Snow in Hanover Square, London 1926
oil on canvas 54.1 x 72.8
1925.32

Porter, Frederick James 1883–1944
Landscape with River
oil on canvas 55.2 x 73.8
1940.5

Porter, Frederick James 1883–1944
Roses
oil on canvas 45.6 x 35.2
1946.43

Porter, Frederick James 1883–1944
Winter Morning
oil on canvas 54.2 x 65
1934.19

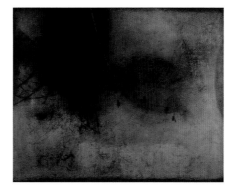

Portway, Douglas 1922–1993
London 1961–1964
oil on canvas 114 x 146
1964.19

Potter, Mary 1900–1981
Hampshire Farm 1939
oil & pencil on panel 61.2 x 76.4
1941.62

Potter, Mary 1900–1981
Night and Day (recto) 1974
oil on board 183.3 x 182.4 (E)
1987.77a

Potter, Mary 1900–1981
Night and Day (verso) 1974
oil on board 183.3 x 182.4 (E)
1987.77b

Potter, Mary 1900–1981
Still Life
oil on plywood 51 x 61.2
1941.121

Facing page: Brockhurst, Gerald Leslie, 1890–1978, *Clytie*, 1920–1924, Manchester City Galleries (p. 45)

Potter, Paulus 1625–1654
Evening Landscape with Cattle and Peasants Dancing to the Sound of a Pipe 1649
oil on panel 37.5 x 50.3
1979.493

Pourbus the elder, Frans 1545–1581
Portrait of an Old Man (possibly Hubertus Langetus) 1580
oil on panel 40.6 x 30.4
1950.298

Poynter, Edward John 1836–1919
The Ides of March 1883
oil on canvas 153 x 112.6
1883.18

Poynter, Edward John 1836–1919
Diana and Endymion 1901
oil on canvas 77.5 x 57.1
1917.254

Poynter, Edward John 1836–1919
The Vision of Endymion 1902
oil on canvas 50.8 x 38.1
1904.2

Poynter, Edward John 1836–1919
Study for 'The Ides of March'
oil on canvas 40.6 x 27.9
1993.3

Praag, Arnold van b.1926
Old Soldier 1963
oil on cardboard 67 x 41.1
1964.49

Priestman, Bertram 1868–1951
The Great Green Hills of Yorkshire 1913
oil on canvas 129.2 x 179.2
1913.18

Prinsep, Valentine Cameron 1838–1904
At the Golden Gate c.1882
oil on canvas 137.5 x 95.8
1883.22

Prinsep, Valentine Cameron 1838–1904
Cinderella 1899
oil on canvas 149.6 x 113.1
1908.17

Prinsep, Valentine Cameron 1838–1904
The Queen was in the Parlour, Eating Bread and Honey
oil on panel 59.6 x 33
1938.487

Pritchett, Edward active c.1828–1879
St Mark's, Venice
oil on canvas 35.7 x 30.8
1902.5

Prout, Margaret Fisher 1875–1963
Mays Farm (recto) 1941
oil on board 47.5 x 58
1957.2

Prout, Margaret Fisher 1875–1963
Mays Farm (verso)
oil (?)
1957.2

Pryde, James Ferrier 1866–1941
The Arch 1926
oil on canvas 73.7 x 71.2
1927.15

Pym, Roland Vivian 1920–2006
Italian Girls 1938
oil on canvas 51 x 69
1939.212

Pyne, James Baker 1800–1870
Boppard on the Rhine 1858
oil on canvas 41.4 x 51.3
1917.159

Raeburn, Henry (attributed to) 1756–1823
Alexander Gordon, 4th Duke of Gordon
oil on canvas 76.5 x 63.6
1902.11

Raeburn, Henry (attributed to) 1756–1823
Mrs Shafto Clarke and Her Daughter
1785–1795
oil on canvas 126 x 100.6
1917.173

Raeburn, Henry (attributed to) 1756–1823
Alexander Campbell of Hillyards c.1808–1812
oil on canvas 75.5 x 62.2
1917.174

Ramsay, Patricia 1886–1974
Tiger Lilies 1896–1974
oil on board 62.5 x 57.9
1934.7

Ranken, William Bruce Ellis 1881–1941
Ernest Thesiger
oil on canvas 128 x 102.4
1942.22

Rankley, Alfred 1819–1872
Music Hath Charms
oil on canvas 44.1 x 56.2
1971.39

Ratcliffe, William Whitehead 1870–1955
Winter Scene, Sweden 1913
oil on canvas 61.6 x 76.7
1946.44

Ratcliffe, William Whitehead 1870–1955
Still Life by the Fire c.1914
oil on canvas 67 x 54
2011.114

Ratcliffe, William Whitehead 1870–1955
Swedish Farm
oil on canvas 61 x 76.4
1955.35

Rawson, James active 1855–1863
Apples, Grapes and Strawberries 1863
oil on panel 19 x 26.7
1920.544

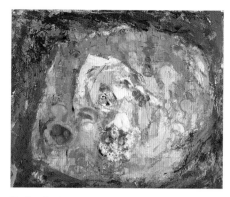

Redpath, Anne 1895–1965
Table Top c.1961
oil on hardboard 86.4 x 106.7
1962.46 ※

Reekie, William Maxwell 1869–1948
A Convoy in the Mediterranean, April 1918
1918
oil on canvas 30.2 x 40.3
1920.134

Reekie, William Maxwell 1869–1948
Llaneillian 1929–1930
oil on canvas 30.2 x 40.4
1930.169

Reekie, William Maxwell 1869–1948
Maclellan's Castle 1936
oil on canvas 45.6 x 60.9
1937.43

Reid, Flora Macdonald 1860–c.1940
A Doubtful Customer 1902
oil on canvas 35.9 x 25.7
1902.16

Reid, Flora Macdonald 1860–c.1940
A Cornish Fishwife 1904
oil on canvas 61.4 x 46.2
1904.19

Reid, George 1841–1913
The Reverend Alexander McLaren 1896
oil on canvas 123.7 x 80.4
1896.28

Reid, George 1841–1913
Alderman Sir James Hoy 1902–1903
oil on canvas 124 x 95.2
1903.16

Reid, George 1841–1913
James Moorhouse
oil on canvas 124 x 102.7
1924.35

Reid, John Robertson 1851–1926
The Mermaid's Arrival
oil on canvas 25.2 x 35.4
1913.13

Reni, Guido 1575–1642
Saint Catherine 1638–1640
oil on canvas 102 x 83.6
1974.88

Renoir, Pierre-Auguste 1841–1919
Seated Woman 1861–1870
oil on canvas 55.2 x 46.5
1947.164

Renoir, Pierre-Auguste 1841–1919
Seated Nude c.1897
oil on canvas 40.1 x 33.8
1972.9

Reynolds, Alan b.1926
Moonlight 1956
oil on hardboard 63.3 x 76.1
1957.9

Reynolds, Joshua 1723–1792
Charles, 9th Lord Cathcart c.1753–1755
oil on canvas 124 x 99
1981.36

Reynolds, Joshua 1723–1792
*Jane Hamilton, Wife of 9th Lord Cathcart, and
Her Daughter Jane, Later Duchess of Atholl*
1754–1755
oil on canvas 124 x 99
1981.37

Reynolds, Joshua 1723–1792
Lady Anstruther c.1763
oil on canvas 76.5 x 62.6
1898.4

Reynolds, Joshua 1723–1792
Admiral Lord Hood c.1783
oil on canvas 127.2 x 100.9
1898.3

Ricci, Marco (attributed to) 1676–1730
A Storm at Sea 1700–1730
oil on canvas 96.3 x 154
1966.335

Ricci, Sebastiano (school of) 1659–1734
Mercury, Herse and Aglauros 1720–1734
oil on canvas 88.5 x 58.8
1954.903

Richards, Albert 1919–1945
Royal Engineers' Dump
oil on cardboard 55.8 x 75.9
1947.43

Richardson, Edward Harrison 1881–1952
Albert Square, Manchester c.1930
oil on canvas 24.7 x 29.7
1980.323

Richardson the elder, Jonathan (attributed to)
c.1664–1667–1745
Portrait of a Gentleman in Red Velvet
oil on canvas 75.4 x 63
1973.291

Richmond, William Blake 1842–1921
*Near Viareggio, Where Shelley's Body Was
Found* 1876
oil on canvas 91.5 x 228.8
1924.63

Richter, Herbert Davis 1874–1955
An Artist's Home 1927
oil on canvas 101.6 x 76.4
1927.17

Ricketts, Charles S. 1866–1931
The Trojan Women 1922–1924
oil on canvas 109 x 79.9
1948.33

Ricketts, Charles S. 1866–1931
Faust and the Centaur
oil on canvas 75.5 x 63
1933.22

Ricketts, Charles S. 1866–1931
Montezuma
oil on canvas 104 x 88.8
1915.1

Rietschoof, Jan Claesz. 1652–1719
Massed Shipping Anchored in the Foreground:
A View of Rotterdam Beyond 1706
oil on panel 65 x 83.7
1979.495

Riley, Bridget b.1931
Zephyr 1976
acrylic on linen 224.5 x 107.3
1977.3

Riley, Cecil b.1917
St Cross Road, Oxford 1941
oil on canvas 61 x 76.5
1943.74

Ritchie, Hannah active 1926–1932
Meije, Upper Savoy 1928
oil on canvas 56 x 46
1930.2

Riviere, Briton 1840–1920
Calves in a Meadow 1864
oil on millboard 20.1 x 25.4
1920.547

Riviere, Briton 1840–1920
His Only Friend 1871
oil on canvas 69.4 x 95.1
1937.124

Riviere, Briton 1840–1920
The Last of the Garrison 1875
oil on canvas 105 x 152.8
1898.7

Riviere, Briton 1840–1920
'In Manus Tuas, Domine' 1879
oil on canvas 147.7 x 217.6
1902.14

Riviere, Briton 1840–1920
Daniel's Answer to the King 1890
oil on canvas 120.5 x 187.9
1937.123

Riviere, Briton 1840–1920
Dead Hector 1892
oil on canvas 76.8 x 122.7
1917.259

Roberts, David 1796–1864
The Lady Chapel, Church of St Pierre, Caen
1832
oil on panel 48.7 x 39.7
1904.8

Roberts, David 1796–1864
*The High Altar of the Church of SS Giovanni e
Paolo at Venice* 1858
oil on canvas 142.3 x 107.5
1920.537

Roberts, Lancelot Percival 1883–1950
A Lancashire Lass 1929
oil on canvas 76.4 x 58.8
1929.13

Roberts, William Patrick 1895–1980
Sarah 1920–1931
oil on canvas 61.2 x 51
1931.1

Roberts, William Patrick 1895–1980
A Woman (Sarah) c.1927
oil on canvas 61 x 50.8
1928.51

Robertson, John Ewart 1820–1879
James Hatton 1830
oil on canvas 91.7 x 101.5
1908.24

Robinson, Bob b.1951
Going to the Wall 1982
oil on canvas 129 x 113.5
1986.462

Roden, William Thomas 1817–1892
John Henry Newman after 1874
oil on canvas 127 x 101.3
1908.25

Rodgers, Roy b.1935
Composition with Sunflowers 1958
acrylic on canvas 91.5 x 91.4
1966.184

Roelofs, Willem 1822–1897
Ferme sous les arbres
oil on canvas 29.9 x 41.4
1979.616

Romiti, Gino 1881–1967
An Old Tuscan Road 1908
oil on canvas 60 x 80
1930.8

Romney, George 1734–1802
Mrs Margaret Ainslie c.1764
oil on canvas 126.5 x 101.4
1917.177

Romney, George 1734–1802
Captain William Peere Williams c.1782
oil on canvas 126.9 x 101
1950.297

Ronaldson, Thomas Martine 1881–1942
Summer 1928
oil on canvas 71.1 x 55.9
1929.32

Rooker, Michael Angelo 1746–1801
Westgate, Winchester 1779
oil on canvas 50.8 x 40
1948.224

Rosoman, Leonard Henry 1913–2012
Auxiliary Fireman Leonard Rosoman,
Cheapside 1940
oil on canvas 56.2 x 66.6
1947.405

Facing page: Wimpenny, George Henry, 1857–1939, *Chetham's Reading Room*, Chetham's Library (p. 11)

Rossetti, Dante Gabriel 1828–1882
The Bower Meadow 1850–1872
oil on canvas 86.3 x 68
1909.15

Rossetti, Dante Gabriel 1828–1882
Joli Coeur 1867
oil on mahogany 38.1 x 30.2
1937.746

Rossetti, Dante Gabriel 1828–1882
Astarte Syriaca 1877
oil on canvas 185 x 109
1891.5

Rothenstein, William 1872–1945
Le grand if vert 1900–1904
oil on canvas 84 x 61.3
1925.275

Rothenstein, William 1872–1945
Alice by the Fireside 1901–1913
oil on canvas 76.2 x 64
1925.269

Rothenstein, William 1872–1945
In the Morning Room c.1905
oil on canvas 107.5 x 76.2
1925.297

Rothenstein, William 1872–1945
The Church of St Seine L'Abbaye 1906
oil on canvas 76.5 x 55.7
1939.1

Rothenstein, William 1872–1945
Reading the Book of Esther 1907–1909
oil on canvas 87 x 106.5
1925.307

Rothenstein, William 1872–1945
Nature's Ramparts 1908
oil on canvas 89.6 x 101.4
1925.276

Rothenstein, William 1872–1945
Eli the Thatcher 1913
oil on canvas 76.5 x 63.3
1939.11

Rothenstein, William 1872–1945
Tree in Winter 1916
oil on canvas 76 x 101.7
1939.12

Rothenstein, William 1872–1945
Self Portrait 1919
oil on canvas 76.2 x 63
1935.158

Rothenstein, William 1872–1945
The Beech Wood c.1923
oil on canvas 101.6 x 76.3
1925.263

Rothenstein, William 1872–1945
Sir Arthur Dixon 1941
oil on canvas 76.3 x 61.2
1947.364

Rothenstein, William 1872–1945
At the Window
oil on canvas 56.2 x 44.9
1925.567

Rothenstein, William 1872–1945
Flower, Fruit and Thorn Piece
oil on canvas 59.8 x 75
1925.294

Rothenstein, William 1872–1945
Ignacio Zuloaga as a Torero
oil on canvas 81.3 x 45.7
1925.558

Rothenstein, William 1872–1945
Iles' Farm, Winter
oil on canvas 71.7 x 92
1925.274

Rothenstein, William 1872–1945
Princess Betty
oil on canvas 96 x 76.4
1925.304

Rothenstein, William 1872–1945
Rachel Queen
oil on canvas 96 x 76.1
1925.31

Rothenstein, William 1872–1945
St Martin's Summer
oil on canvas 84.4 x 91.8
1925.29

Rothenstein, William 1872–1945
The Church at Bourlon
oil on canvas 80.5 x 100
1920.82

Rotius, Jan Albertsz. 1624–1666
Portrait of a Boy with a Dog 1660
oil on canvas 114.6 x 88
1930.54

Roworth, Edward 1880–1964
W. Maxwell Reekie
oil on canvas 120.8 x 99.5
1988.107

Royle, Herbert F. 1870–1958
Haymakers
oil on canvas 71 x 91.5
1916.6

Rubin, Reuven 1893–1974
Bethlehem
oil on canvas 60 x 73
1938.538

Ruisdael, Jacob van 1628/1629–1682
Landscape with a Woman and Child Walking along a Wooded Country Lane 1649
oil on panel 25.9 x 21.4
1979.496

Ruisdael, Jacob van 1628/1629–1682
A Storm off the Dutch Coast 1660–1670
oil on canvas 85.3 x 100.4
1955.124

Rutherford, Harry 1903–1985
Penzance 1930
oil on millboard 63.2 x 76
1930.167

Rutherford, Harry 1903–1985
Suburban Summer 1935
oil & charcoal on canvas 63.3 x 76.1
1936.3

Rutherford, Harry 1903–1985
Sennen Cove
oil on canvas 40.6 x 50.8
1957.85

Rutherston, Albert 1881–1953
The Chicken Market, Bourbonnais 1905
oil on canvas 46.1 x 60.8
1925.293

Ruysdael, Salomon van c.1602–1670
*River Scene with Sailing Boats Unloading at
the Shore* 1630–1660
oil on panel 42.2 x 59.7
1979.498

Ruysdael, Salomon van c.1602–1670
*Winter Scene with Sledges and Skaters on a
River* 1656
oil on panel 39.6 x 59.1
1979.497

Ryan, Adrian 1920–1998
Daffodils and Tulips 1951
oil on canvas 61.1 x 41
1954.896

Rysbrack, Pieter Andreas c.1684–1690–1748
Dead Game 1740
oil on canvas 72.2 x 91.7
1908.36

Sadler, Walter Dendy 1854–1923
In the Camp of the Amalekites 1888
oil on canvas 99.6 x 138
1889.1

Salanson, Eugénie Marie 1864–1892
Head of a Girl
oil on canvas 41 x 33
1917.219

Salanson, Eugénie Marie 1864–1892
La Francine de Grandville
oil on canvas 55.2 x 46.2
1917.218

Sandys, Frederick 1829–1904
Vivien 1863
oil on canvas 64 x 52.5
1925.7

Sant, James 1820–1916
A Thorn amidst the Roses 1887
oil on canvas 111.8 x 86.5
1887.12

Santoro, Rubens 1859–1942
A Siesta in Sunshine 1878
oil on canvas 35.5 x 61.9
1918.405

Santoro, Rubens 1859–1942
Basket Makers in Naples 1878
oil on canvas 67.5 x 64.1
1918.4

Sargent, Frederick 1837–1899 & **Saunders, H. L.** d.1899
Interior of the Manchester Royal Exchange 1877
oil on canvas 153.4 x 215.5
1968.245

Sargent, John Singer 1856–1925
Albanian Olive Gatherers 1909
oil on canvas 96 x 115.1
1910.2

Sargent, John Singer 1856–1925
An Italian Sailor
oil on canvas 77 x 63.5
1926.35

Sargent, John Singer 1856–1925
Mrs Duxbury and Daughter
oil on canvas 144.5 x 97.1
1945.41

Satchwell, Eric b.1926
Playing Fields 1953
oil on canvas 25.2 x 34
1954.1064

Sayers, Reuben Thomas William 1815–1888
The Water Lily 1850
oil on canvas 79 x 48.2
1882.24

Scheffer, Ary 1795–1858
The Holy Women at the Sepulchre
oil on panel 108.8 x 86
1924.17

Schooten, Floris Gerritsz. van c.1585–after 1655
Still Life: Fruit, Bread and a Goblet on a Table 1630–1635
oil on panel 34.2 x 55.5
1979.499

Schreyer, Christian Adolphe 1828–1899
Abandoned
oil on canvas 130 x 250
1888.3

Schwabe, Randolph 1885–1948
Head of an Old Woman
oil on panel 34.5 x 25.1
1925.564

Schweitzer, Adolf Gustav 1847–1914
The Old Diligence in Winter 1877
oil on canvas 106.6 x 77.6
1918.402

Scott, William Bell (after) 1811–1890
Peter Vischer (1487–1528)
oil on canvas 278 x 100
1907.39

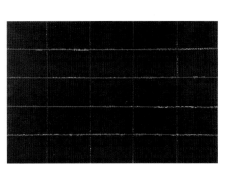

Scully, Sean b.1945
Drawing No.4 1974
acrylic on paper
1975.76

Seabrooke, Elliott 1886–1950
Wallflowers 1928–1932
oil on millboard 50.3 x 60.7
1976.124

Seabrooke, Elliott 1886–1950
Lock House, Heybridge Basin 1948–1950
oil on canvas 51 x 61.2
1976.122

Seabrooke, Elliott 1886–1950
Aix-en-Provence
oil on canvas 70.8 x 91.3
1976.123

Seeman, Isaac d.1751
George Lloyd 1734
oil on canvas 76 x 64
1982.157

Semenowsky, Emile Eisman 1857–1911
Autumn 1870–1890
oil on panel 56.1 x 37.8
1917.211

Severdonck, Franz van 1809–1889
Domestic Fowl in a Landscape 1867
oil on panel 17.8 x 24
1938.504

Shackleton, William 1872–1933
The Sailor's Funeral 1908–1925
oil on cardboard 34.3 x 35.6
1925.559

Facing page: Bomberg, David, 1890–1957, *Figure Composition*, c.1913, Manchester City Galleries (p. 34)

Shackleton, William 1872–1933
Bed Time 1925
oil on canvas 45.2 x 49.1
1938.409

Shackleton, William 1872–1933
Grass of Parnassus 1925–1933
oil on canvas 54.6 x 64
1938.41

Shannon, Charles Haslewood 1863–1937
The Mill Pond 1905
oil on canvas 109.2 x 103.5
1909.21

Shannon, Charles Haslewood 1863–1937
Toilet Scene I
oil on canvas 53.3 x 53.3
1948.27

Shannon, Charles Haslewood 1863–1937
Toilet Scene II
oil on canvas 51.4 x 55.7
1948.271

Sharp, Dorothea 1874–1955
The Yellow Balloon 1937
oil on canvas 63.3 x 76.3
1938.486

Shaw, Peter 1926–1982
Kinder Scout 1972
oil on canvas 84.4 x 109.4
1973.1

Shayer, William 1787–1879
Landscape with Cattle by a Stream
oil on canvas 71.4 x 91.8
1917.251

Shee, Martin Archer 1769–1850
Major General Sir Barry Close, Bt 1811–1850
oil on canvas 127 x 101.9
1955.25

Sheffield Junior, George 1839–1892
A Hundred Years Ago 1890
oil on canvas 117.3 x 166
1890.6

Shephard, Rupert 1909–1992
Hedgerow 1943
oil on canvas 51 x 41
1946.77

Shepherd, Juliana Charlotte c.1832–1898
Thoughts of the Future
oil on canvas 40.2 x 30.4
1899.1

Shields, Frederick James 1833–1911
William Blake's Room 1882–1911
oil on canvas 30.5 x 39.5
1917.675

Shields, Frederick James 1833–1911
The Annunciation 1894
oil on canvas 84.5 x 53.5
1917.282

Shields, Frederick James 1833–1911
The Wild Sea's Engulfing Maw (The Gouliot Caves, Sark) 1894
oil on canvas 64 x 78.1
1917.287

Shields, Frederick James 1833–1911
Hamlet and the Ghost 1901
oil on canvas 60 x 41
1917.676

Shields, Frederick James 1833–1911
Edwin Gibbs
oil on canvas 76 x 63
1903.14

Shields, Frederick James 1833–1911
Kiss Me, Baby
oil on canvas 17.3 x 43.5
1917.302

Shields, Frederick James 1833–1911
The Good Shepherd
oil on canvas 164 x 105.8
1913.17

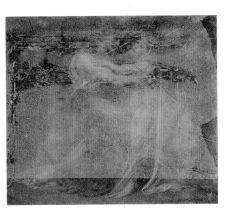

Shields, Frederick James 1833–1911
The Widow's Son
oil on canvas 56 x 65.1
1917.304

Shields, Frederick James 1833–1911
Touch Me Not
oil on canvas 30.1 x 55.7
1917.305

Sickert, Walter Richard 1860–1942
The Grey Dress 1884
oil on canvas 50.9 x 30.2
1947.76

Sickert, Walter Richard 1860–1942
Dieppe c.1885
oil on panel 22.5 x 35.3
1947.91

Sickert, Walter Richard 1860–1942
Charles Bradlaugh at the Bar of the House of Commons c.1892–1893
oil on canvas 228.4 x 121.6
1911.49

Sickert, Walter Richard 1860–1942
Mamma Mia Poveretta 1901–1906
oil on canvas 46 x 38.2
1911.103

Sickert, Walter Richard 1860–1942
Jack the Ripper's Bedroom 1906–1907
oil on canvas 50.8 x 40.7
1980.303

Sickert, Walter Richard 1860–1942
The Blue Hat 1911–1915
oil on canvas 50.7 x 40.6
1925.265

Sickert, Walter Richard 1860–1942
Hubby and Marie c.1912
oil on canvas 51 x 40.7
1925.576

Sickert, Walter Richard 1860–1942
Interior with Nude 1914
oil on canvas 50.8 x 40.8
1925.578

Sickert, Walter Richard 1860–1942
Paradise Row, Bath 1917
oil on canvas 51.5 x 43.6
1925.311

Sickert, Walter Richard 1860–1942
Victor Lecour 1922–1924
oil on canvas 81.3 x 60.5
1947.165

Sickert, Walter Richard 1860–1942
O nuit d'amour c.1922
oil on canvas 90.2 x 69.8
1998.42

Sickert, Walter Richard 1860–1942
Cicely Hey c.1922–1923
oil on canvas 61 x 50.8
1980.304

Sickert, Walter Richard 1860–1942
Le Grand Duquesne, Dieppe
oil on canvas 131.6 x 104.8
1935.159

Sickert, Walter Richard 1860–1942
The Mirror
oil on canvas 27.1 x 21.7
1925.272

Sickert, Walter Richard (attributed to)
1860–1942
Les Modistes 1885–1887
oil on canvas 55.7 x 43
1928.1

Siefert, Arthur b.1858
Devotion
oil on panel 35 x 27.2
1917.24

Simcock, Jack 1929–2012
Hay Shed and Head I 1964
oil on hardboard 33 x 50.8
1965.266

Simon, J. 1861–1945
Israeli Scene with Figures
oil on hardboard 35.2 x 44.8
1968.153

Sisley, Alfred 1839–1899
A Normandy Farm 1874
oil on canvas 49.6 x 59.8
1927.19

Smallfield, Frederick 1829–1915
Early Lovers 1858
oil on canvas 76.4 x 46.1
1903.7

Smart, Edgar Rowley 1887–1934
Quai St Michel, Paris 1928
oil on canvas 54 x 65
1928.12

Smart, Edgar Rowley 1887–1934
'Wheatsheaf Hotel' 1932
oil on canvas 50.8 x 66
1934.1

Smart, Edgar Rowley 1887–1934
Landscape: A Mountain Valley with a Church
oil on canvas 51 x 61
1960.38

Smart, Edgar Rowley 1887–1934
The Mill, Giverny
oil on canvas 51 x 60.9
1927.36

Smith, David Murray 1865–1952
On the Sussex Downs
oil on canvas 51.5 x 61.7
1914.52

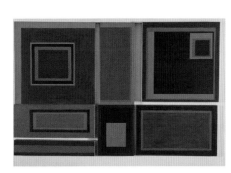

Smith, Donald b.1934
Estate V 1968
acrylic on wood 75.6 x 101.5
1968.101

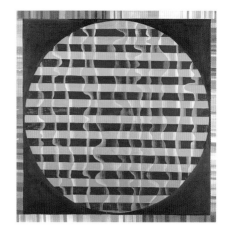

Smith, Jack 1928–2011
Shimmer: Red and Orange 1962
oil on canvas 137.3 x 137.7
1965.1

Smith, James H. active 1781–1789
Sir Thomas Egerton, Bt, as an Archer in Heaton Park 1781–1785
oil on canvas 228.6 x 147.3
1958.54

Smith, Mary W. active 1947–1956
Girl with a Book 1947
oil on canvas 60.7 x 50.7
1956.101

Smith, Matthew Arnold Bracy 1879–1959
Pomegranates 1928–1959
oil on canvas 38 x 46
1928.42

Smith, Matthew Arnold Bracy 1879–1959
Dahlias 1929
oil on canvas 60.9 x 61
1931.19

Smith, Matthew Arnold Bracy 1879–1959
Model Reclining 1933
oil on canvas 54.3 x 65
1934.193

Smith, Matthew Arnold Bracy 1879–1959
Reclining Female Nude
oil on canvas 45 x 54
1995.51

Smith, Ray b.1949
Celebration 1978
acrylic on cotton duck 182.9 x 136.5
1986.229

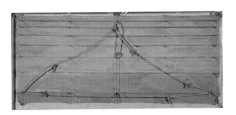

Smith, Richard b.1931
Grey/Blue (Coathanger) 1972
acrylic on canvas 85.2 x 200.3
1992.115

Smith, Thomas c.1720–1767
View from Durdham Down, near Bristol
oil on canvas 70 x 109.3
1919.1

Snyders, Frans 1579–1657
The Leopards
oil on canvas 117.5 x 165.4
1908.19

Soens, Jan 1547/1548–1611/1614
The Holy Family with the Infant Baptist
1560–1570
oil on canvas 158.3 x 110.8
1961.74

Solomon, Simeon 1840–1905
Study: Female Figure 1873
oil on paper 25 x 15.1
1933.7

Solomon, Simeon 1840–1905
The Magic Crystal (Study: Male Figure) 1878
oil on paper 32 x 18.1
1933.71

Somerset, Richard Gay 1848–1928
A Surrey Pastoral 1878
oil on canvas 61 x 120.9
1904.11

Somerset, Richard Gay 1848–1928
Conway Quay
oil on canvas 76.1 x 114.2
1896.16

Somerset, Richard Gay 1848–1928
Evening
oil on canvas 35.4 x 55
1896.17

Somerset, Richard Gay 1848–1928
On the Elwy, Denbighshire
oil on canvas 65.7 x 101.5
1883.2

Sorgh, Hendrik Martensz. 1609/1611–1670
A Fish Stall by a Harbour 1650–1670
oil on panel 31.2 x 26.2
1979.5

Sorgh, Hendrik Martensz. 1609/1611–1670
Kitchen Interior with a Man Bringing Fish for Sale 1657
oil on panel 47 x 62.9
1979.501

Sorgh, Hendrik Martensz. 1609/1611–1670
Fishing Boats in a Choppy Sea 1666
oil on panel 35.7 x 49.6
1979.502

Sorrell, Alan 1904–1974
Marching Down to the Station 1945
acrylic on paper 32.5 x 43.6
1947.413

Souch, John c.1593–1645
Sir Thomas Aston at the Deathbed of His Wife 1635
oil on canvas 203.2 x 215.1
1927.15

Southall, Joseph Edward 1861–1944
A Bucket of Salt Water 1912
tempera on linen 40.6 x 23.5
1925.285

Southall, Joseph Edward 1861–1944
The Lickey, Worcestershire 1921–1925
tempera on cardboard 23.3 x 30.5
1925.283

Soyer, Paul Constant 1823–1903
A Young Artist 1840–1900
oil on canvas 22.7 x 18
1918.421

Spear, Ruskin 1911–1990
Airgraphs on Drying Drums in the Dark Room
oil on canvas 63.2 x 76.2
1947.398 🐝

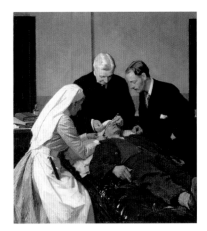

Speed, Harold 1872–1957
Dr David Little Operating for Cataract 1919
oil on canvas 136.3 x 122.2
1919.27

Spencelayh, Charles 1865–1958
The White Rat 1899
oil on canvas 30.6 x 25.4
1926.1 🐝

Spencelayh, Charles 1865–1958
Generation to Generation 1949
oil on canvas 82.6 x 62.8
1954.6 🐝

Spencer, Gilbert 1892–1979
Blackmoor Vale 1931
oil on canvas 61 x 106.7
1932.43 🐝

Spencer, Gilbert 1892–1979
Burdens Farm with Melbury Beacon c.1943
oil on canvas 50.9 x 61.4
1943.41 🐝

Spencer, Gilbert 1892–1979
The Cottage Window
oil on canvas 46 x 56.1
1937.674 🐝

Spencer, Gilbert 1892–1979
Twyford Dorset
oil on canvas 50.8 x 76.5
1937.21 🐝

Facing page: Millais, John Everett, 1829–1896, *Victory O Lord*, 1871, Manchester City Galleries (p. 167)

Spencer, Jean 1942–1998
4 Part Painting (Nuremberg) 1989
oil on canvas 113 x 75
2002.67 (1)

Spencer, Jean 1942–1998
4 Part Painting (Nuremberg) 1989
oil on canvas 113 x 75
2002.67 (2)

Spencer, Jean 1942–1998
4 Part Painting (Nuremberg) 1989
oil on canvas 113 x 75
2002.67 (3)

Spencer, Jean 1942–1998
4 Part Painting (Nuremberg) 1989
oil on canvas 113 x 75
2002.67 (4)

Spencer, Liam David b.1964
Cakebread Street (Sunshine after Rain) 1998
oil on board 17 x 21
2002.1

Spencer, Liam David b.1964
Chapel Street And Blackfriars, 2001 2001
oil on board 15 x 126
2003.152 (P)

Spencer, Liam David b.1964
City of Manchester Stadium 2008
oil on board 30.3 x 40.6
2011.86

Spencer, Stanley 1891–1959
The Boatbuilder's Yard, Cookham 1936
oil on canvas 86.6 x 71.4
1936.272

Spencer, Stanley 1891–1959
A Village in Heaven 1937
oil on canvas 43.5 x 183.5
1937.707

Spencer, Stanley 1891–1959
Cookham Moor 1937
oil on canvas 50.9 x 76.3
1937.706

Spender, John Humphrey 1910–2005
Still Life with Pears 1947
oil, ink & wax on canvas 27.1 x 36.8
1947.447

Spenlove-Spenlove, Frank 1866–1933
The Little White Cross 1902
oil on canvas 91.5 x 60.9
1904.5

Spenlove-Spenlove, Frank 1866–1933
In the Shadow of the Church, Dordrecht, Holland 1903
oil on canvas 101.5 x 106.8
1904.2

Spindler, Louis Pierre 1800–1889
Eliza Crosfield 1843
oil on canvas 76.1 x 63.2
1971.63

Spindler, Louis Pierre 1800–1889
William Crosfield 1843
oil on canvas 77 x 64
1971.62

Stamper, James William 1873–1947
Wallflowers 1926
oil on canvas 45.7 x 35.7
1926.69

Stanfield, Clarkson Frederick 1793–1867
The Last of the Crew 1853
oil on canvas 83.5 x 121.5
1920.532

Stanhope, John Roddam Spencer 1829–1908
Eve Tempted c.1877
tempera on panel 161.2 x 75.5
1883.29

Stanhope, John Roddam Spencer 1829–1908
The Waters of Lethe by the Plains of Elysium
c.1880
tempera on canvas 147.5 x 282.4
1889.4

Stanzione, Massimo 1585–1656
Salome with the Head of John the Baptist
oil on canvas 106 x 126.9
1958.1007

Stark, James 1794–1859
A Barge on the Yare: Sunset
oil on panel 26.8 x 36.5
1917.161

Stark, James 1794–1859
Landscape in Norfolk
oil on canvas 52.1 x 70.5
1903.6

Stark, James 1794–1859
Landscape with a Path Between Cottages
oil on panel 17.4 x 21.5
1917.152

Steen, Jan 1625/1626–1679
The Rommelpot: Interior with Three Figures
1650–1679
oil on panel 32.8 x 26.1
1979.503

Steer, Philip Wilson 1860–1942
Summer at Cowes 1888
oil on canvas 50.9 x 61.2
1970.191

Steer, Philip Wilson 1860–1942
A Young Girl in a White Dress 1892
oil on canvas 46 x 38.2
1947.79

Steer, Philip Wilson 1860–1942
The Mill, Bridgnorth 1901
oil on canvas 46 x 61.1
1925.301

Steer, Philip Wilson 1860–1942
A Lady in Black 1904–1925
oil on canvas 112.5 x 87.3
1925.282

Steer, Philip Wilson 1860–1942
Summer 1905
oil on canvas 111.9 x 86.5
1932.52

Steer, Philip Wilson 1860–1942
The Mauve Dress 1905
oil on canvas 54 x 43.2
1930.21

Steer, Philip Wilson 1860–1942
The Horseshoe Bend of the Severn 1909
oil on canvas 76.4 x 101.6
1923.25

Steer, Philip Wilson 1860–1942
The Deserted Quarry, Ironbridge 1910
oil on canvas 92 x 137
1929.44

Steer, Philip Wilson 1860–1942
Mist over the Needles 1919–1929
oil on canvas 45.9 x 76.7
1929.377

Steer, Philip Wilson 1860–1942
Return of the Fishing Fleet 1920–1942
oil on canvas 46 x 76.4
1947.146

Steer, Philip Wilson 1860–1942
The Ferry, Avonmouth 1922
oil on canvas 51.2 x 76.1
1925.286

Steer, Philip Wilson 1860–1942
The Embarkment
oil on canvas 55.8 x 69
1947.127

Steggles, Harold 1911–1971
Essex Landscape 1930
oil on canvas 36 x 45.9
1931.2

Steggles, Walter James 1908–1997
Norfolk Small Holding
oil on panel 32.4 x 35.8
1946.78

Steggles, Walter James 1908–1997
The Quay, Walberswick
oil on canvas 40.9 x 61.4
1977.87

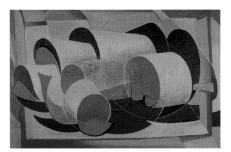

Stephenson, Cecil 1889–1965
Scrolls I 1933
oil on canvas 63.5 x 101.4
1977.1

Stevens, Harry 1919–2008
Kite in the Sea 1949
oil on canvas 43 x 58.7
1970.3

Stevenson, William Lennie b.1911
Still Life 1953
oil on hardboard 60.7 x 76
1955.135

Stokes, Adrian Scott 1854–1935
Snow in the Tyrol 1900–1917
oil on canvas 112.5 x 132.3
1917.203

Stokes, Adrian Scott 1854–1935
November in the Dolomites 1904
oil on canvas 50.2 x 65.9
1904.21

Stone, Frank 1800–1859
Self Portrait 1820–1825
oil on canvas 77 x 63.3
1893.19

Stone, Henry 1616–1653
Thomas Fairfax, 3rd Baron Fairfax
oil on canvas 76.8 x 63.2
1903.13

Stone, Marcus C. 1840–1921
Two's Company, Three's None c.1860–1892
oil on panel 31.1 x 51.6
1917.196

Stone, Marcus C. 1840–1921
A Girl in a Garden 1879
oil on canvas 74 x 49 (E)
1917.198

Stone, Marcus C. 1840–1921
The Lost Bird 1883
oil on canvas 108.2 x 56
1884.14

Stone, Marcus C. 1840–1921
Reverie 1899–1917
oil on canvas 76.5 x 51
1917.231

Stone, Marcus C. 1840–1921
A Passing Cloud
oil on canvas 24.7 x 40
1917.209

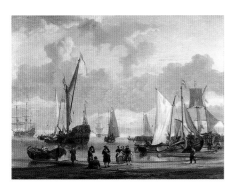

Storck, Abraham Jansz. 1644–1708
*Coast Scene with Shipping Anchored Off-Shore
and Figures on a Beach in the Foreground*
1664–1704
oil on panel 36.4 x 49.1
1979.504

Storck, Abraham Jansz. 1644–1708
Shipping off Amsterdam 1664–1704
oil on canvas 29.3 x 34.5
1908.31

Stott, Edward William 1859–1918
Feeding the Ducks 1885
oil on canvas 48 x 39.4
1947.72

Stott, Edward William 1859–1918
Noonday
oil on canvas 71.8 x 91.5
1917.204

Stott, Edward William 1859–1918
Sunday Morning
oil on canvas 88 x 101.8
1913.6

Stott, Edward William 1859–1918
The Bird Cage
oil on canvas 76.6 x 52 (E)
1917.212

Stott, Edward William 1859–1918
The Old Gate
oil on canvas 81.6 x 97.6
1912.3

Stott, Edward William 1859–1918
The Riverbank
oil on canvas 69.9 x 96
1908.1

Stott, William 1857–1900
The Eiger 1880–1900
oil on canvas 94.3 x 149.2
1912.57

Stott, William 1857–1900
A Summer's Day
oil on canvas 132.9 x 189.3
1915.8

Stott, William 1857–1900
Awakening of the Spirit of the Rose
oil on canvas 94.6 x 142.2
1914.22

Stott, William 1857–1900
Ravenglass
oil on panel 44.9 x 53.1
1947.131

Facing page: Souch, John, c.1593–1645, *Sir Thomas Aston at the Deathbed of His Wife*, 1635,
Manchester City Galleries (p. 225)

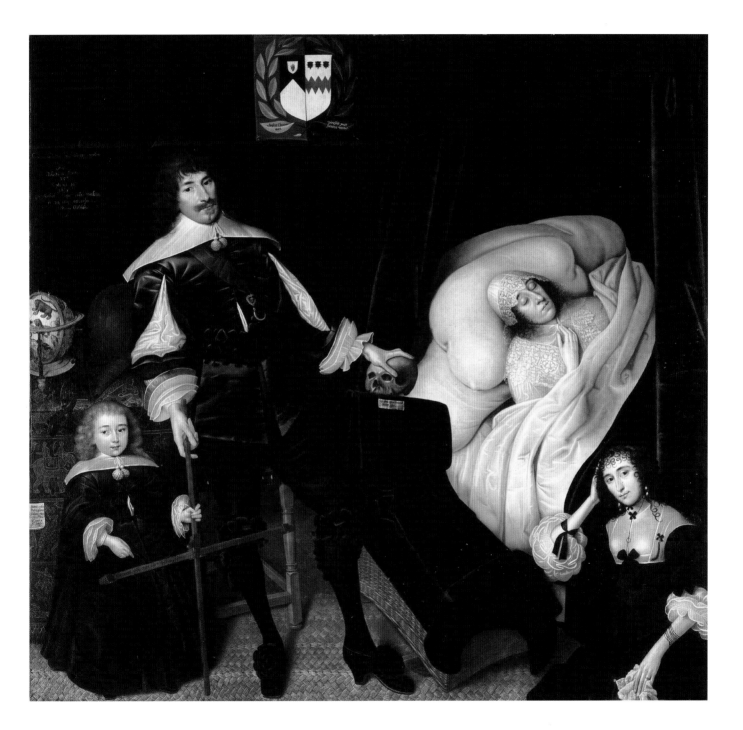

Stralen, Antoni van c.1594–1641
*Skating Scene with Numerous Figures on the
Ice and an Island Fort*
oil on panel 23.7 x 35.8
1979.505

Strang, Ian 1886–1952
Mount Kemmel 1919
oil on canvas 101.5 x 121.5
1920.9

Strang, William 1859–1921
John Masefield 1912
oil on canvas 61.1 x 45.9
1930.152

Strang, William 1859–1921
A Belgian Peasant Girl 1914–1915
oil on canvas 76.4 x 63.6
1915.2

Strang, William 1859–1921
Panchita Zorolla 1916
oil on canvas 76.7 x 61
1944.26

Streater, Robert (attributed to) 1621–1679
*Brancepeth Castle and the Church of St
Brandon, County Durham*
oil on canvas 79.5 x 116
1967.269

Stringer, Daniel 1754–1806
Self Portrait
oil on canvas 92.5 x 80
1986.46

Stringer, Thomas 1722–1790
'Driver' with Owner and Groom 1732–1790
oil on canvas 63 x 75.3
1979.609

Stringer, Thomas 1722–1790
View, Supposedly of Poynton Hall, Cheshire
c.1750
oil on canvas 120.6 x 102.9
1981.62

Stringer, Thomas 1722–1790
Huntsman in a Landscape
oil on canvas 62 x 91
1979.61

Strudwick, John Melhuish 1849–1937
When Apples Were Golden and Songs Were Sweet but Summer Had Passed Away c.1906
oil on canvas 76.4 x 48.4
1906.103

Stuart, Charles active 1854–1904
Still Life with Grapes, Brambles and Bird's Nest 1862
oil on canvas 35.5 x 53
1971.38

Stubbs, George 1724–1806
Cheetah and Stag with Two Indians c.1765
oil on canvas 182.7 x 275.3
1970.34

Suddaby, Rowland 1912–1972
Still Life 1936
oil, tempera & pencil on paper 55.8 x 60.7
1936.26

Sugars, Fanny 1856–1933
My Mother
oil on canvas 36.2 x 31.2
1933.17

Sutherland, Graham Vivian 1903–1980
Press for Making Shells 1941
oil on hardboard 77.2 x 45.9
1947.418

Sutherland, Graham Vivian 1903–1980
Bird in Landscape 1944
oil on paper 62.7 x 46.5
1955.106

Sutton, Philip b.1928
Orange and Blue Still Life
oil on canvas 122 x 91.5
1960.299

Swan, John Macallan 1847–1910
Miss Alexandra Ionides 1901–1903
oil on canvas 183.2 x 76.4
1934.484

Swimmer, Thomas b.1932
Village in Russia 1954
oil on canvas 58 x 76
1970.5

Swiss School
Landscape with Bathers
oil on canvas 29.3 x 36
1947.69

Swynnerton, Annie Louisa 1844–1933
The Town of Siena 1854–1933
oil on canvas 37.8 x 51
1936.21

Swynnerton, Annie Louisa 1844–1933
The Reverend William Gaskell 1879
oil on canvas 86.6 x 71.1
1914.1

Swynnerton, Annie Louisa 1844–1933
S. Isabel Dacre 1880–1932
oil on canvas 70.3 x 51.9
1932.15

Swynnerton, Annie Louisa 1844–1933
Interior of San Miniato, Florence 1881
oil on canvas 26 x 30.4
1936.211

Swynnerton, Annie Louisa 1844–1933
An Italian Mother and Child 1886
oil on canvas 125.8 x 73.5
1936.208

Swynnerton, Annie Louisa 1844–1933
The Dreamer 1887
oil on canvas 53.3 x 42.8
1936.267

Swynnerton, Annie Louisa 1844–1933
The Olive Gatherers 1889
oil on canvas 38.5 x 71
1936.268

Swynnerton, Annie Louisa 1844–1933
Rain Clouds, Monte Gennaro 1904
oil on canvas 30.6 x 63
1936.206

Swynnerton, Annie Louisa 1844–1933
The Southing of the Sun 1911
oil on canvas 111.9 x 88.9
1923.47

Swynnerton, Annie Louisa 1844–1933
Mrs A. Scott-Elliot and Children 1912–1923
oil on canvas 168.4 x 169.3
1923.38

Swynnerton, Annie Louisa 1844–1933
Montagna Mia c.1923
oil on canvas 112.3 x 183
1934.13

Swynnerton, Annie Louisa 1844–1933
Adoration of the Infant Christ (after Perugino)
oil on canvas 59.7 x 90.6
1934.12

Swynnerton, Annie Louisa 1844–1933
Crossing the Stream (unfinished)
oil on canvas 126.2 x 74
1936.212

Swynnerton, Annie Louisa 1844–1933
Illusions
oil on canvas 68 x 51
1936.207

Swynnerton, Annie Louisa 1844–1933
Italian Landscape
oil on canvas 84.3 x 119.1
1939.2

Swynnerton, Annie Louisa 1844–1933
The Vagrant
oil on canvas 74 x 59.4
1934.14

Tait, Arthur Fitzwilliam 1819–1905
London Road, Manchester 1844–1850
oil on canvas 61 x 86
2007.72

Tait, Arthur Fitzwilliam 1819–1905
Victoria Street, Manchester 1844–1850
oil on canvas 61 x 86
2007.71

Tal-Coat, Pierre 1905–1985
French Village 1933
oil on canvas 49.9 x 60.8
1952.6

Tal-Coat, Pierre 1905–1985
Landscape with a Rainbow 1933
oil on canvas 53.8 x 64.8
1952.7

Talmage, Algernon 1871–1939
The Old Hunter 1924
oil on canvas 64 x 76.7
1926.62

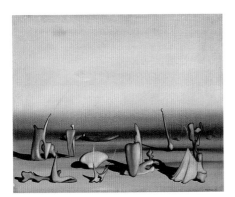

Tanguy, Yves 1900–1955
Echelles 1935
oil on canvas 34.1 x 39.3 (E)
1995.37

Tavaré, Frederick Lawrence 1847–1930
Robinson's Bank, Smithy Door 1877
oil on card 37 x 35.3
1938.368

Taylor, Doris 1890–1978
Springtime Group 1931
oil on canvas 60.9 x 50.9
1932.2

Taylor, Doris 1890–1978
Fruit Bowl 1939
oil on canvas 45.5 x 61
1941.64

Taylor, Leonard Campbell 1874–1969
Battledore 1906
oil on panel 25.6 x 35.3
1917.195 🐝

Ten Kate, Herman Frederik Carel 1822–1891
Interior of a Dutch Inn 1851
oil on canvas 28.4 x 33.6
1931.51

Teniers II, David 1610–1690
Peasants Playing Cards and Skittles in a Yard
1650–1660
oil on panel 27.8 x 37.3
1979.507

Teniers II, David 1610–1690
The Dentist 1652
oil on panel 32.7 x 46.8
1979.506

Teniers II, David 1610–1690
Cottage in a Landscape 1660–1670
oil on panel 24.3 x 35
1908.21

Tennant, John F. 1796–1872
The Old Squire 1838
oil on canvas 89 x 124.4
1918.404

Terborch II, Gerard 1617–1681
*Gerbrand Pancras, Formerly Known as
Hendrick Casimir II, Prince of Nassau-Dietz*
1670
oil on canvas 33.4 x 27.8
1979.447

Terborch II, Gerard 1617–1681
Cornelis Vos, Burgomaster of Deventer
oil on copper 22.7 x 19
1979.446

Thomson, John 1835–1878
Study of a Head 1863
oil on canvas 37.5 x 29.5
1906.101

Thomson, John 1778–1840
Craigmillar Castle (near Edinburgh)
oil on canvas 46 x 61
1916.5

Thomson, John Leslie 1851–1929
Changing Pasture
oil on canvas 43.3 x 71.1
1901.6

Thornhill, James 1675/1676–1734
Time, Truth and Justice 1712–1720
oil on canvas 24.5 x 48.5
1964.57

Thornhill, James 1675/1676–1734
The Victory of Apollo c.1716
oil on canvas 24.5 x 48.5
1964.59

Thornhill, James 1675/1676–1734
Time, Prudence and Vigilance c.1716
oil on canvas 24.5 x 48.5
1964.58

Thornton, Alfred Henry Robinson 1863–1939
Monday Morning 1937–1939
oil on millboard 36 x 46.2
1943.66

Tibble, Geoffrey Arthur 1909–1952
The Studio 1944
oil on canvas 77.5 x 94
1946.161

Tibble, Geoffrey Arthur 1909–1952
Woman at a Table 1946
oil on canvas 51 x 41
1946.162

Tilborgh, Gillis van (attributed to)
c.1635–c.1678
The Card Players
oil on copper 37.5 x 42.9
1908.35

Tisdall, Hans 1910–1997
Moorings at Kew 1946
oil on hardboard 42.4 x 52.2
1946.1

Tisdall, Hans 1910–1997
Still Life
oil on cardboard 42 x 32
1946.61

Tissot, James 1836–1902
Hush! 1875
oil on canvas 73.7 x 112.2
1933.56

Tissot, James 1836–1902
A Convalescent
oil on panel 36.2 x 21.8
1925.47

Todd, Arthur Ralph Middleton 1891–1966
Sub-Officer Henry E. Shaw, BEM, London Fire Service
oil on canvas 35.6 x 23
1947.429

Todd, Frederick 1860–1942
Warburton Church
oil on canvas 32.9 x 39.4
1927.151

Tomson, Arthur 1858–1905
Apple Blossom
oil on canvas 45.6 x 60.8
1907.2

Tonks, Henry 1862–1937
Strolling Players 1906
oil on canvas 118.2 x 128.3
1926.2

Tonks, Henry 1862–1937
The Little Invalid 1912
oil on panel 76.5 x 63.7
1925.288

Tresham, Henry 1751–1814
*The Earl of Warwick's Vow Previous to the
Battle of Towton* 1797
oil on canvas 44 x 35.8
1966.334

Trevelyan, Julian 1910–1988
Gulls 1959
oil on hardboard 48.5 x 37.4
1968.156

Troin
French Landscape
oil on canvas 49.3 x 61.6
1946.45

Troyon, Constant 1810–1865
A Pasture in Normandy 1854
oil on canvas 54 x 73.1
1911.17

Tunnard, John 1900–1971
Iconoclasm 1944
oil on hardboard 50.8 x 76
1961.252

Tunnicliffe, Charles Frederick 1901–1979
The Small Niece 1929
oil on canvas 41.3 x 31.1
1930.18

Tunnicliffe, Charles Frederick 1901–1979
Young Swan 1935
oil on linen 47.2 x 84.3
1938.252

Tunnicliffe, Charles Frederick 1901–1979
Cob
oil on silk 102 x 69
1938.412

Facing page: Draper, Herbert James, 1864–1920, *A Water Baby*, c.1900, Manchester City Galleries (p. 83)

Tunnicliffe, Charles Frederick 1901–1979
July Gulls
oil on board 50.2 x 60.6
1938.411

Turchi, Alessandro 1578–1649
The Flight into Egypt
oil on canvas 307.5 x 180
1978.259

Turner, Francis Calcraft 1795–1851
Heaton Park Races, Manchester
oil on canvas 34.4 x 62.3
1931.17

Turner, Joseph Mallord William 1775–1851
Thomson's Aeolian Harp 1809
oil on canvas 166.7 x 306
1979.7

Turner, Joseph Mallord William 1775–1851
*'Now for the Painter' (Rope) – Passengers
Going on Board* 1827
oil on canvas 174.3 x 223.5
1947.507

Tuson, Robert active c.1950–c.1960
Flower Piece 1955
oil on panel 65.5 x 55
1955.132

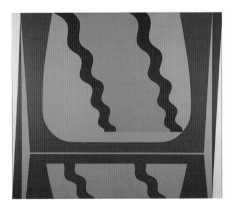

Tyzack, Michael 1933–2007
Candy Man 1965
acrylic on canvas 183 x 214
1968.105

Uhlman, Fred 1901–1985
Near Lyme Regis 1948–1950
oil on cardboard 31.1 x 41.4
1950.29

Underwood, Leon 1890–1975
Concrete Observation Post, Mount Kemmel
1919
oil on canvas 47.8 x 65.8
1920.91

unknown artist
Andieoli Giorgio (c.1465/1470–1555)
oil on canvas 277 x 100
1907.45

unknown artist
Fra B. G. D'Ulma
oil on canvas 277 x 100
1907.43

unknown artist
Jean Goujon (c.1510–c.1572)
oil on canvas 278 x 100
1907.38

unknown artist
Lorenzo Ghilberti (c.1381–1455)
oil on canvas 277 x 100
1907.44

unknown artist
Raphael D'Urbino (1483–1520)
oil on canvas 278 x 100
1907.47

unknown artist
Torrigiano
oil on canvas 277 x 100
1907.46

Uwins, Thomas 1782–1857
*Neapolitan Peasants at the Festa of the
Madonna del Arco* 1840
oil on panel 55 x 41.7
1896.6

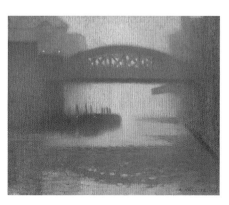

Valette, Adolphe 1876–1942
Windsor Bridge on the Irwell 1909
oil on jute 50.4 x 61.1
1928.33

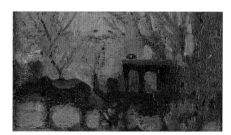

Valette, Adolphe 1876–1942
Study of a 'Cab at All Saints' 1909–1911
oil on board 21.9 x 28.8
2008.244

Valette, Adolphe 1876–1942
Albert Square, Manchester 1910
oil on jute 152 x 114
1928.37

Valette, Adolphe 1876–1942
Hansom Cab at All Saints 1910
oil on jute 115.5 x 155.3
1928.35

Valette, Adolphe 1876–1942
Oxford Road, Manchester 1910
oil on canvas 127.4 x 101.5
1928.31

Valette, Adolphe 1876–1942
Central Station 1910–1911
oil on panel 16.5 x 17.5
2010.1

Valette, Adolphe 1876–1942
Study for 'Albert Square' c.1910
oil on cardboard 12 x 15.5
1991.76

Valette, Adolphe 1876–1942
Study for 'Albert Square' c.1910
oil on board 31.6 x 24 (E)
1996.32

Valette, Adolphe 1876–1942
Study for 'Albert Square' c.1910
oil on board 14.5 x 23
1999.19

Valette, Adolphe 1876–1942
Study for 'Base of Statues, Albert Square'
c.1910
oil on board 8 x 15
1997.24

Valette, Adolphe 1876–1942
Old Cab at All Saints, Manchester 1911
oil on jute 115.5 x 155.3
1928.34

Valette, Adolphe 1876–1942
Bailey Bridge, Manchester 1912
oil on jute 155 x 115
1928.36

Valette, Adolphe 1876–1942
Castlegate, Salford 1912
oil on canvas
1986.5

Valette, Adolphe 1876–1942
India House, Manchester 1912
oil on jute 142.4 x 86.1
1928.38

Valette, Adolphe 1876–1942
*Under Windsor Bridge on the Irwell,
Manchester* 1912
oil on jute 48.2 x 61
1928.32

Valette, Adolphe 1876–1942
Self Portrait Study c.1912
oil on canvas mounted on board 60.8 x 48
2000.22

Valette, Adolphe 1876–1942
*York Street Leading to Charles Street,
Manchester* 1913
oil on linen 81.3 x 60
1928.3

Valette, Adolphe 1876–1942
Annie Barnett 1917
oil on board 39.5 x 46.9
1938.405

Valette, Adolphe 1876–1942
Flowers and Fruit 1917
oil on canvas 49.8 x 58.8
1938.408

Valette, Adolphe 1876–1942
Self Portrait c.1917
oil on linen 45 x 60.4
1938.407

Valette, Adolphe 1876–1942
May Aimee Smith 1918
oil on panel 55.5 x 38.1
2001.14

Valette, Adolphe 1876–1942
John Henry Reynolds 1919
oil on canvas 81.7 x 56.2
1927.51

Valette, Adolphe 1876–1942
Le Puy 1920–1942
oil on canvas 14.6 x 23
1999.191

Valette, Adolphe 1876–1942
Rowley Smart 1925
oil on panel 66.3 x 55
1998.183

Valette, Adolphe 1876–1942
E. H. Mooney
oil on canvas 40.4 x 32.8
2001.134

Valette, Adolphe 1876–1942
Girl at Her Toilet
oil on millboard 40.1 x 32.3
1938.406

Vanderbank, John 1694–1739
Scene from 'Don Quixote': Zoraida Pretending to Swoon in the Garden 1730
oil on panel 40 x 28.6
1967.225

Vanderbank, John 1694–1739
Scene from 'Don Quixote': The Arrival at the Supposed Castle c.1730–1736
oil on panel 40.7 x 43.5
1967.224

Vasey, Gladys 1889–1981
Madeleine (the artist's daughter) 1938
oil on canvas 61.1 x 51
1938.491

Vasey, Gladys 1889–1981
Lamorna Lane, Lamorna Cove, Cornwall 1941
oil on board 45.6 x 40.5
1957.7

Vasey, Gladys 1889–1981
Lamorna Lane 1942
oil on plywood 32.9 x 40.5
1968.213

Vaughan, John Keith 1912–1977
Coast above Berwick I 1952
oil on board 35.5 x 42.3
1953.331

Vaughan, John Keith 1912–1977
Assembly of Figures 1953
oil on soft board 101.5 x 121.9
1957.8

Velde, Adriaen van de 1636–1672
Winter Scene with a Group of Golfers on a Frozen River
oil on panel 22.4 x 28.4
1979.508

Velde I, Esaias van de 1587–1630
Landscape with Riders in a Carriage Passing a Church 1623
oil on panel 40 x 68.6
1979.509

Velde I, Willem van de (studio of) 1611–1693
Sailing Vessels Passing a Coast of Sand Dunes 1657
oil on canvas 30.8 x 40.1
1979.510

Velde II, Willem van de 1633–1707
Men of War at Anchor in a Calm
oil on canvas 64.4 x 80.5
1979.512

Velde II, Willem van de 1633–1707
Seascape: With a Yacht Sailing under a Rainy Sky
oil on panel 19.2 x 15.2
1979.511

Velde II, Willem van de (follower of) 1633–1707
Seascape with Yachts Moored in a Calm
1650–1707
oil on canvas 33.7 x 41
1979.513

Venard, Claude 1913–1999
Still Life with Green Apple
oil on canvas 73 x 59.9
1956.4

Verboeckhoven, Eugène Joseph 1798–1881
Cattle near a Lake 1842
oil on panel 18.6 x 27.2
1934.396

Verboeckhoven, Eugène Joseph 1798–1881
Sheep and Dogs 1861
oil on canvas 77.5 x 58.4
1917.187

Verboeckhoven, Eugène Joseph 1798–1881
Startled 1864
oil on panel 72.2 x 100.3
1934.399

Verbruggen the elder, Gaspar Peeter de
1635–1681
Roses, Tulips, Tobacco Plants and Other Flowers in a Glass Vase 1663
oil on canvas 56.4 x 41.4
1979.535

Vernet, Claude-Joseph 1714–1789
Coast Scene with a British Man of War 1766
oil on canvas 81.8 x 131.2
1977.53

Verveer, Salomon Leonardus 1813–1876
Village with a Church
oil on panel 14.3 x 30.5
1979.617

Veyrassat, Jules Jacques 1828–1893
Returning Home
oil on canvas 22.2 x 35.2
1917.22

Facing page: Copley, John, 1875–1950, *Chamber Music*, Manchester City Galleries (p. 67)

Vincent, George 1796–1831
Wooded Landscape with Figures and Gate
c.1820
oil on canvas 27.8 x 35.5
1938.51

Vincent, George 1796–1831
View near Wroxham, Norfolk
oil on canvas 49.1 x 38.8
1904.1

Vitofski, Henry 1892–1964
The Seamstress 1928
oil on canvas 43.4 x 56
1928.121

Vlaminck, Maurice de 1876–1958
Road through Trees 1900–1920
oil on canvas 60 x 73
1949.101

Vlieger, Simon de 1601–1653
River Estuary with Shipping on a Windy Day
oil on canvas 30 x 38.9
1979.514

Vliet, Hendrick Cornelisz. van c.1611–1675
Portrait of a Man
oil on canvas 100.5 x 91.7
1909.34

Vliet, Hendrick Cornelisz. van c.1611–1675
Portrait of a Young Woman
oil on canvas 100.9 x 91.3
1909.35

Vliet, Hendrick Cornelisz. van (after)
c.1611–1675
Interior of the Oude Kerk at Delft 1660–1675
oil on canvas 77 x 69
1953.207

Vollon, Antoine 1833–1900
Strawberries
oil on panel 67.1 x 75.5
1914.64

Voltz, Friedrich 1817–1886
Cattle Drinking 1875
oil on panel 37.5 x 92.4
1918.939

Vouet, Simon (attributed to) 1590–1649
Apollo in His Chariot with Time
oil on canvas 37.3 x 31.9
1966.295

Waddington, John Barton 1835–1918
View of Manchester from Kersal 1856
oil on canvas 17.6 x 27.8
1927.42

Wadsworth, Edward Alexander 1889–1949
Dunkerque 1924
tempera on canvas 84 x 89.2
1928.88

Wadsworth, Edward Alexander 1889–1949
Souvenir of Fiumicino 1937
tempera on linen 61 x 50.9
1943.77

Wagner, Alexander von 1838–1919
The Chariot Race c.1882
oil on canvas 138.2 x 347
1898.12

Waite, Robert Thorne 1842–1935
New Mown Hay
oil on canvas 99.1 x 135
1901.1

Walker, Ethel 1861–1951
Flora 1930–1933
oil on canvas 61.2 x 51.2
1933.34 🐝

Walker, Ethel 1861–1951
Eileen 1931
oil on canvas 61 x 50.8
1931.2 🐝

Walker, Ethel 1861–1951
An August Morning 1938
oil on canvas 63.5 x 91.5
1941.63 🐝

Walker, Ethel 1861–1951
The Bouquet of Flowers 1938–1939
oil on canvas 76.5 x 64.2
1941.5 🐝

Walker, Ethel 1861–1951
The Miniature
oil on canvas 76.3 x 51.2
1939.21 🐝

Wallace, Robin 1897–1952
The Friary Wall, Norfolk 1934
oil on canvas 63.6 x 76.4
1935.134

Wallis, Alfred 1855–1942
Trawler and Pier
oil on card 22.2 x 32.5
1995.44

Wallis, Hugh 1871–1943
Flowers in the Window 1922
oil on canvas 54.6 x 60.3
1944.8

Walton, Allan 1891–1948
Swiss Interior 1923
oil on canvas 40.9 x 33
1925.26

Walton, Allan 1891–1948
Farmyard
oil on canvas 32.9 x 39.2
1946.46

Walton, Allan 1891–1948
Lowestoft Harbour
oil on canvas 33.3 x 39.5
1946.47

Walton, Allan 1891–1948
The Sand Boat
oil on hardboard 45.4 x 50.9
1929.51

Waplington, Paul Anthony b.1938
Basford Hill Silver Prize Band 1975
acrylic on canvas 122.3 x 157.8
1986.2

Ward, Edward Matthew 1816–1879
Byron's Early Love, 'A Dream of Annesley Hall'
1856
oil on canvas 62 x 51.3
1917.273

Wasse, Arthur 1854–1930
A Courtyard in Bavaria 1906
oil on canvas 102.4 x 138.5
1913.7

Waterhouse, John William 1849–1917
Hylas and the Nymphs 1896
oil on canvas 98.2 x 163.3
1896.15

Waterlow, Ernest Albert 1850–1919
Warkworth Castle, Northumberland 1903
oil on canvas 122 x 183.3
1903.11

Waterlow, Ernest Albert 1850–1919
On the Mediterranean
oil on canvas 101.9 x 153.3
1928.84

Watson, John Dawson 1832–1892
Inspiration 1866
oil on panel 30.4 x 24.9
1917.317

Watson, John Dawson (after) 1832–1892
Grinling Gibbons (1648–1721)
oil on canvas 278 x 100
1907.40

Watson, William d.1921
Morning, Loch Goil 1893
oil on canvas 61 x 91.5
1917.199

Watson, William d.1921
Morning on the Goil 1897
oil on canvas 60.3 x 91
1917.228

Watson, William Ferguson 1895–1966
Still Life with Dead Pigeon, Finches and Falcons' Hoods
oil on canvas 73.1 x 59.7
1965.309

Watts, George Frederic 1817–1904
The Good Samaritan 1850
oil on canvas 254.7 x 189.2
1882.149

Watts, George Frederic 1817–1904
The Honourable John Lothrop Motley 1861
oil on panel 60.8 x 50.1
1906.99

Watts, George Frederic 1817–1904
Charles Hilditch Rickards 1866
oil on canvas 82.8 x 67.4
1886.9

Watts, George Frederic 1817–1904
Prayer 1867–1887
oil on canvas 102.6 x 69.6
1887.1

Watts, George Frederic 1817–1904
Paolo and Francesca 1870
oil on canvas 66.1 x 52.5
1907.7

Watts, George Frederic 1817–1904
The Ulster 1874
oil on canvas 198.7 x 99.7
1922.3

Watts, George Frederic 1817–1904
Study: Head of a Girl 1876
oil on canvas 66 x 53.1
1934.405

Watts, George Frederic 1817–1904
The Coquette 1878–1882
oil on canvas 66.2 x 53.4
1947.129

Watts, George Frederic 1817–1904
A Greek Idyll 1894
oil on canvas 91 x 125.7
1934.412

Waugh, Eric b.1929
Sheep
oil on hardboard 91.3 x 121.7
1968.149

Waugh, Eric b.1929
Suffolk Farm
oil on hardboard 39.6 x 49.4
1968.15

Weatherby, William c.1891–1966
The Old Barn 1923
oil on board 50.7 x 38.1
1924.2

Webb, James 1825–1895
The Signal mid-19th C–late 19th C
oil on canvas 138 x 207
1984.34

Webb, James 1825–1895
Fishing on a Squally Day 1861
oil on canvas 92.5 x 153.6
1920.1346

Webb, James 1825–1895
After the Storm (off Mont Orgueil and Gorey, Jersey)
oil on canvas 77.2 x 115
1932.86

Webb, James 1825–1895
Constantinople
oil on canvas 61.3 x 91.7
1934.409

Webb, William J. c.1830–c.1904
The Lost Sheep 1864
oil on panel 33.1 x 25.1
1920.94

Weber, Philipp 1849–1921
A Winter Evening 1873
oil on canvas 61 x 101.5
1918.1153

Wedgbury, David 1937–1998
Bobby Charlton (b.1937) 1974
oil on canvas 45.7 x 45.6
1974.103

Wehnert, Edward Henry (after) 1813–1868
Andreas Mantegna (c.1431–1506)
oil on canvas 277 x 100
1907.42

Weight, Carel Victor Morlais 1908–1997
Escape of the Zebra from the Zoo during an Air Raid
oil on panel 22 x 34.6
1947.425 🐝

Weight, Carel Victor Morlais 1908–1997
The First Cricket Match of Spring
oil on canvas 40.5 x 51
1945.27 🐝

Weisbrod, Richard 1906–1991
Harbour 1963
oil on hardboard 37.4 x 81
1968.151

Weiss, José 1859–1919
Clear Morning
oil on canvas 50.8 x 76.2
1910.2

West, Joan M. active 1913–c.1940
Ennui 1940
oil on canvas 38.2 x 27.9
1940.712

Westall, Richard 1765–1836
The Bower of Pan 1800
oil on canvas 88.5 x 106.2
1971.91

Westcott, Philip 1815–1878
George Cornwall Legh, MP 1850
oil on canvas 142.5 x 111.7
1967.109

Westcott, Philip 1815–1878
Cogitating the Poor Law Bill
oil on canvas 61.5 x 47.1
1918.417

Westcott, Philip 1815–1878
Cromwell's Protest against the Persecution of the Waldensian Ambassadors
oil on canvas 144 x 212.5
1979.602

Wetherbee, George Faulkner 1851–1920
A Sylvan Stream
oil on canvas 127.4 x 81.3
1900.13

Whaite, Henry Clarence 1828–1912
The Heart of Cambria 1886
oil on canvas 190.3 x 122.2
1886.6

Whaite, Henry Clarence 1828–1912
Just Arrived by the Sloop (in the Conway Valley, North Wales) 1889
oil on canvas 86.3 x 152.6
1908.8

Whaite, Henry Clarence 1895–1978
Walberswick, Boats on the Blythe at a Wooden Jetty 1936–1940
oil on canvas 38.7 x 48.5
1980.239

Whaite, Henry Clarence 1828–1912
Gipsy Camp, Sunrise
oil on canvas 86.3 x 152.6
1979.611

Whaite, Henry Clarence 1828–1912
Llyn Dylun, the Llandudno Water Supply
oil on canvas 55.3 x 78.3
1898.9

Wheatley, Francis 1747–1801
A Scene in 'Twelfth Night', Act III 1771–1772
oil on canvas 99.8 x 124.8
1953.4

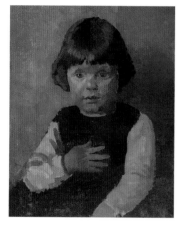

Wheatley, John 1892–1955
A Little Girl
oil on board 41 x 32.3
1925.48

White, Ethelbert 1891–1972
Boats at Aldeburgh
oil on canvas 64.2 x 76.5
1933.12

White, Ethelbert 1891–1972
Suffolk Landscape
oil on canvas 61.6 x 76.6
1936.264

Wijnants, Jan c.1635–1684
Landscape with Cattle 1670
oil on canvas 84 x 100
1923.15

Wijnants, Jan c.1635–1684
*Wooded Landscape with Figures Walking by a
Sandy Bank*
oil on canvas 26.7 x 30.7
1979.517

Wild, David b.1931
The River Hodder 1967
oil on hardboard 76.1 x 101.4
1970.192

Facing page: Egg, Augustus Leopold, 1816–1863, *A Walk on the Beach*, c.1855–1860, Manchester City Galleries (p. 87)

Wilde, Samuel de 1748–1832
Music 1801
oil on canvas 71.1 x 90.7
1910.8

Wildman, William Ainsworth 1882–1950
Oyster Dredger, Heybridge, Essex 1930
oil on hardboard 60.7 x 76.4
1932.6

Wilkie, David 1785–1841
Sir Alexander Keith 1830
oil on panel 71.8 x 48.3
1972.53

Wilkinson, Derek 1929–2001
The Harbour 1957
oil on hardboard 56.3 x 122
1958.19

Wilkinson, Derek 1929–2001
The Beach 1958
oil & emulsion on hardboard 72.5 x 84.4
1959.23

Wilkinson, Derek 1929–2001
Industrial Scene 1961
oil on hardboard 73.4 x 42.6
1968.148

Wilkinson, Derek 1929–2001
Still Life 1961
oil on hardboard 61.8 x 71.6
1968.146

Wilkinson, William Henry 1856–1925
An Italian 1912–1914
oil on canvas 61.6 x 50.8
1933.21

Wilkinson, William Henry 1856–1925
Self Portrait 1927
oil on canvas 50.8 x 40.8
1927.5

Williams, Terrick John 1860–1936
The Harbour, Dieppe 1931
oil on canvas 76.2 x 94.3
1937.643

Williams, Terrick John 1860–1936
The Rialto Market, Venice
oil on canvas 51 x 76.9
1968.211

Williamson, Harold 1898–1972
Patsy
oil on hardboard 50.8 x 43.2
1947.34

Willock, John Smith 1887–1976
Seaside Circus 1934
oil on canvas 50.7 x 61
1935.9

Wilson, Alexander 1803–1846
A Horse in Platt Fields, Manchester, with Platt Hall in the Distance 1822
oil on canvas 71.8 x 86.4
1963.297

Wilson, Frank Avray 1914–2009
Configuration, Green and Black
oil on hardboard 122 x 61
1960.117

Wilson, Richard 1713/1714–1782
Cicero's Villa 1760–1763
oil on canvas 101.3 x 136.8
1897.1

Wilson, Richard 1713/1714–1782
Hadrian's Villa, near Tivoli 1763–1765
oil on canvas 42.8 x 52.9
1917.175

Wilson, Richard 1713/1714–1782
A Summer Evening 1764
oil on canvas 123.5 x 105.9
1969.182

Wilson, Richard 1713/1714–1782
Valley of the Mawddach with Cader Idris Beyond 1770–1775
oil on canvas 91.7 x 106.7
1905.21

Wilson, Richard 1713/1714–1782
The Keep of Okehampton Castle 1771–1772
oil on canvas 169.5 x 163.5
1903.5

Wilson, Richard (after) 1713/1714–1782
Dolbadarn Castle and Llyn Peris
oil on canvas 43.2 x 68.5
1924.57

Wilson, Richard (after) 1713/1714–1782
Pembroke Castle
oil on canvas 62.2 x 89.5
1908.38

Wilson, Richard (follower of) 1713/1714–1782
Italian Landscape
oil on canvas 69.1 x 68.7
1909.14

Wimperis, Edmund Morison 1835–1900
Watering Horses 1893–1896
oil on canvas 70.3 x 108.2
1896.18

Wimperis, Edmund Morison 1835–1900
The Ferry 1894
oil on canvas 61 x 91.3
1917.252

Windus, William Lindsay 1822–1907
The Outlaw 1861
oil on canvas 35.7 x 34.3
1937.28

Windus, William Lindsay 1822–1907
Samuel Teed
oil on canvas 71.7 x 61
1954.1058

Wissing, Willem 1656–1687
Queen Mary, Wife of William of Orange
1670–1687
oil on canvas 144.8 x 99.8
1917.183

Wit, Jacob de 1695–1754
Sketch for a Ceiling: Bacchus and Ariadne
oil on canvas 48.2 x 61
1965.135

Witherop, Jack Coburn 1906–1984
Washing Day, St Ives 1940
tempera on hardboard 60.9 x 81.1
1943.68

Wolfe, Edward 1897–1982
Zinnias 1930
oil on canvas 73.7 x 107.9
1934.447

Wolfe, Edward 1897–1982
Ian 1931
oil on canvas 87 x 61.4
1934.2

Wolfe, Edward 1897–1982
Penrhyndeudraeth 1947
oil on canvas 67 x 84.5
1985.11

Wolfe, Edward 1897–1982
Aisha of the Kasba
oil on canvas 53.6 x 43.3
1931.33

Wolfe, Edward 1897–1982
Self Portrait
oil on canvas 68 x 56.5
1985.12

Wolfe, Edward 1897–1982
Sunflowers
oil on canvas 63.5 x 63.5
1946.48

Wood, Christopher 1901–1930
Poppies in a Decorated Jar 1925
oil on canvas 61.3 x 51.1
1939.143

Wood, Christopher 1901–1930
Loading the Boats, St Ives 1926
oil on canvas 51.2 x 61.3
1936.114

Wood, Christopher 1901–1930
Cumberland Landscape 1928
oil on plywood 50.8 x 60.8
1933.125

Wood, Christopher 1901–1930
'Ship Inn', Mousehole 1930
oil on board 49 x 86.5
1995.45

Wood, Edgar 1860–1935
The Garden, Redcroft 1915
oil on canvas 40.5 x 35.5
1981.334

Wood, Edgar 1860–1935
Italian Hilltop Farm 1921
oil on canvas 29.2 x 34.2
2007.7

Wood, Edgar 1860–1935
St Mark's, Venice 1922
oil on card on millboard 22.6 x 27.7
1981.335

Wood, Ursula 1868–c.1925
Going through the Lock 1897
oil on canvas 23.2 x 30.7
1939.19

Woodrow, Joash 1927–2006
Jacob Kramer in Hat and Coat 1959–1961
oil on hessian 63 x 35
2006.3

Wootton, John c.1682–1764
Landscape with Fishermen 1750–1755
oil on canvas 98.4 x 120
1953.111

Workman, Harold 1897–1975
Market Carts 1920–1940
oil on canvas 63.7 x 76.5
1940.1

Workman, Harold 1897–1975
Manette Street, Soho 1935
oil on canvas 45.7 x 51.2
1936.5

Workman, Harold 1897–1975
Printing Camouflage Cloth 1945
oil on canvas 87.8 x 115.6
1945.254

Worsley, John 1919–2000
Away Walrus from HMS 'Devonshire' at Sea
1943
oil on canvas 122 x 91.2
1947.392

Wouwerman, Philips 1619–1668
*Landscape with a Large Number of Peasants
Merrymaking in front of a Cottage* 1646
oil on canvas 52.5 x 75.1
1979.516

Wouwerman, Philips (follower of) 1619–1668
Battle Scene
oil on canvas 50.7 x 65.2
1931.129

Wright, John Michael 1617–1694
Murrough O'Brien, 1st Earl of Inchiquin
1660–1670
oil on canvas 115.5 x 106
1945.255

Wright, Nelson 1880–1930
A Cumberland Slate Quarry 1926
oil on canvas 63.6 x 76.4
1930.25

Wright, William Matvyn 1910–1983
Firemen on a Roof 1941
oil on panel 122 x 121.1
1947.395

Wright of Derby, Joseph 1734–1797
Thomas Day 1770
oil on canvas 127 x 100.4
1975.194

Wright of Derby, Joseph 1734–1797
Portrait of a Gentleman 1777–1780
oil on canvas 75.5 x 63.2
1901.5

Wright of Derby, Joseph 1734–1797
Caernarvon Castle by Moonlight c.1780–1785
oil on canvas 54 x 64.4
1905.7

Wright of Derby, Joseph (after) 1734–1797
Sir Richard Arkwright
oil on canvas 76.5 x 63.8
1968.239

Wyatt, Irene 1903–1987
Summer Flowers 1935
oil on canvas 45.7 x 35.7
1935.395

Wyatt, Maria C. active 1940–1950
The Potteries
oil on canvas 50.7 x 63.1
1947.35

Wyllie, James W. active c.1940–c.1950
Flowers in a Blue Jug
oil on canvas 47.6 x 62.8
1946.126

Wyndham, Richard 1896–1948
The Medway near Tonbridge 1936
oil on canvas 63.5 x 76.7
1937.211

Facing page: Gear, William, 1915–1997, *Gray Vertical*, 1956, Whitworth Art Gallery, The University of Manchester (p. 358)

Yeames, William Frederick 1835–1918
Prince Arthur and Hubert 1882
oil on canvas 201.3 x 125.8
1883.19

Youngman, Nan 1906–1995
Convolvulus 1943
oil on canvas 61 x 51
1945.15

Youngman, Nan 1906–1995
Waste Land, Tredegar, South Wales 1951
oil on plywood 38 x 50.9
1953.332

Yvon, Adolphe 1817–1893
*Marshal Ney Supporting the Rear Guard
during the Retreat from Moscow* 1856
oil on canvas 179.8 x 301
1882.7

Zick, Januarius 1730–1797
Christ Healing the Sick
oil on canvas 116.9 x 148.2
1979.612

Zoffany, Johann 1733–1810
Venus Bringing Arms to Aeneas 1759
oil on canvas 27.6 x 37.8
1966.4

Zuccarelli, Francesco 1702–1788
Pastoral Landscape c.1760
oil on canvas 59.8 x 84.5
1972.91

Manchester Jewish Museum

Coventry, Gertrude Mary 1886–1964
*Alderman Leslie Lever (1905–1977), Lord
Mayor of Manchester*
oil on canvas 68 x 62
1986-115

Flax, J.
*Manchester Central Synagogue During
Shavuot*
acrylic on paper 55 x 76
1984-356

Gardener, R. S.
*The Manchester Spanish and Portugese
Synagogue*
oil on board 24.5 x 29
1984-174

Midgley, Donald G.
A Hebrew Teacher 1939
oil on canvas 76 x 62
1989-42

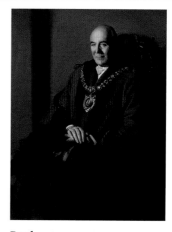

Reed
*Alderman A. Moss, Lord Mayor of Manchester
(1953–1954)*
oil on canvas 126 x 100
MJMP1

Schlesinger, M.
Central Synagogue, Manchester 1976
oil on canvas 40 x 50
MJM35

Stiasteny, Anton
Gunner Elias Harris (1881–1968)
oil on canvas 39 x 28
2000-4

unknown artist
Abraham Lazarus Kastenburg (d.1874) c.1893
oil on canvas 56 x 46
1982-49

unknown artist
Memorial to Holocaust Victims 1945–1950
oil on canvas 53 x 42
1983-271

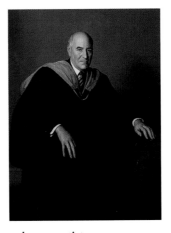

unknown artist
Abraham Moss, Lord Mayor of Manchester
oil on canvas 127 x 101
1986-114

unknown artist
David M. Gouldman
oil on canvas 56 x 47
1984-451/A

unknown artist
Emmanuel Nove
oil on canvas 60 x 49
1984-409

unknown artist
H. Bornstein, Chief Cantor
oil on board 88 x 66
1986-245

unknown artist
Mark Bloom
oil on canvas 62 x 49
1983-274

unknown artist
Mordacae Davide Basso (b.1815)
oil on canvas 71 x 53
1995-56

unknown artist
Mrs David M. Gouldman
oil on canvas 56 x 47
1984-451/B

unknown artist
Portrait of an Unknown Man
oil on canvas 75 x 62
MJM27

unknown artist
Reverend Professor David Myer Isaacs
(1810–1879)
oil on canvas 40 x 33
1989-20/5

unknown artist
Two Orthodox Jews in Discussion
oil on board 46.5 x 65
1984-328

Virotski, Henry
Ephraim Marks
oil on canvas 60 x 49
1984-410

Manchester Metropolitan University

Adams, Alastair Christian b.1969
Dame Sandra Burslem 2006
acrylic (?) on board 200 x 120
PCF26

Aherne, J.
Jerusalem Bazaar 1985
oil on canvas 92 x 121
PCF17

Craddock, A.
Cockerel and Head
acrylic on paper 110 x 56
PCF23

Horowitz, S. J.
Abstract
oil on canvas 41 x 41
PCF19

Hyatt, John b.1958
The Source 2008
oil on canvas 100 x 100
PCF50

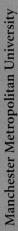

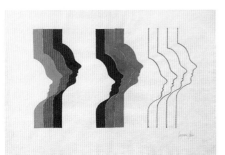

Jones, Cayman
Faces
acrylic on paper 38.5 x 56
PCF21

Morrocco, Alberto 1917–1998
A. H. Body, Founder, Principal (1946–1966)
1966
oil on canvas 74 x 62
PCF16

Philipson, Robin 1916–1992
Dusk
acrylic on canvas 25 x 25
PCF18

Riley, Harold b.1934
Sir Kenneth Green (1934–2010) 1998
oil on canvas 154 x 120
PCF27

unknown artist
Figures
acrylic on paper 76 x 50
PCF22

unknown artist
Figures and Buildings
oil on board 30 x 30
PCF24

unknown artist
Landscape
acrylic on board 55 x 74
PCF25

unknown artist
River Scene
oil on canvas 49 x 75
PCF20

Manchester Metropolitan University Special Collections

Billyard, Kenneth Harry 1943–1977
'Landscape Metamorphosis No.1' 1974
acrylic on board 56 x 115
11211

Bradbury, Emma Louise 1866–1959
Study of Sculpture 1891
oil on canvas 61 x 51
11227

Bradbury, Emma Louise 1866–1959
Study of a Male Nude* 1892
oil on canvas 76 x 51
11231

Brannan, Peter 1926–1994
The Barman 1940–1959
oil on canvas 24 x 19
U204

Brannan, Peter 1926–1994
Reading in Bed 1959
oil on canvas 40 x 29.5
U206

Browne, Michael J. b.1963
Path 1993
oil on canvas 158 x 173
MANMU2006.29

Dakin, Andrew
View from a Window* 1991
oil on canvas 43 x 31
2006.25

Farleigh, John F. W. C 1900–1965
Sunset from Tower Bridge 1959
oil on canvas 74 x 52
FAR/2/2/12

Hagan-Burt, Dympna b.1968
Drifting Off 1998
oil on canvas 175 x 144
MANMU : 1998.1

Hagan-Burt, Dympna b.1968
Looking Back 1998
oil on canvas 177 x 136
MANMU :1998.2

Hargreaves, Joan 1921–2007
*Still Life** 1946
oil on canvas 50 x 61
HAR.659

Hargreaves, Joan 1921–2007
*Dutch Girl** 1948
oil on canvas 76 x 51
HAR.841

Hargreaves, Joan 1921–2007
*Two Men at a Table** 1948
oil on canvas 64 x 76
HAR.840

Hargreaves, Joan 1921–2007
*Female Nude** 1949
oil on canvas 76 x 51
HAR.648

Hargreaves, Joan 1921–2007
*Surrey Landscape** 1949
oil on canvas 43 x 56
HAR.829

Hargreaves, Joan 1921–2007
*Still Life 9** 1950
oil on canvas 61 x 71
HAR.842

Hargreaves, Joan 1921–2007
*Still Life 5** 1950–1951
oil on canvas 63 x 76
HAR.826

Hargreaves, Joan 1921–2007
*Pink Still Life** 1951
oil on canvas 51 x 61
HAR.828

Hargreaves, Joan 1921–2007
*Boats** 1953
oil on canvas 76 x 51
HAR.650

Hargreaves, Joan 1921–2007
*House with Black Shadows** 1953
oil on canvas 76 x 63
HAR.839

Hargreaves, Joan 1921–2007
*Boats**
oil on canvas 51 x 76
HAR.643

Hargreaves, Joan 1921–2007
*City Painting**
oil on canvas 51 x 76
HAR.848

Hargreaves, Joan 1921–2007
*Dancers**
oil on canvas 51 x 76
HAR.647

Hargreaves, Joan 1921–2007
*Elvaston Crescent**
oil on canvas 40 x 49
HAR.830

Hargreaves, Joan 1921–2007
*Family**
oil on canvas 71 x 91
HAR.832

Hargreaves, Joan 1921–2007
*Two Nudes in a Garden** (recto)
oil on canvas 61 x 51
HAR.652

Hargreaves, Joan 1921–2007
*Figures in a Park** (verso)
oil on canvas 42 x 52
652B

Hargreaves, Joan 1921–2007
*Flowers in a Pot**
oil on canvas 51 x 61
HAR.641

Hargreaves, Joan 1921–2007
*Flowers in a Vase**
oil on canvas 43 x 51
HAR.656

Hargreaves, Joan 1921–2007
*Landscape 1**
oil on canvas 41 x 51
HAR.654

Hargreaves, Joan 1921–2007
*Landscape 2**
oil on canvas 63 x 76
HAR.831

Hargreaves, Joan 1921–2007
*Landscape**
oil on wood 25 x 35
HAR.325

Hargreaves, Joan 1921–2007
*Male Nude 1**
oil on canvas 76 x 51
HAR.645

Hargreaves, Joan 1921–2007
*Male Nude 2**
oil on canvas 76 x 63
HAR.835

Hargreaves, Joan 1921–2007
*Male Nude with Boxes**
oil on canvas 76 x 51
HAR.649

Facing page: Peake, Mervyn, 1911–1968, *The Glassblower*, 1944, Manchester City Galleries (p. 189)

Hargreaves, Joan 1921–2007
Male Nude with Still Life*
oil on canvas 76 x 51
HAR.646

Hargreaves, Joan 1921–2007
Nude Woman 1*
oil on canvas 51 x 41
HAR.634

Hargreaves, Joan 1921–2007
Nude Woman 2*
oil on canvas 66 x 56
HAR.640

Hargreaves, Joan 1921–2007
Park Scene*
oil on canvas 50 x 76
HAR.824

Hargreaves, Joan 1921–2007
Portrait of a Lady in Red*
oil on canvas 61 x 51
HAR.658

Hargreaves, Joan 1921–2007
Portrait of an Unknown Lady 1*
oil on canvas 55.5 x 45.5
HAR.637

Hargreaves, Joan 1921–2007
Portrait of an Unknown Lady 2*
oil on canvas 64 x 35.5
HAR. 638

Hargreaves, Joan 1921–2007
Portrait of an Unknown Lady 3*
oil on canvas 51 x 41
HAR.655

Hargreaves, Joan 1921–2007
Seated Nude*
oil on canvas 76 x 61
HAR.642

Hargreaves, Joan 1921–2007
*Still Life 1**
oil on canvas 61 x 51
HAR.639

Hargreaves, Joan 1921–2007
*Still Life 2**
oil on canvas 76 x 51
HAR.644

Hargreaves, Joan 1921–2007
*Still Life 3**
oil on canvas 61 x 51
HAR.653

Hargreaves, Joan 1921–2007
*Still Life 4**
oil on canvas 63 x 76
HAR.825

Hargreaves, Joan 1921–2007
*Still Life 6**
oil on canvas 71 x 92
HAR.834

Hargreaves, Joan 1921–2007
*Still Life 7**
oil on canvas 63.5 x 76
HAR.836

Hargreaves, Joan 1921–2007
*Still Life 8**
oil on canvas 63.5 x 76
HAR.838

Hargreaves, Joan 1921–2007
*Still Life with a Cézanne Book**
oil on canvas 71 x 92
HAR.833

Hargreaves, Joan 1921–2007
*Still Life with Flowers**
oil on canvas 63 x 76
HAR.837

Hargreaves, Joan 1921–2007
Portrait of an Unknown Lady 4* (recto)
oil on canvas 61 x 46
HAR.657

Hargreaves, Joan 1921–2007
Still Life* (verso)
oil on canvas 35 x 51
657B

Hargreaves, Joan 1921–2007
Two Male Nudes*
oil on canvas 51 x 41
HAR. 635

Hargreaves, Joan 1921–2007
Vase of Flowers*
oil on canvas 46 x 35.5
HAR.636

Hewison, Jim M.
The Hall 1940
oil on canvas 40 x 25
11250

Howard, Ghislaine b.1953
Collette in Rehearsal 1994
oil on canvas 27.5 x 21
MANMU : 1994.3

Howard, Ghislaine b.1953
Dennis in Rehearsal 1994
oil on canvas 21 x 27.5
MANMU : 1994.4

Hyatt, John b.1958
*No.15: Tall Tales and Short Stories from the
Collection of the Angel of History* 1998
oil on canvas 34.5 x 43.5
MANMU : 1999.3

Hyatt, John b.1958
*Tall Tales and Short Stories from the Collection
of the Angel of History #7* 1998
oil on canvas 44.5 x 54
MANMU : 1999.2

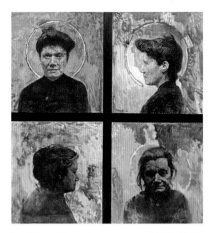

McAleer, Mary Agnes active 1970–1990
Four Portraits of an Unknown Man★
oil on canvas 111 x 105
12662

McAleer, Mary Agnes active 1970–1990
Four Portraits of an Unknown Woman★
oil on canvas 111 x 105
12661

McAleer, Mary Agnes active 1970–1990
Two Figures★
oil on canvas 158 x 59
Unknown

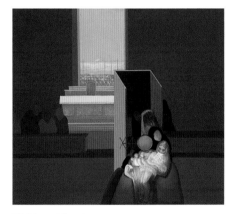

Muckley, Louis Fairfax 1862–1926
William Jabez Muckley (1829–1905) 1895
oil on canvas 121 x 97.5
MANMU : 2005.1

Picking, John b.1939
Confessionale No.7 1972
oil on canvas 90 x 101
PCF2

unknown artist
Portrait of an Unknown Man★
oil on canvas 70 x 52
PCF15

Weinberger, Harry 1924–2009
'Studio 1'
oil on canvas 191 x 121
PCF11

Whittam, William Wright 1931–1996
All Saints Park, Manchester 1952–1954
oil or acrylic on board 69 x 89
PCF6

Whittam, William Wright 1931–1996
Female Nude★ 1952–1954
oil on canvas 76 x 61
PCF14

Whittam, William Wright 1931–1996
Female Nude* 1952–1954
oil or acrylic on canvas 76 x 61
PCF7

Whittam, William Wright 1931–1996
Figures in a Park* 1952–1954
oil or acrylic on canvas 71 x 91
PCF10

Whittam, William Wright 1931–1996
Pigeons on Pavement* 1952–1954
oil or acrylic on canvas 51 x 76
PCF5

Whittam, William Wright 1931–1996
Portrait of an Unknown Man in a White Shirt*
1952–1954
oil or acrylic on board 68 x 30
PCF9

Whittam, William Wright 1931–1996
*Portrait of an Unknown Woman Lying on
Fabric** 1952–1954
oil or acrylic on board 61 x 76
PCF8

Wolfendon, Christopher
'69' 1999
oil or acrylic on canvas 123 x 90
MANMU : 1999.10

Wolfendon, Christopher
The Black Death 1999
oil or acrylic on canvas 122 x 92
MANMU : 1999.11

Wood, Edgar 1860–1935
Tunisia 1914
oil on canvas 18.5 x 26
MANMU : 1983.1

Manchester Metropolitan University, Arts for Health Archive

Brown, Gilford b.1965
Man on a Horse 1987
oil on canvas 90 x 120
PCF12 (P)

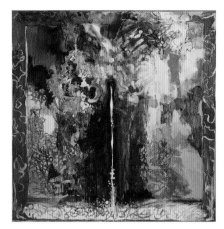

Chantrey, Melvyn b.1945
Waterfall 1992–1993
oil on board 122 x 122
PCF13

Manchester Metropolitan University, Faculty of Art and Design

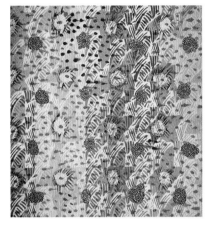

Woolley, Hannah
Colour Abstract
acrylic on canvas 244 x 214
PCF28

Manchester Town Hall

Allen, Joseph William (attributed to)
1803–1852
John Dalton
oil on canvas 227 x 166.5
THP008001

Benson, Edward 1808–1863
Sir Joseph Heron
oil on canvas 76 x 64
THP052001

Bradley, William 1801–1857
Joseph Brotherton 1832–1849
oil on canvas 230 x 135
THP028001

Bradley, William (attributed to) 1801–1857
James Kershaw 1842–1850
oil on canvas 230 x 135
THP025001

Bradley, William (circle of) 1801–1857
Sir Thomas Potter 1842
oil on canvas 273 x 180
THP037001

Cartledge, William 1891–1976
Sir William Kay 1921
oil on canvas 120 x 90
THP017001

Cartledge, William 1891–1976
Alderman James Henry Swales 1926
oil on canvas 110 x 85
THP018001

Desanges, Louis William 1822–1906
The Earl of Derby
oil on canvas 273 x 180
THP039001

Dugdale, Thomas Cantrell 1880–1952
W. B. Pritchard 1912
oil on canvas 140 x 112
THP004001

Faulkner, Benjamin Rawlinson 1787–1849
William Nield 1849
oil on canvas 230 x 135
THP024001

Gabain, Ethel Leontine 1883–1950
Dame Mary Latchford Kingsmill Jones
1947–1950
oil on canvas 105 x 82
THP019001

Facing page: Léger, Fernand, 1881–1955, *Painting*, 1926, Manchester City Galleries (p. 148)

Grant, Francis (attributed to) 1803–1878
Sergeant R. B. Armstrong, QC, MP
oil on canvas 273 x 180
THP035001

Guttenberg
William Cundiff
oil on canvas 150 x 99
THP046001

Hooke, Richard 1820–1908
Benjamin Nicholls
oil on canvas 186 x 156
THP010001

Hooke, Richard 1820–1908
Ivie Mackie
oil on canvas 186 x 156
THP009001

Johnson, Herbert 1848–1906
John Hinchcliffe 1891
oil on canvas 98 x 75
THP020001

Knight, John Prescott 1803–1881
Sir Joseph Heron 1813–1881
oil on canvas 273 x 180
THP054001

Knight, John Prescott 1803–1881
John Bright
oil on canvas 270 x 180
THP036001

Lecomte-Vernet, Charles Émile Hippolyte 1821–1900
Henry Julius Leppoc 1877
oil on canvas 163 x 128
THP012001

Mooney, Edward Hartley 1877–1938
Edward Holt 1928
oil on canvas 110 x 90
THP015001

Mooney, Edward Hartley 1877–1938
George Westcott 1929
oil on canvas 110 x 90
THP016001

Mostyn, Thomas Edwin 1864–1930
John Foulkes Roberts 1898
oil on canvas 273 x 180
THP041001

Mostyn, Thomas Edwin 1864–1930
Sir William Henry Talbot 1907
oil on canvas 150 x 123
THP007001

Muckley, William Jabez 1829–1905
Thomas Goadsby 1861–1866
oil on canvas 230 x 135
THP026001

Munns, Henry Turner 1832–1898
Abel Heywood 1889
oil on canvas 273 x 180
THP033001

Munns, Henry Turner 1832–1898
Sir John Harwood 1892
oil on canvas 273 x 180
THP034001

Munns, Henry Turner 1832–1898
Sir Anthony Marshall 1895
oil on canvas 273 x 180
THP040001

Noakes, Michael b.1933
Her Majesty Queen Elizabeth II (b.1926) 1977
oil on canvas 240 x 143
THP056001

Patten, George 1801–1865
Mark Phillips 1832–1852
oil on canvas 230 x 135
THP027001

Patten, George 1801–1865
Alexander Kay 1850
oil on canvas 230 x 135
THP029001

Patten, George 1801–1865
John Potter 1850
oil on canvas 230 x 135
THP032001

Patten, George 1801–1865
William Benjamin Watkins 1850
oil on canvas 230 x 135
THP030001

Patten, George 1801–1865
George Wilson c.1851
oil on canvas 165 x 138
THP006001

Patten, George 1801–1865
Charles James Stanley Walker 1852
oil on canvas 163 x 138
THP011001

Patten, George 1801–1865
Elkanah Armitage 1852
oil on canvas 230 x 135
THP031001

Penny, Edward 1714–1791
James, Lord Strange
oil on canvas 210 x 143
THP078001

Percy, William 1820–1893
John Grave 1876
oil on canvas 273 x 180
THP042001

Reynolds, Samuel William 1773–1835
Alderman Sir Thomas Potter
oil on canvas 130 x 110
THP081001

Reynolds, Samuel William 1773–1835
Richard Potter
oil on canvas 90 x 69.4
THP080001

Sidley, Samuel 1829–1896
Daniel Adamson 1885
oil on canvas 195 x 130
THP014001

Snyders, Frans 1579–1657
Landscape with Birds and Animals
oil on canvas 228 x 300
THP079001

unknown artist
Abel Heywood
oil on canvas 115 x 90
THP013001

unknown artist
Alderman Sir Thomas Baker
oil on canvas 110 x 90 (E)
THP087001

unknown artist
Charles Behrens
oil on canvas 160 x 124
THP043001

unknown artist
James Bake
oil on canvas 76 x 60
THP044001

unknown artist
Portrait of an Unknown Gentleman
oil on canvas 92 x 71
THP001001

unknown artist
R. A. D. Carter
oil on canvas 147 x 122
THP003001

unknown artist
Sir John Mark
oil on canvas 122 x 87
THP021001

unknown artist
Sir Joseph Heron
oil on canvas 114 x 79
THP050001

unknown artist
Sir Philip Dingle
oil on canvas 76 x 61
THP051001

unknown artist
The Central Executive Cotton Famine Relief Committee
oil on canvas 190 x 350
THP038001

unknown artist
William Booth
oil on canvas 145 x 120
THP005001

Vasey, Gladys 1889–1981
Thomas Henry Adams
oil on canvas 105 x 82
THP023001

Williams, Margaret Lindsay 1888–1960
Elizabeth II (b.1926) 1953
oil on canvas 99 x 73
THP082001

Williamson, Harold 1898–1972
Douglas Gosling 1908–1972
oil on canvas 82 x 60
THP022001

Museum of
Science and
Industry

B., R.
*Mary George, Director of the Electrical Association for Women (1956–1976)** c.1960
oil on canvas 61 x 51
A1989.338 ESI 1/14/1

Baxter, Gib
*Avro Vulcan en route to the Falklands** 1982
acrylic on board 45.5 x 56
S11/1998

Copnall, Frank Thomas 1870–1949
*Percy Norris** 1926
oil on canvas 45.5 x 30.5
A1970.36

Eastman, Frank S. 1878–1964
*A. V. Roe** 1948
oil on canvas 90.5 x 69.5
MS 0619

Garratt, Agnes M. 1867–1944
While at Alloa, Scotland c.1880
oil on board 12.5 x 17.7
A1984.178/MS0497/3/1/1/8

Garratt, Herbert William 1864–1913
*Cavalier** (recto) c.1890
oil on board 27.5 x 26
A1984.178/MS0497/3/1/2

Garratt, Herbert William 1864–1913
Cavalier (verso) c.1890
oil on board 27.5 x 26
A1984.178/MS0497/3/1/2A

Garratt, Herbert William 1864–1913
*Ship in a Stormy Sea** c.1890
oil on board 15 x 23
A1984.178/MS0497/3/1/1/6

Garratt, Herbert William 1864–1913
View of a Ship from the Coast at Worthing*
1901
oil on board 20.7 x 34
A1984.178/MS0497/3/1/1/14

Garratt, Herbert William 1864–1913
Ship at Sea* c.1901
oil on board 25 x 38.5
A1984.178/MS0497/3/1/1/15

Garratt, Herbert William 1864–1913
0-6-0+0-6-0 Garratt Locomotive* c.1909
oil on canvas 41 x 61
A1978.72/3

Garratt, Herbert William 1864–1913
Great Eastern Railway Locomotive No.603*
c.1909
oil on canvas 50.5 x 76
A1978.72/1

Garratt, Herbert William 1864–1913
Steam Locomotive No.310* c.1909
oil on canvas 61 x 45.5
A1978.72/2

Garratt, Herbert William 1864–1913
View of York Station* c.1909
oil on canvas 41 x 61
A1978.72/4

Garratt, Herbert William 1864–1913
*View through the Front Window of a Steam
Locomotive** c.1909
oil on canvas 41 x 61
A1978.72/5

Harris, Alfred Peter b.1932
1830 Warehouse and Liverpool Road Station*
1980
oil on canvas 75.5 x 121
12A.1

Jagger, David (attributed to) 1891–1958
Dr S. Z. de Ferranti, FRS* 1931
oil on canvas 89.5 x 69.5
A1996.10

Kay, Rupert active 1973–1978
*Pott Street Pumping Station** 1973
acrylic on board 45.5 x 30.5
A1978.19/1

Miller, Edmund b.1929
*'The Quiet Test-Pilot'** 1989
oil on board 49.5 x 59
A1989.435

Miller, Edmund b.1929
Airborne Pioneers 1991
oil on canvas 89.5 x 130
A1987.431

Miller, Edmund b.1929
*Roy Chadwick** 1991
oil on canvas 59 x 74
A1992.130

T., R.
Firgrove Mill Engine, 1907 c.1988
oil on canvas 65 x 49.5
GMMSI/1988

unknown artist
Richard Johnson (1809–1881) c.1849
oil on canvas 73 x 61
A2010.63

unknown artist
*Charles Beyer** c.1870
oil on canvas 68 x 56
MS 0594

unknown artist
*Aerial View of a Factory on the River Avon**
c.1950
oil on board 114.5 x 205.5
2A.1

National Football Museum

Adamson, Sean
Ball Game
oil on canvas (?) 38 x 28
FIFA A80

Avery, Stuart J. C.
Pride of the Nation 1990
oil on canvas 90 x 120
TEMP.723

Beaton, Cecil Walter Hardy 1904–1980
Footballers c.1955
oil on canvas (?) 82 x 97.5
E857.161 (P)

Beaton, Cecil Walter Hardy 1904–1980
The Tackle c.1960
oil on canvas 57 x 48
E857.245 (P)

Brand, Doris
Boots (They Were Christopher's)
oil on canvas 66 x 87
FIFA A39

Brandao, Joyce
Football at Rio de Janeiro 1955
oil (?) & mixed media on canvas 14 x 23
FIFA A37

Bratby, John Randall 1928–1992
Jimmy Hill
oil on board 66 x 40.5
E237.26 (P) ※

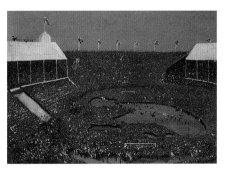

Brown, Reginald
Wembley 1923 1923 (?)
oil on canvas (?) 34 x 49
E549.20 (P)

Facing page: Rossetti, Dante Gabriel, 1828–1882, *Astarte Syriaca*, 1877, Manchester City Galleries (p. 210)

Browne, Michael J. b.1963
The Art of The Game 1997
oil on canvas 305.5 x 254
E1406 (P)

Buza, Kustim
Sunset 1989
oil on board 36 x 56.5
E239.300 (P)

Cains, Gerald Albert b.1932
Saturday Taxpayers
oil on canvas (?) 72 x 90
LANGTON 013

Chart, Daphne c.1910–2006
Clapham Common c.1953
oil on canvas 62 x 75
LANGTON 014

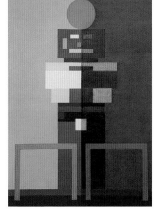

Colquhoun, Ithell 1906–1988
The Game of The Year 1953
oil on canvas 132.2 x 96
FIFA A1

Coverley-Price, Victor 1901–1988
Study of Textures 1960
oil on canvas (?) 50 x 60
FIFA A29

Deykin, Henry Cotterill 1905–1989
Aston Villa v West Bromwich Albion 1950
oil on canvas (?) 61 x 81
E857.168 (P)

Deykin, Henry Cotterill 1905–1989
Wembley Cup Final 1951 1951
oil on canvas 49 x 61
FIFA A31

Edwards, Peter Douglas b.1955
Bobby Charlton 1991
oil on canvas 98 x 72
E1355 (P)

Elford, N.
Portsmouth 1, Manchester United 1, Fratton Park, 1924 1924
oil on deckchair canvas 45 x 35
E857.147 (P)

Freeth, Hubert Andrew 1913–1986
Watford Dressing Room 1953
oil on canvas 70 x 90
E857.133

Goodman
Everton F. C. 1997
acrylic on board 52.5 x 52.5
PCF1

Hackney, Arthur 1925–2010
Spectators Returning Home After Port Vale v Accrington Stanley
oil (?) & mixed media on canvas (?) 35 x 70
E857.208

Hall, Clifford 1904–1973
Football Match c.1933
oil on board 14 x 20
E857.85 (P)

Higgs, J.
A Huddersfield Town Footballer Meets King George V 1932
oil on board 75 x 55
FIFA A9

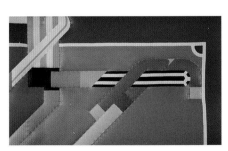

Holwell, Chris
Phew What a Scorcher/Maradona Goal 1970s
acrylic on upholstered canvas 79 x 142
FIFA A44

Horridge
Aston Villa
acrylic on board 53 x 53
PCF3

Howell, Chris
Goal Mouth Scramble 1994
acrylic on upholstered canvas 122 x 54
LANGTON 106

Jennings, Chris
Via Goldoni, Milano, 1908
acrylic on canvas 122 x 183
FIFA A75

Lambert, Albert
At the Match c.1925
oil on canvas (?) 80 x 67
E857.186 (P)

Lancaster, Edward
Village Football
oil on canvas 56 x 70
FIFA A43

M., G. O.
In the Dressing Room
oil on board 59 x 65
FIFA A3

Martin, Benito Quinquela 1890–1977
Rincon de la Boca 1963
oil on canvas 88 x 98
TEMP.722

Pearce, William H.
A Tense Moment 1953
oil on canvas (?) 48 x 72
E857.185 (P)

Petts, J.
The Goalkeeper c.1930s
oil on canvas (?) 25 x 50
FIFA A8

Powell, John
Soccer in the Suburbs 1950
oil on board 29 x 39
E857.128 (P)

Riordon, Eric 1906–1948
Canadian Tour, 1950
oil or acrylic on canvas (?) 30 x 39
E239.304 (P)

Samuelson, Peter 1912–1996
Football Match 1950–1960
oil on canvas 85 x 110
E857.204 (P)

Scott, Septimus Edwin 1879–1962
Big Match 1953
oil or acrylic on paper 71 x 147
FIFA A41

Slater, Paul b.1953
Burnley F. C. 1997
acrylic on board 54 x 54
PCF2

Smith, Paul
The Day Before War Broke Out (A Football Match, 1939) 2006
oil on board 74 x 100
E869

unknown artist
Fureball
acrylic on paper & board 56 x 74
FIFA A48

unknown artist
Penalty
acrylic on board 52 x 69
PCF4

unknown artist
Tom Finney
oil on board 53 x 38
PCF5

unknown artist
Willie Cunningham in Preston North End Kit
oil on board 44 x 34
E549.23.37 (P)

unknown artist
Camp Ball 1825–1850
oil on canvas 29.5 x 40
FIFA A49

unknown artist
William Charles Cuff 1946 (?)
oil on canvas 81 x 63
TEMP.607

unknown artist
John Charles 1955–1960
acrylic on card 36.5 x 26
E857.133 (P)

unknown artist
Village Green Soccer c.1950
oil on canvas 71 x 92
FIFA A69

Vaudou, Gaston 1891–1957
A Soccer Match 1920
oil on canvas 45 x 60
FIFA A4

Webster, Thomas George 1800–1886
Football 1839
oil on canvas 63 x 150
FIFA A20

Webster, Thomas George 1800–1886
A Football Game 1839 (?)
oil on canvas 15 x 32
FIFA A21

Webster, Thomas George (after) 1800–1886
Football c.1870
oil on canvas 69 x 94
E857.162 (P)

People's History Museum

The People's History Museum is the national museum of democracy. It is the only museum dedicated to telling the story of the development of democracy in Britain. Originally founded in Limehouse Town Hall in London in 1975, and known as the National Museum of Labour History, the museum and its collections were relocated to Manchester in the late 1980s. The museum galleries on Princess Street opened to the public in 1990 in the building where the TUC held its first ever meeting over 100 years ago. The museum and its public galleries moved to its current site at the Pump house in 1994. The museum closed in 2007 for a £12.5 million major capital development project, reopening in February 2010, in a purpose built home.

The museum places its collection at the heart of everything it does and uses it to tell the story of the development of democracy. The galleries and collections allow exploration of Friendly societies, temperance societies, the Primrose League, and women's struggles to win the vote, amongst many other campaigns. The paintings and painted banners of the People's History Museum uniquely depict 'history from below', powerfully illustrating the lives of working people in Britain and their achievements.

The museum acquired Designated Status in 1998 for its entire collection, which in addition to its paintings and painted banners, also includes posters, political prints, tokens and ceramics. With its unparalleled banner collection, the museum holds an immensely important and hitherto neglected part of Britain's heritage. Many of the museum's earlier banners are double-sided and have stunning, full-scale emblems painted in oils. A large percentage of the banners were produced and painted by Britain's main banner maker, George Tutill, City Road, London. Tutill employed professional painters to carry out this work. A number of these banners came from two of Britain's foremost labour history collectors, John Gorman and John Smethurst.

While not a fine art museum, and holding no great number of oils on canvas, the museum does hold a significant amount of paintings. The vast majority of these are by Cliff Rowe, received by the museum when based in Limehouse. Highlights of the Cliff Rowe paintings include his large Smithfield Market meat porters and many of women workers, such as textile workers and locomotive engine cleaners. Largely produced between the 1930s and the 1970s, many of these works are unsigned and undated, and have brief names, such as 'Women silkscreen printers'.

The majority of the non-Rowe oils and acrylic paintings were also acquired by the former museum, as were many of the painted and non-painted banners. The paintings, some of them on boards, cover individual portraits, workers, strikes and disputes, trade union emblems, and large-scale depictions of certain labour struggles. The highlights of the paintings include A. J. Waudby's large painted emblem design for the Operative Bricklayers' Society, two paintings of industrial workers works by J. Ashford, a portrait of Arthur Henderson, portraits of 1945 Labour government figures, Clement Attlee, Nye Bevan, Herbert Morrison, and Manny Shinwell, and a full-length portrait drape of British Communist Party leader, Harry Pollitt, holding the 1951 publication produced by the Party's executive, 'The British Road To Socialism'.

'Star' painted banners include the early nineteenth-century 'Success to Miners' banner, the Duns Shoemakers' banner, the Liverpool Tinplate

Workers' banner, thought to be the oldest trade union banner still in existence, and the Sunderland Employers' 'Nine Hours' campaign banner.

In the coming years, the museum will continue to actively collect artefacts relating to British democracy, keeping the collection and the museum's story alive and fresh. Please note, these paintings represent approximately one-third of the People's History Museum.

Philip Dunn, Museum Registrar

Alston, W. P.
Aneurin Bevan (1897–1960) 1980
acrylic on canvas 61 x 46
NMLH.1992.716

Ashford, J.
Railway Worker Holding Bunch of Red Roses* 1955
oil on board 123 x 84
NMLH.1992.790.2

Ashton, J.
Two Workers and White Dove* 1952
oil on canvas 102 x 76
NMLH.1992.790.1

Bernasconi, George Henry 1841–1916
Merchant Shipping Bill Banner 1884
oil on linen 177 x 129
NMLH.1993.628

Brooks, Ern 1911–1993
Still Life, 'Daily Worker' Newspaper*
oil on board 76.5 x 75.5
NMLH.1994.168.19

Brooks, Ern 1911–1993
Zeus and Europa* c.1950
acrylic on canvas 91.5 x 71
NMLH.2005.43.2

Facing page: Modigliani, Amedeo, 1884–1920, *Portrait of an Unknown Model*, c.1918, Manchester City Galleries (p. 168)

Carr, Dorothy
Mining Village (possibly Spennymoor) c.1951
oil on paper 29.5 x 40
NMLH.1998.21.9

Carr, Dorothy
*Spennymoor** c.1951
oil on board 50 x 81.5
NMLH.1998.21.32

Carr, Dorothy
*Spennymoor** c.1951
oil on paper 28 x 37.7
NMLH.1998.21.8

Dixon, William
*Tin-Plate Workers' Banner, Liverpool** 1821
oil on linen 150 x 266
NMLH.1990.26

Easton, A. F.
Mrs Florence Willard, Founder Member of TULC and National Museum of Labour History (now People's History Museum) 1975
oil on canvas 70 x 61
NMLH.1992.717

Eisler, Georg 1928–1998
*Miners' Strike, 1984–1985** 1988
oil on canvas 298 x 398
NMLH.1989.2

Galeotti, Renzo
James Klugmann (1912–1977) 1977
tempera & ink on canvas 76 x 56
NMHL.1994.168.15

Gibbons, Geoff P. active 1984–1990
*Solidarity, 1984–1985**
oil on board 128 x 128
NMLH.1991.105

Glover, Margaret b.c.1940
Lord Fenner Brockway: Towards Tomorrow 1980
oil on canvas 68 x 55
NMLH.1991.111

Gray, Stuart
Hatted and Bearded Man c.1890s
oil on canvas 67 x 59
NMLH.1992.718

Hancock, Samuel Harry 1862–1932
Landlord and Tenants c.1920s
oil on canvas 112 x 87
NMLH.2011.1

Healey, Christine 1945–2010
Faces of Barbara Castle c.1991
acrylic on canvas 132 x 97
NMLH.1993.763

Healey, Christine 1945–2010
Faces of Foot c.1991
acrylic on canvas 104 x 215
NMLH.1993.762

Locket, D.
Coal Mining, 1985
oil on board 91 x 130
NMLH.1992.806

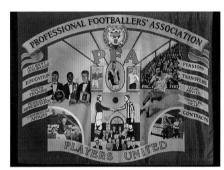

Midgely, John
Professional Footballers' Association Banner
1991
acrylic on polyester 180 x 200
IRN7561;entry 0344

Moscheles, Felix Stone 1833–1917
Robert Cunningham Graham (?)
oil on canvas 61 x 51
NMLH.1 UD

Rowe, Cliff 1904–1989
Girl with Skipping Rope 1931
oil on board 91 x 61
PCF115

Rowe, Cliff 1904–1989
Woman Sitting on Doorstep 1931
oil on panel 90 x 60
PCF84

Rowe, Cliff 1904–1989
Woman with Birdcage in Window 1931
oil on board 61 x 91
PCF88

Rowe, Cliff 1904–1989
Two Women and Pram 1937
oil on board 61 x 91
PCF124

Rowe, Cliff 1904–1989
Two Young Girls on Doorstep 1937
oil on panel 59 x 80
PCF171

Rowe, Cliff 1904–1989
Child Knocking on Door 1954
oil on board 61 x 91
PCF83

Rowe, Cliff 1904–1989
Sorting Pencils 1961
oil on paper on board 60 x 122
PCF147

Rowe, Cliff 1904–1989
Impulse Panel 1963
oil & emulsion on board 61 x 122
PCF135

Rowe, Cliff 1904–1989
Man on Long Boot Machine 1963
oil on paper on board 60 x 165
PCF155

Rowe, Cliff 1904–1989
Gloved Machine Operator 1965
oil on paper on board 103 x 181
PCF43

Rowe, Cliff 1904–1989
Woman at Bottle Machine 1965
oil on paper on board 100 x 230
PCF180

Rowe, Cliff 1904–1989
Woman Looking Through a Microscope 1966
oil on board 120 x 106
PCF148

Rowe, Cliff 1904–1989
Woman Machinist 1966
oil on board 130 x 103
PCF1

Rowe, Cliff 1904–1989
Centrifugal Pump 1967
oil on board 120 x 106
PCF151

Rowe, Cliff 1904–1989
Man with Goggles at Machine 1967
acrylic on board 120 x 90
PCF57

Rowe, Cliff 1904–1989
Pulping Machine 1967
oil on panel 53 x 86
PCF145

Rowe, Cliff 1904–1989
Still Life with Spectacles 1967
oil on board 55 x 123
PCF163

Rowe, Cliff 1904–1989
Black Singer 1969
oil on board 97 x 152
PCF70

Rowe, Cliff 1904–1989
Street Corner 1969
oil on board 56 x 122
PCF82

Rowe, Cliff 1904–1989
Acrobats 1970
oil on board 122 x 90
PCF64

Rowe, Cliff 1904–1989
Child in Pushchair (unfinished) 1970
oil on board 64 x 122
PCF74

Rowe, Cliff 1904–1989
Dancer in Two Positions 1970
oil on board 122 x 82
PCF66

Rowe, Cliff 1904–1989
Emblematic Figure and Bird 1970
oil on board 118 x 88
PCF153

Rowe, Cliff 1904–1989
Ships Moored Together 1971
oil on panel 27 x 90
PCF169

Rowe, Cliff 1904–1989
Southend 1971
oil on board 90 x 122
PCF59

Rowe, Cliff 1904–1989
Man at Conveyor Machine 1973
oil on board 103 x 174
PCF98

Rowe, Cliff 1904–1989
Old Lighthouse, Harwich 1973
acrylic on board 34 x 93
PCF75

Rowe, Cliff 1904–1989
Boat Hulls 1974
oil on board 58 x 126
PCF77

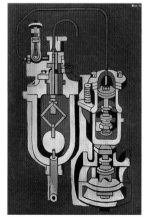

Rowe, Cliff 1904–1989
Section of Machine Part 1974
oil on board 90 x 59
PCF174

Rowe, Cliff 1904–1989
Shapes 1974
oil on board 122 x 65
PCF161

Rowe, Cliff 1904–1989
Millworker in Headscarf 1976
oil on canvas 60 x 89
PCF168

Rowe, Cliff 1904–1989
Astronaut
oil & emulsion on board 122 x 61
PCF136

Rowe, Cliff 1904–1989
Baker
oil on board 61 x 125
PCF45

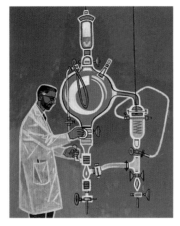

Rowe, Cliff 1904–1989
Bearded Scientist
oil on board 120 x 90
PCF164

Rowe, Cliff 1904–1989
Bike Racers Cornering
oil on board 46 x 121
PCF48

Rowe, Cliff 1904–1989
Bootmaking
oil on paper on board 85 x 165
PCF157

Rowe, Cliff 1904–1989
Buoys on Quay
oil on board 60 x 110
PCF162

Rowe, Cliff 1904–1989
By Chance
oil on board 128 x 57
PCF160

Rowe, Cliff 1904–1989
Casting
acrylic on board 122 x 61
PCF55

Rowe, Cliff 1904–1989
Chemist
oil on paper on board 61 x 125
PCF91

Rowe, Cliff 1904–1989
Child on Rocking Horse
oil on board 121 x 90
PCF60

Rowe, Cliff 1904–1989
Crane Operator
oil on paper on board 122 x 61
PCF165

Rowe, Cliff 1904–1989
Drying Enamel Plates
oil on board 122 x 61
PCF137

Rowe, Cliff 1904–1989
Electrical Engineer
oil on board 70 x 122
PCF78

Rowe, Cliff 1904–1989
Engine Assembler
oil on board 122 x 46
PCF90

Rowe, Cliff 1904–1989
Female Glass Worker
oil on board 61 x 122
PCF94

Rowe, Cliff 1904–1989
Female Guitarist
oil on board 92 x 121
PCF107

Rowe, Cliff 1904–1989
Fireside
oil on board 90 x 121
PCF152

Rowe, Cliff 1904–1989
Fishing Boat
oil on board 81 x 122
PCF67

Rowe, Cliff 1904–1989
Fishing Boat on the Stocks
oil on board 92 x 120
PCF134

Rowe, Cliff 1904–1989
Fruit Basket
oil on board 69 x 40
PCF176

Rowe, Cliff 1904–1989
Glass Blower
oil on paper on board 190 x 83
PCF182

Rowe, Cliff 1904–1989
Glassblower at Red Furnace
oil on board 62 x 122
PCF10

Rowe, Cliff 1904–1989
Guitarist
oil on board 122 x 61
PCF52

Rowe, Cliff 1904–1989
Hospital Laundry Workers
oil on board 20 x 33
PCF14

Rowe, Cliff 1904–1989
Human Pattern
oil on board 90 x 122
PCF61

Rowe, Cliff 1904–1989
Industrial Plant
oil on board 68 x 150
PCF188

Rowe, Cliff 1904–1989
Kentish Town
oil on panel 60 x 88
PCF170

Rowe, Cliff 1904–1989
Kentish Town, 1937
oil on board 46 x 100
PCF186

Rowe, Cliff 1904–1989
Loco Cleaners
oil on board 38 x 38
PCF189

Rowe, Cliff 1904–1989
Man and Machine (unfinished)
oil & pencil on board 122 x 59
PCF92

Rowe, Cliff 1904–1989
Man and Microscope
oil on board 122 x 61
PCF93

Rowe, Cliff 1904–1989
Man at Boot Machine
oil on board 101 x 117
PCF105

Rowe, Cliff 1904–1989
Man at Metal Press
oil on paper 60 x 185
PCF33

Rowe, Cliff 1904–1989
Man Drawing Out Molten Glass
oil on paper on board 89 x 185
PCF179

Facing page: Millais, John Everett, 1829–1896, *Autumn Leaves,* 1856, Manchester City Galleries (p. 167)

Rowe, Cliff 1904–1989
Man Leaning Over Woman
oil on board 60 x 126
PCF54

Rowe, Cliff 1904–1989
Man Pouring Liquid into Tank
oil on board 61 x 125
PCF44

Rowe, Cliff 1904–1989
Man Shaping a Bottle
oil on board 197 x 106
PCF99

Rowe, Cliff 1904–1989
Men and Women in Doorway
oil on board 91 x 61
PCF86

Rowe, Cliff 1904–1989
Men Hoisting Machine Section
oil on board 122 x 61
PCF46

Rowe, Cliff 1904–1989
Mexican Guerrillas
oil on board 61 x 91
PCF85

Rowe, Cliff 1904–1989
Operating Theatre Nurse
oil on canvas 90 x 60
PCF167

Rowe, Cliff 1904–1989
Pipe Cutter
acrylic on board 122 x 83
PCF56

Rowe, Cliff 1904–1989
Plating Bicycle Frames
oil on panel 133 x 73
PCF149

Rowe, Cliff 1904–1989
Railway Wheeltapper
oil on board 145 x 56
PCF158

Rowe, Cliff 1904–1989
Removal Men
oil on board 61 x 91
PCF12

Rowe, Cliff 1904–1989
Riveters
oil on canvas 45 x 91
PCF144

Rowe, Cliff 1904–1989
Roofer
oil on paper on board 76 x 56
PCF5

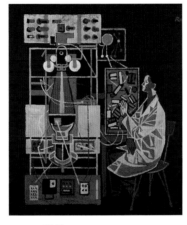

Rowe, Cliff 1904–1989
Scientist at Lab Bench
oil on paper on board 109 x 97
PCF143

Rowe, Cliff 1904–1989
Sorting Tobacco Leaves
oil on board 122 x 61
PCF139

Rowe, Cliff 1904–1989
Street Scene (unfinished)
acrylic on board 58 x 126
PCF53

Rowe, Cliff 1904–1989
Sun Furnace
oil on board 190 x 83
PCF183

Rowe, Cliff 1904–1989
Textile Worker
oil on canvas 70 x 100
PCF8

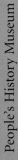

Rowe, Cliff 1904–1989
Textile Workers
oil on board 100 x 164
PCF7

Rowe, Cliff 1904–1989
The Steps
oil on board 91 x 61
PCF175

Rowe, Cliff 1904–1989
The Three Graces
oil on paper on board 80 x 200
PCF156

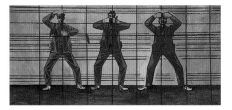

Rowe, Cliff 1904–1989
Three Men Building Frame
oil on board 90 x 192
PCF97

Rowe, Cliff 1904–1989
Three Toy Bears
oil on canvas 61 x 122
PCF102

Rowe, Cliff 1904–1989
Three Women Talking
acrylic on board 60.8 x 91.3
PCF210

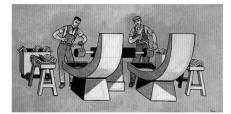

Rowe, Cliff 1904–1989
Two Bicycle Makers
oil on chipboard 61 x 122
PCF100

Rowe, Cliff 1904–1989
Village Harbour
oil on paper on board 57 x 122
PCF166

Rowe, Cliff 1904–1989
Weaver
oil on paper on board 61 x 121
PCF111

Rowe, Cliff 1904–1989
White Roses
oil on panel 59 x 50
PCF177

Rowe, Cliff 1904–1989
Woman Cleaning Loco Boiler
oil on board 122 x 80
PCF178

Rowe, Cliff 1904–1989
Woman Cleaning Loco Boiler
oil on board 159 x 100
PCF190

Rowe, Cliff 1904–1989
Woman Cleaning Loco Boiler
oil on board 120 x 100
PCF191

Rowe, Cliff 1904–1989
Woman Cleaning Loco Boiler
oil on board 93 x 61
PCF9

Rowe, Cliff 1904–1989
Woman in Bottling Plant
oil on board 81 x 137
PCF95

Rowe, Cliff 1904–1989
Woman Machinist
oil on board 61 x 120
PCF192

Rowe, Cliff 1904–1989
Woman Millworker
oil on paper on board 103 x 220
PCF96

Rowe, Cliff 1904–1989
Woman on Moped
oil on board 61 x 122
PCF80

Rowe, Cliff 1904–1989
Woman Potter
oil on board 122 x 61
PCF47

Rowe, Cliff 1904–1989
Woman Reclining on Bed
oil on canvas 61 x 122
PCF103

Rowe, Cliff 1904–1989
Woman Sat at Machine Controls
oil on paper on board 86 x 170
PCF146

Rowe, Cliff 1904–1989
Woman Silkscreen Printer
acrylic on board 90 x 49
PCF187

Rowe, Cliff 1904–1989
Woman Sunbathing in Park
oil on board 54 x 122
PCF49

Rowe, Cliff 1904–1989
Woman Working
oil on paper on board 86 x 144
PCF150

Rowe, Cliff 1904–1989
Women and Pram
oil on board 61 x 91
PCF87

Scott, Maureen b.1940
The History of Labour 1975
oil on canvas 173 x 124
NMLH.1992.808

Stone, Marcus active 1934–1951
Aneurin Bevan (1897–1960) 1945
acrylic on card 54 x 60
NMLH.1992.715

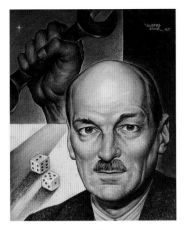

Stone, Marcus active 1934–1951
Clement Attlee (1883–1967) 1945
acrylic on card 63 x 57
NMLH.1993.373.11 (P)

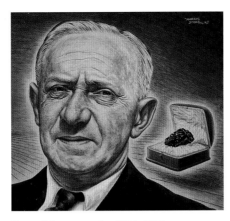

Stone, Marcus active 1934–1951
Emmanuel Shinwell (1884–1986) 1945
acrylic on canvas 50 x 63
NMLH.1993.373.13 (P)

Stone, Marcus active 1934–1951
Herbert Morrison (1888–1965) 1945
acrylic on canvas 63 x 50.5
NMLH.1993.373.12 (P)

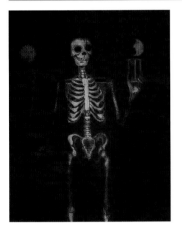

unknown artist
Skeleton c.1820
oil & bitumen on textile 227 x 142
NMLH.2005.32

unknown artist
Friendly United Mechanics Cabinet Emblem* c.1830
oil on wood 127 x 95
NMLH.1992.66

unknown artist
Success To Miners Banner* c.1830
oil on silk 161 x 158
NMLH.2007.1.2

unknown artist
Plumbers' Banner* 1832
oil on cotton & silk 238 x 194
NMLH.1998.24

unknown artist
Shoemakers' Banner* 1832
oil on cotton 212 x 174
NMLH.1997.7.1

unknown artist
Shoemakers' Apron* c.1832
oil on textile 67.4 x 45.5
PCF201

unknown artist
Typographical Association Banner (recto)
1849–1882
oil on linen & silk 200 x 180
NMLH1993.703

unknown artist
Typographical Association Banner (verso)
1849–1882
oil on textile 200 x 180
NMLH1993.703

unknown artist
*Co-operative Smiths Banner** c.1870
oil on cotton 350 x 250
NMLH.2005.44.4

unknown artist
The Sunderland Employers Banner 1871
oil on linen 200 x 180
NMLH.1993.690

unknown artist
Dockers Union Banner (recto) 1890s
oil on silk 200 x 190 (E)
NMLH1993.58

unknown artist
Dockers Union Banner (verso) 1890s
oil on silk 200 x 190 (E)
NMLH1993.58B

unknown artist
Arthur Henderson (1863–1935) 1917
oil on canvas 130 x 104
NMLH.2010.25.1 (P)

unknown artist
*National Builders Labourers And Construction
Workers Society Banner* (recto) c.1921
oil on silk 200 x 180
NMLH.1993.559

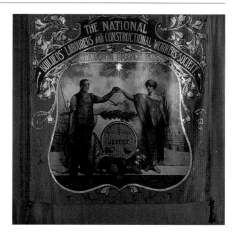

unknown artist
*National Builders Labourers And Construction
Workers Society Banner* (verso) c.1921
oil on textile 200 x 180
NMLH.1993.559B

Facing page: Rothenstein, William, 1872–1945, *In the Morning Room*, c.1905, Manchester City Galleries (p. 210)

unknown artist
National Union of Railwaymen Smithfield Branch Banner (recto) c.1925
oil on silk 264 x 290
NMLH.1993.651A

unknown artist
National Union of Railwaymen Smithfield Branch Banner (verso) c.1925
oil on textile 264 x 290
NMLH.1993.651B

unknown artist
Harry Pollitt (1890–1960) c.1951
oil on canvas drape 253 x 134
NMLH.1994.168.17

unknown artist
Fellowship is Life I c.1950s
oil on board 61 x 183
NMLH.1992.786.1.2A

unknown artist
Fellowship is Life II c.1950s
oil on board 61 x 183
NMLH.1992.786.1.2B

unknown artist
Liberty Fraternity & Peace* c.1960
oil on board 122 x 182.5
NMLH.1992.784

unknown artist
The Tolpuddle Martyrs* c.1960
oil on board 121.5 x 183
NMLH.1992.783

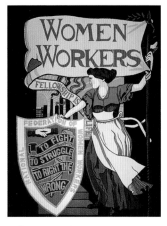

unknown artist
National Federation of Women Workers Banner 1970s
acrylic on linen 132 x 91
NMLH1993.593

unknown artist
Taking Scabs To Work c.1984
oil on board 113 x 161
NMLH.1992.807

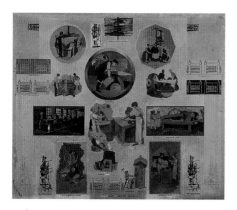

unknown artist
Metalworkers and Engineers from the
Thirteenth Century to the Nineteenth Century*
1980s
oil on canvas 125 x 144
NMLH.1994.161

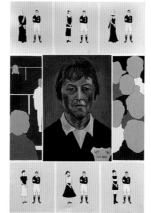

unknown artist
Dick Kerrs (1917–1960)* c.1992
oil on canvas 184 x 121
NMLH.1994.166.11

unknown artist
Robert Blatchford (1851–1943)
oil on canvas 80.02 x 66.02
NMLH.2010.25.2 (P)

unknown artist
William Rust (1903–1949), Editor of 'Daily
Worker' Newspaper
oil on canvas 64 x 81.5
NMLH.1994.168.14

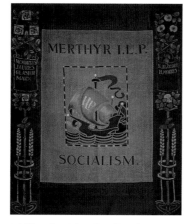

Wallhead, Richard Collingham
Merthyr Independent Labour Party Banner
c.1920
oil on cotton, velvet & silk 185 x 143
NMLH.1993.496

Waudby, A. J.
Operative Bricklayers Society Emblem* 1869
oil on textile 248 x 189
NMLH.1993.773

Royal Northern
College of Music

Bradford, Dorothy 1918–2008
Allegri String Quartet, Rodewald, Liverpool, 20
October 1964 1964
oil on board 91 x 213
PCF1

Bradford, Dorothy 1918–2008
Quartet
oil on board 60 x 182
PCF11

Cartledge, William 1891–1976
Adolph Brodsky (1851–1929) 1924
oil on canvas 107 x 87
PCF2

Davies, Austin (attributed to) 1926–2012
Gordon Green late 1950s
oil on canvas 61 x 85
PCF8

Durkin, Tom (possibly) 1928–1990
Country Scene
oil on board 37 x 51
PCF4

Fischer, Paula 1873–1950
Carl Fuchs (1845–1951)
oil on canvas 78 x 67.5
PCF6

Gregson, Julie
'La Rondine'
acrylic on canvas 123 x 122
PCF12

Hood, Barbara M. b.1915
Eva Turner (1892–1990), as Turandot
oil on canvas 61 x 49
PCF14

Howorth, Ray 1914–1985
Hilda Collens (1883–1956) 1957
oil on canvas 70 x 45
PCF3

Purser, Sarah Henrietta 1848–1943
Carl Fuchs (1845–1951)
oil on canvas 72 x 61
PCF5

unknown artist
Charles Hallé (1819–1895)
oil on canvas 53 x 42
PCF15

unknown artist
Greek Scene
oil on canvas 59 x 79.9
PCF7

The Christie NHS Foundation Trust

Brown, Nicola
Landscape 2006
mixed media on paper 24 x 18
PCF49

Cyprus, Chris b.1971
Canal Scene at Night c.2005
acrylic on canvas 100 x 100
PCF7

Cyprus, Chris b.1971
Landscape with Cows c.2005
acrylic on canvas 100 x 100
PCF6

Cyprus, Chris b.1971
Woodland c.2005
acrylic on canvas (?) 92 x 92
PCF8

Cyprus, Chris b.1971
Tatton Park 2009
acrylic on canvas 58 x 79
PCF66

Dunn, Kevin Lancelot b.1962
Landscape 2006
mixed media on paper 27 x 18
PCF50

Dunn, Kevin Lancelot b.1962
Landscape 2009
acrylic on canvas 60 x 46
PCF38

Dunn, Kevin Lancelot b.1962
Lindisfarne, View to the Mainland 2009
acrylic on canvas 91 x 61
PCF4

Dunn, Kevin Lancelot b.1962
Bow Lane, Manchester 2011
acrylic on canvas 40 x 30
PCF27

Dunn, Kevin Lancelot b.1962
Lizard Street, Manchester 2011
acrylic on canvas 40 x 30
PCF26

Dunn, Kevin Lancelot b.1962
Parliament Building, Budapest 2011
acrylic on canvas 41 x 50.5
PCF18

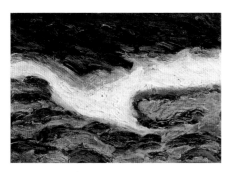

Fox, Doreen b.1953
Seascape 2011
acrylic on canvas 23 x 32
PCF31

Fox, Doreen b.1953
Seascape 2011
acrylic on canvas 30.5 x 30
PCF32

George, Kevin
The Christie Hospital 2011
acrylic on canvas 90 x 120
PCF5

Greenhalgh, Gillian A. b.1950
People in a Garden 2011
acrylic on canvas 30 x 40
PCF25

Kushnick, Patricia b.1940
Landscape 2006
mixed media on paper 28 x 13.5
PCF53

Kushnick, Patricia b.1940
Dream Candy 2011
acrylic on canvas 25 x 12.5
PCF41

Kushnick, Patricia b.1940
Dream Farm 2011
acrylic on canvas 20 x 20
PCF40

Kushnick, Patricia b.1940
Flowers 2011
acrylic on canvas 40 x 40
PCF20

Kushnick, Patricia b.1940
Halos and Flowers 2011
acrylic on canvas 30.5 x 25.5
PCF42

Lily, Rooney b.1950
Portrait of an Unknown Woman 2011
acrylic on canvas 40 x 30
PCF28

Lily, Rooney b.1950
Portrait of an Unknown Woman 2011
acrylic on canvas 40.5 x 30
PCF29

Mountford, Patricia Ann b.1957
Landscape 2007
mixed media on paper 42 x 29
PCF58

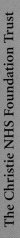

Mountford, Patricia Ann b.1957
Scaffolding 2009
acrylic on canvas 80 x 120
PCF35

Mountford, Patricia Ann b.1957
Flowers 2011
acrylic on canvas 76 x 76
PCF64A

Mountford, Patricia Ann b.1957
Flowers 2011
acrylic on canvas 76 x 30.5
PCF64B

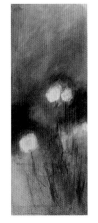

Mountford, Patricia Ann b.1957
Flowers 2011
acrylic on canvas
PCF65A

Mountford, Patricia Ann b.1957
Flowers 2011
acrylic on canvas 76 x 30.5
PCF65B

Murray, Gill b.1940
Landscape 2006
mixed media on paper 23 x 11
PCF47

Murray, Gill b.1940
Landscape 2006
mixed media on paper 31 x 17
PCF54

Murray, Gill b.1940
Woodland in Snow 2008
acrylic on canvas 40.5 x 40.5
PCF63

Murray, Gill b.1940
Woodland Scene 2008
acrylic on canvas 51 x 41
PCF62

Murray, Gill b.1940
Beach Scene 2011
acrylic on canvas 40 x 40
PCF16

Murray, Gill b.1940
Beach Scene 2011
acrylic on canvas 46 x 35.5
PCF21

Murray, Gill b.1940
Mountains 2011
acrylic on canvas 50 x 50
PCF33

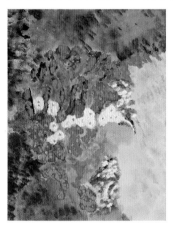

Oliver, Jo
Flowers 2011
acrylic on canvas 46 x 35.5
PCF15

Routledge, Jacki b.1957
Seascape 2011
acrylic on canvas 51 x 40
PCF17

Siraj, Zia b.1941
Dervishes 2011
acrylic on canvas 41 x 51
PCF13

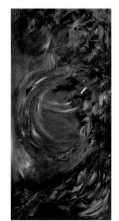

Tait, Eileen
Above the Clouds
acrylic on canvas 122 x 152
PCF67

Tait, Eileen
Autumn
acrylic on canvas 122 x 61
PCF71

Tait, Eileen
Spring
acrylic on canvas 122 x 61
PCF68

Tait, Eileen
Summer
acrylic on canvas 122 x 61
PCF70

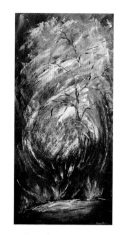

Tait, Eileen
Winter
acrylic on canvas 122 x 61
PCF69

unknown artist
The Christie 1980–1990
acrylic on canvas 61 x 59
PCF45

unknown artist
Landscape 2006
mixed media on paper 25 x 22
PCF46

unknown artist
Landscape 2006
mixed media on paper 23 x 22
PCF51

unknown artist
Landscape 2006
mixed media on paper 28 x 19
PCF52

unknown artist
Landscape 2006
mixed media on paper 24 x 20
PCF55

unknown artist
Landscape 2006
mixed media on paper 29 x 15.5
PCF56

unknown artist
Landscape 2006
mixed media on paper 28.5 x 16
PCF57

Facing page: Martineau, Robert Braithwaite, 1826–1869, *A Lady with a Gold Chain and Earrings*, 1861,
Manchester City Galleries (p. 160)

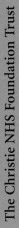

unknown artist
Fish 2008
acrylic on canvas 15 x 15
PCF60_1

unknown artist
Fish 2008
acrylic on canvas 15 x 15
PCF60_2

unknown artist
Landscape 2008
acrylic on canvas 25 x 12.5
PCF59_1

unknown artist
Landscape 2008
acrylic on canvas 25 x 12.5
PCF59_2

unknown artist
Landscape 2008
acrylic on canvas 25 x 12.5
PCF59_3

unknown artist
Landscape 2008
acrylic on canvas 25 x 12.5
PCF59_4

unknown artist
Landscape 2008
acrylic on canvas 25 x 12.5
PCF59_5

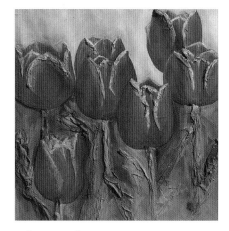

unknown artist
Tulips 2008
acrylic on canvas 17.5 x 17.5
PCF61

unknown artist
Peacock 2011
acrylic on canvas 23 x 30
PCF30

unknown artist
Venice 2011
acrylic on canvas 35.5 x 25
PCF10

Walker, Anne b.1959
Sunflowers 2009
acrylic on canvas 76 x 31
PCF4_1

Walker, Anne b.1959
Sunflowers 2009
acrylic on canvas 76 x 31
PCF4_2

Walker, Anne b.1959
Sunflowers 2009
acrylic on canvas 76 x 31
PCF4_3

Walker, Anne b.1959
Portrait of an Unknown Child 2011
acrylic on canvas 15 x 15
PCF37

Walker, Anne b.1959
Portrait of an Unknown Man 2011
acrylic on canvas 18 x 13
PCF24

Walker, Anne b.1959
Portrait of an Unknown Woman 2011
acrylic on canvas 20 x 20
PCF11

Walker, Anne b.1959
Portrait of an Unknown Woman 2011
acrylic on canvas 20 x 20
PCF12

Walker, Anne b.1959
Portrait of an Unknown Woman 2011
acrylic on canvas 12.5 x 12.5
PCF22

Walker, Anne b.1959
Portrait of an Unknown Woman 2011
acrylic on canvas 15 x 15
PCF23

Walker, Anne b.1959
Portrait of Unknown Children 2011
acrylic on canvas 13 x 18
PCF36

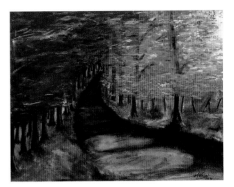

Walker, Anne b.1959
Woodland Scene 2011
acrylic on canvas 46 x 60
PCF34

Wilkinson, Pat b.1964
Fire 2011
acrylic on canvas 20 x 20
PCF44

Wilkinson, Pat b.1964
Ice 2011
acrylic on canvas 20 x 20
PCF43

Wilkinson, Pat b.1964
Up 2011
acrylic on canvas 40 x 40
PCF14

Yeoman, Neill b.1966
Trees 2009
acrylic on canvas 91.5 x 61
PCF2

Yeoman, Neill b.1966
Portrait of an Unknown Woman 2011
acrylic on canvas 50 x 39
PCF19

The Portico Library and Gallery

Benjamin, Norman
The Portico Library
oil on board 41 x 50
PCF5

Bernieri, Luigi c.1862–1944
Joseph Sunlight
oil on canvas 205 x 85 (E)
PCF1

Bernieri, Luigi c.1862–1944
*Portrait of an Unidentified Lady of the
Sunlight Family*
oil on canvas 118 x 82.5
PCF3

Smith, Phill W. active 1890–1932
*Portrait of an Unidentified Lady of the
Sunlight Family*
oil on canvas 100 x 75
PCF2

The University of Manchester

Ashurst, Stephen b.1956
Christopher Rose-Innes 2003
oil on canvas 180 x 106
MH1

Ashurst, Stephen b.1956
*Professor Graham Wood, UMIST (1961–
2000), Britain's First Professor of Corrosion
Science (1972–1997)* 2003
oil on canvas 212 x 151
EPS/Mill/003

Ashurst, Stephen b.1956
Brian Launder (b.1939) 2004
oil on canvas 200 x 115 (E)
EPS/Begg/029

Ashurst, Stephen b.1956
Lord Alliance 2004
oil on canvas 180 x 115 (E)
HUM021

Ashurst, Stephen b.1956
*Professor John Gartside, Professor Alan Gilbert
and Professor Sir Martin Harris* 2005
oil on board 180 x 240
PCF12

Ashurst, Stephen b.1956
*Professor Edwin Smith, Head of Department,
UMIST (1962–1990)* 2006
oil on canvas 110 x 26 (E)
EPS/MatSci/001

Ashurst, Stephen b.1956
*Professor Kenneth Entwhistle, Head of
Department, UMIST (1962–1990)* 2006
oil on canvas 110 x 26 (E)
EPS/MatSci/002

Ashurst, Stephen b.1956
The Four Deans 2006
oil on canvas 250 x 180 (E)
EPS/MIB/001

Ashurst, Stephen b.1956
*Professor Tom Hinchcliffe and Dr Roger
Pannone* 2009
oil on canvas 150 x 180
PCF11

Ashurst, Stephen b.1956
Sir Terry Leahy
oil on canvas 200 x 120 (E)
PCF10

Atack, David b.1949
*Professor H. C. A. Hankins, Principal and
Vice-Chancellor (1984–1995)*
oil on canvas 100 x 100 (E)
EPS/Sack/030

Atack, David b.1949
Professor R. F. Boucher, Principal and Vice-Chancellor (1995–2000)
oil on canvas 110 x 90 (E)
EPS/Sack/029

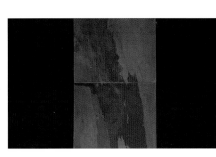

Blease, G. D. b.1970
Landscape 1993
acrylic on canvas 184 x 122
HUM014

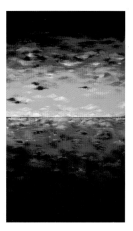

Chadwick, Heidi b.1973
Descent 1
oil on board 182 x 122
HUM030A

Chadwick, Heidi b.1973
Descent 2
oil on board 183 x 122
HUM030B

Chirnside, J. active 1957–1979
David Cardwell, Acting Principal (1951–1953) 1957
oil on canvas 85 x 64 (E)
EPS/Sack/031

Chirnside, J. active 1957–1979
Joe Burgess, Secretary and Registrar of UMIST (1954–1973)
oil on canvas 85 x 64 (E)
EPS/Sack/027

Close
Portrait of an Unknown Scientist
oil on canvas 125 x 80
MH3

Collier, John 1850–1934
Osborne Reynolds 1904
oil on canvas 92 x 72
MH2

Coventry, Gertrude Mary 1886–1964
Norman Smith
oil on canvas 60 x 48
CEN24

Darmesteter, Helena 1849–1940
Michael Sadler, Professor of History and Administration of Education 1908
oil on canvas 110 x 90 (E)
CEN01

Eley, William b.1938
Legs 1973
oil on canvas 91 x 71
HUM060

Eley, William b.1938
Herta
oil on canvas 61 x 122
MH22

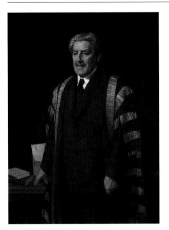

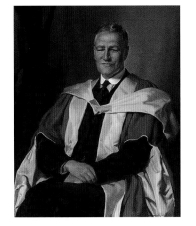

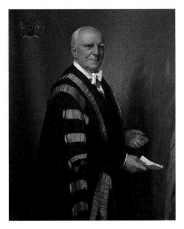

Gunn, Herbert James 1893–1964
The Right Honourable David Alexander Edward Lindsay 1939
oil on canvas 130 x 110 (E)
PCF1

Gunn, Herbert James 1893–1964
Sir Walter Hamilton Moberly (1881–1974)
oil on canvas 110 x 90 (E)
PCF4

Gunn, Herbert James 1893–1964
The Right Honourable Frederick James Marquis
oil on canvas 120 x 100 (E)
PCf2

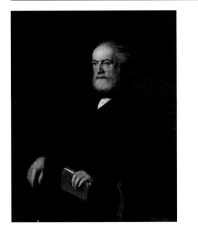

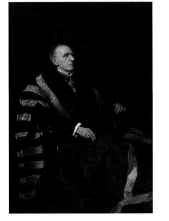

Herkomer, Hubert von 1849–1914
Alfred Angus Nield, Chairman of the Council of Owen College (1864–1887) c.1889
oil on canvas 90 x 70 (E)
CEN03

Herkomer, Hubert von 1849–1914
The Right Honourable Viscount Morley of Blackburn, Chancellor of the Victoria University of Manchester
oil on canvas 180 x 120
CEN04

Hussain, Shameela
Kshitij (Unlimited Horizon)
acrylic on canvas 84 x 119
MH5

Facing page: Heemskerck, Maerten van, 1498–1574, *Margaretha Banken*, 1540–1542, Manchester City Galleries (p. 199)

Isherwood
Edinburgh 1964
oil on canvas 52 x 77
HUM007

Isherwood
Southport Beach
oil on canvas 40 x 50
MH12

Jellicoe, Colin b.1942
Two Figures in a Landscape 1967
oil on canvas 54 x 43
HUM008

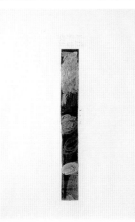

Kettle, Alice b.1961
Design I, Martin Harris Building, University of Manchester 2009
acrylic on foil 65 x 57
MH8

Kettle, Alice b.1961
Design II, Martin Harris Building, University of Manchester 2009
acrylic on foil 65 x 57
MH9

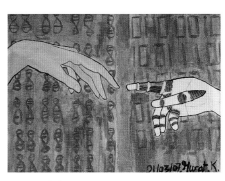

Korur, Philippe Murat b.1986
Pointing Fingers 2007
acrylic on canvas 29 x 41
EPS/Begg/018

Lazell, Katherine
Flight 2007
acrylic on canvas 42 x 29
EPS/Begg/019

Lovatt, William active 1824–1836
John Owens
oil on canvas 100 x 70 (E)
CEN19

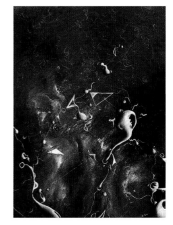

Minor, E.
Abstract
oil on canvas 59 x 42
MH18

Minor, E.
Shapes
oil on board 30 x 40
MH17

Myers, William H. 1890–1924
Hans Renold
oil on canvas 89 x 69
EPS/Sack/057

Nancollis, Robert b.1947
*Man as Bird**
acrylic on panel 36 x 31
HUM029A

Nancollis, Robert b.1947
*Man with Crocodile on His Head**
acrylic on panel 36 x 31
HUM029A

Nancollis, Robert b.1947
Quality Not Quantity Is Our Motto
acrylic on panel 92 x 61
HUM028

Nancollis, Robert b.1947
Witton Albion
acrylic on panel 82 x 43
HUM027

Noakes, Michael b.1933
*Professor Sir Rowland Smith, Chancellor
(1996–2002)* 2001–2002
oil on canvas 100 x 74
EPS/Sack/056

Noakes, Michael b.1933
*Lord Bowden of Chesterfield, Principal
(1953–1976)*
oil on canvas 85 x 64 (E)
EPS/Sack/028

Richardson-Jones, Keith 1925–2005
Counterpoint Red/Green
acrylic on canvas 198 x 104
MH26

Riley, Harold b.1934
The Urchin 1969
oil on canvas 48.5 x 38
HUM010

Sclettia
Text Book 1962
oil on canvas 76 x 63
MH15

Scott, Megan
Untitled 1982
oil on canvas 90 x 60
HUM011

Servion, Peter
Abstract 1968
oil on board 65 x 89
MH25

Stubley, Trevor 1932–2010
Professor Sir Mark Henry Richmond
oil on canvas 90 x 70 (E)
PCF8

unknown artist
Livesley 1949
oil on canvas 60 x 51
MH6

unknown artist
*A. W. Ward, Principal of Owens College
(1895–1897)*
oil on canvas 140 x 100 (E)
CEN14

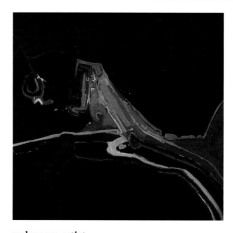

unknown artist
Abstract
oil on board 120 x 152
MH24

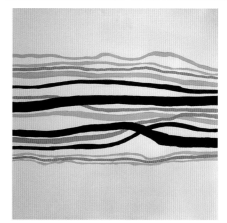

unknown artist
Abstract 1
acrylic on canvas 100 x 100
EPS/Begg/024

unknown artist
Abstract 2
acrylic on canvas 50 x 50
EPS/Begg/025

unknown artist
Abstract 3
acrylic on canvas 100 x 100
EPS/Begg/026

unknown artist
Abstract 4
acrylic on canvas 50 x 50
EPS/Begg/027

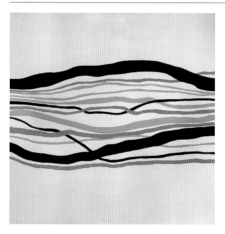

unknown artist
Abstract 5
acrylic on canvas 100 x 100
EPS/Begg/028

unknown artist
Daniel John Leech
oil on canvas 160 x 110 (E)
FLS/CTF/001

unknown artist
George Faulkner
oil on canvas 120 x 100 (E)
CEN07

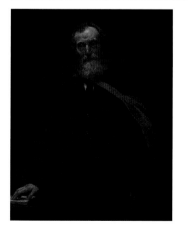

unknown artist
*J. G. Greenwood, Principal of Owen's College
and First Vice-Chancellor of the Victoria
University*
oil on canvas 126 x 95
MH11

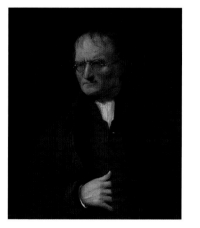

unknown artist
*John Dalton, Vice Principal, Manchester
Mechanics Institute, UMIST (1839–1841)*
oil on canvas 85 x 64 (E)
EPS/Sack/032

unknown artist
*John Henry Renolds, First Principal of the
Manchester School of Technology, UMIST
(1902–1912)*
oil on canvas 85 x 64 (E)
EPS/Sack/033

unknown artist
Joseph Jordan
oil on canvas 43 x 32
MHS/Simon/004

unknown artist
Joseph Jordan
oil on canvas 56 x 43
MHS/Simon/005

unknown artist
Landscape
oil on canvas 46 x 74
MH14

unknown artist
Lord L. Turnberg
oil on canvas 89 x 101
MHS/Stop/009

unknown artist
Portrait of an Unknown Academic
oil on canvas 90 x 70
EPS/Sack/055

unknown artist
Portrait of an Unknown Man
oil on canvas 102 x 79
HUM044

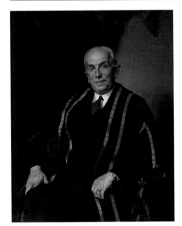

unknown artist
Portrait of an Unknown Man
oil on canvas 120 x 100 (E)
PCF3

unknown artist
Portrait of an Unknown Man
oil on canvas 160 x 120
PCF9

unknown artist
Professor Julius Dreschfeld
oil on canvas 94 x 73
MHS/Stop/014

unknown artist
Professor Ross
oil on canvas 52 x 40
MHS/Stop/008

unknown artist
Samuel Elsworth Cottam, Secretary of the
Manchester Mechanics Institute (1832–1838)
oil on canvas 70 x 50 (E)
EPS/Sack/035

unknown artist
Sir Henry E. Roscoe (1833–1915), Professor of
Chemisty (1857–1886)
oil on canvas 119 x 96
HUM040

unknown artist
Sir Martin Harris
oil on canvas 150 x 110 (E)
CEN13

unknown artist
Sir William Dawkins
oil on canvas 110 x 110
CEN06

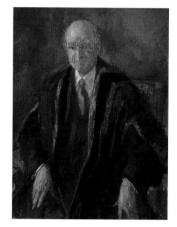

unknown artist
Sir William Mansfield Cooper
oil on canvas 90 x 70 (E)
CEN12

unknown artist
William Crawford Williamson, Professor of
Natural History (1851–1892)
oil on canvas 73 x 59
EPS/Will/003

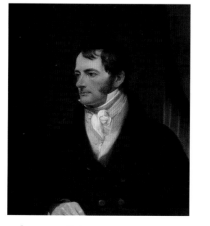

unknown artist
William Henry, Supported the Foundation of
the Manchester Mechanics Institute, 1824
oil on canvas 85 x 64 (E)
EPS/Sack/034

Ward, John Stanton 1917–2007
Emeritus Professor Sir Anthony Llewellyn
Armitage 1979
oil on canvas 110 x 90 (E)
PCF5 🐝

Whittam, William Wright 1931–1996
Building 60
oil on canvas 60 x 49
MH23

Wilson, Alastair
Kilburn's Machines 2002
oil on board 180 x 358
EPS/Kilburn/007

Victoria Baths Trust

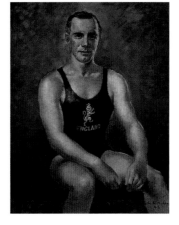

Worsley, John 1919–2000
John Henry 'Rob' Derbyshire (1878–1938)
1948
oil on canvas 90 x 70
PCF1 (P)

Whitworth Art Gallery, The University of Manchester

The Whitworth Art Gallery was founded more than 120 years ago as a source of pleasure and enjoyment for the citizens of Manchester and to provide opportunities for all to learn about the visual arts. It houses collections of international significance including outstanding works on paper, ranging from Renaissance prints to British landscape watercolours, and modern and contemporary work by artists from Pablo Picasso to Lucian Freud, Francis Bacon and Tracey Emin. The holdings of fine art are matched in terms of interest and importance by large collections of world textiles and wallpapers.

Throughout its history, the Whitworth Art Gallery has aimed to be a great gallery in a great city. It was founded in 1889, as the Whitworth Institute and Park, during the heroic period of Victorian philanthropy and was originally a voluntary cultural, educational and technical institution marking the memory of one of the North West's great industrialists, Sir Joseph Whitworth. The building and its park were sited in the southern suburbs of Manchester, which, as the world's first industrial city, was intent on establishing important cultural institutions to match its pre-eminent international status. The Whitworth became a leading cultural player in the city, supported by around 60 eminent Mancunians as Governors of the Institute, including C. P. Scott, the editor of the Manchester Guardian.

The Whitworth's founders drew inspiration from contemporary museums and galleries in Continental Europe for their conception of what an art gallery could be, and from the start had ambitions for the Whitworth to house collections of international importance. By the time the first building was completed in 1908, with its strong influence from the Arts and Crafts movement, the Whitworth had become an important forum for the arts, humanities and technology, and a centre of excellence for research and learning. The Whitworth's already close ties with The University of Manchester were formalised in 1958 when the responsibility for caring for the Gallery and its collections was transferred to University trusteeship. The late 1950s and early 1960s was a period of unprecedented growth in higher education in Britain, and the University of Manchester recognised the value of the Whitworth as a cultural asset that would contribute to its ambitious programme of expansion and help to attract new generations of British and overseas students and staff to Manchester. The University invested heavily in the Whitworth during this period, working closely with Gallery staff to modernise much of the building and expand the modern and contemporary collections of fine art. By the mid-1960s, the refurbished Whitworth had acquired a reputation in the national and international press as 'The Tate of the North'.

The Whitworth acquired its first abstract painting, Alan Davie's *Elephant's Eyeful* in 1960. This acquisition sparked a period of active collection, driven by a need to redress an imbalance within the gallery's holdings which were dominated by historic fine art. Several purchases, including Edward Burra's *John Deth (Homage to Conrad Aitken)* 1931 and John Piper's *Abstract Construction*, strengthened the Gallery's collection of works by artists influenced by Surrealism. Following the Whitworth's transference to the University in 1958 the gallery broadened its acquisition policy and took up the challenge of creating a collection that could truly represent modern and

contemporary art for a young student audience. In pursuit of this ambition, the gallery received generous support from many quarters.

Artists too, facilitated purchases by the gallery at favourable rates. This was particularly true of Howard Hodgkin whose work was bought at the height of his international fame and when prices would have been beyond the Gallery's means. With support from the Friends of the Whitworth, the Gallery purchased Hodgkin's *Interior at Oakwood Court*, 1978–1983, a vibrant gem within the Whitworth's collection of paintings. The Friends also helped with major purchases including Francis Bacon's *Lucian Freud*, 1951 and Freud's *Man's Head (Self Portrait I)*.

The gallery has benefited by generous gifts and bequests including five oil paintings by L. S. Lowry. Lowry himself donated *Industrial Scene,* 1965, a haunting image of the composite Northern Industrial landscape. Three other important oils by Lowry were donated to the Gallery during the 1970s and a further one, *A Couple Crossing the Road*, 1953 was bequeathed in 2001.

The generous bequests of Margaret Pilkington, who was Honorary Director of the Whitworth, and her sister Dorothy included oil paintings by Ben Nicholson, Lucien Pissarro, Jean Edouard Vuillard, Ivon Hitchens and John Keith Vaughan.

The Whitworth's painting collection is particularly strong in works from the 1960s, reflecting a period of diverse movements and painterly approaches. These include Peter Blake's archetypal work of 'Pop', *Got a Girl*, 1960–1961 as well as significant, large paintings by R. B. Kitaj, Patrick Procktor, Patrick Caulfield and Derek Boshier.

Historic art is perhaps most widely represented at the Whitworth by its extensive collection of works on paper but it also holds several highly significant historic oil paintings such as G. F. Watts' *Love and Death*, c.1877–1887 and John Frederick Lewis' *Indoor Gossip, Cairo*, 1873. The Whitworth has also, recently, had a work reattributed to J. M. W. Turner; a late oil on canvas depicting an atmospheric view of the beach at Margate.

Helen Stalker, Assistant Curator, Fine Art

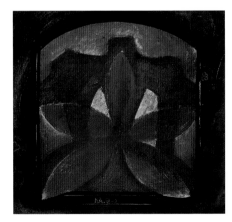

Adams, Norman 1927–2005
Golgotha 1961–1962
oil on canvas 40.5 x 45.5
O.1990.3

Adams, Norman 1927–2005
Time Piece 1980
oil on canvas 208 x 195
O.2001.4

Aldrich, Richard b.1975
Cold Sand 2004
oil & wax on board 59.7 x 39.4
O.2011.11

Facing page: Wadsworth, Edward Alexander, 1889–1949, *Coquillages*, 1926, Whitworth Art Gallery, The University of Manchester (p. 373)

Andrews, Michael 1928–1995
The Blue and Yellow of the Yacht Club 1969
oil on hardboard 61 x 61
O.1974.1

Appelbee, Leonard 1914–2000
Study of a Lobster
oil on canvas 25.1 x 66.4
O.1999.4

Auerbach, Frank Helmuth b.1931
Head of Laurie Owen 1971
oil on board 59 x 80.5
O.1972.1

Ayres, Gillian b.1930
Reef (detail) 1957
oil on hardboard 26.8 x 34.9
O.2003.4

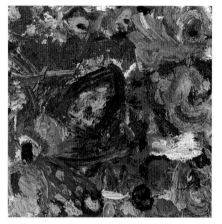

Ayres, Gillian b.1930
Galatea 1981–1982
oil on hessian 91.5 x 91.5
O.1983.6

Bacon, Francis 1909–1992
Lucian Freud 1951
oil on canvas 198.3 x 137.1
O.1980.3

Beaton, Cecil Walter Hardy 1904–1980
Hal Burton
oil on canvas 76 x 56
O.1987.1

Beaumont, Frederick Samuel 1861–1954
Mr Horsfall 1914
oil on canvas 106.5 x 87.6
O.1916.1

Bidauld, Jean Joseph Xavier 1758–1846
Monte Cavo from Lake Albano
oil on canvas 33 x 46
O.1999.3

Birch, Samuel John Lamorna 1869–1955
The Wave
oil on panel 19.8 x 26.8
O.1999.2

Blackadder, Elizabeth V. b.1931
Still Life with Flowers 1972
oil on canvas 127.1 x 127.1
O.2001.3

Bomberg, David 1890–1957
Composition with Figures 1912–1913
oil on wood 41 x 32.8
O.1981.1

Boshier, Derek b.1937
Megaloxenophobia 1962
oil on canvas 142 x 75.8
O.1975.6

Bradshaw, Brian b.1923
The Croal at Churchgate, Bolton 1978–1979
oil on board 76.2 x 61
O.1982.4

Brown, Ford Madox 1821–1893
Execution of Mary, Queen of Scots 1839–1841
oil on canvas 77.9 x 69.1
O.1927.1

Bussy, Simon 1870–1954
The Black Panther
oil on canvas 132 x 107
O.1979.4

Castiglione, Giovanni Benedetto 1609–1664
A Patriarchal Journey
oil on canvas 27.3 x 37.5
O.1958.1

Caulfield, Patrick 1936–2005
Smokeless Coal Fire 1969
acrylic on canvas 152.5 x 91.5
O.1969.3

Clausen, George 1852–1944
Willow Tree 1901
oil on canvas 48 x 38
O.2009.2

Clérisseau, Charles Louis 1722–1820
Capriccio with Classical Ruins
oil on canvas 89.5 x 116.7
O.1962.1

Clough, Prunella 1919–1999
Anchor and Float 1951
oil on canvas 48.9 x 34.3
O.1983.8

Collier, John 1850–1934
S. Wilkins 1904
oil on canvas 95 x 72
PCF3

Collins, William 1788–1847
Coast Scene 1839
oil on wood 10.7 x 16.5
O.1910.4

Conroy, Stephen b.1964
The Red Room 1987–1988
oil on canvas 137.8 x 122.5
O.1989.2

Constable, John 1776–1837
Study of Clouds
oil on canvas 23.8 x 33
O.1970.2

Cook, Ben b.1967
TV2 1993
acrylic on canvas 121.8 x 146
O.1995.1

Cooper, Gladys 1899–1975
A Day among the Crocuses
oil on board 52 x 60
PCF4

Cox the elder, David 1783–1859
Landscape with Sheep
oil on wood 25.6 x 25.6
O.1910.1

Cozens, Alexander 1717–1786
Setting Sun 1770–1773
oil on canvas 24.2 x 30.8
O.1997.3

Crane, Thomas 1808–1859
Walter Crane as a Child c.1846
oil on canvas 42 x 36
O.2011.4

Crane, Walter 1845–1915
Beatrice and Lionel Crane c.1880
oil on canvas 48 x 66
O.2011.5

Davie, Alan b.1920
Elephant's Eyeful 1960
oil on board 121.8 x 152.4
O.1961.2

De Chirico, Giorgio 1888–1978
The Philosopher 1927
oil on canvas 116.7 x 89.5
O.1931.1

De Wint, Peter 1784–1849
Study of Sorrel, Cow Parsley and Willow Saplings 1805–1810
oil on paper on canvas 26.7 x 34.3
O.1996.1

Downton, John 1906–1991
Girl Conducting c.1950
tempera on board 45.5 x 30.4
O.1998.1

Dughet, Gaspard 1615–1675
View of Tivoli
oil on canvas 36.7 x 47
O.1960.1

Dutch School
River Scene 1625–1699
oil on panel 41.5 x 69.6
O.1972.3

Faed, Thomas 1826–1900
'What shall I say to him?' 1888
oil on canvas 46.2 x 61.4
O.1910.5

Fedden, Mary 1915–2012
Fruit at Christmas 2002
oil on canvas 20 x 26
O.2003.1

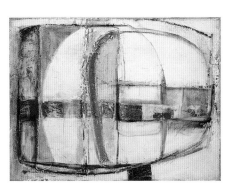

Feiler, Paul b.1918
Overlapping Forms Brown 1964
oil on canvas 45.7 x 61
O.2006.1 🐝

Forbes, Stanhope Alexander 1857–1947
Châteaudun, Street Scene 1901
oil on board 48 x 38
O.2009.3 🐝

Freud, Lucian 1922–2011
Man's Head (Self Portrait I) 1963
oil on canvas 53.3 x 50.8
O.1977.2

Frost, Terry 1915–2003
Blue, Red and Black 1958
oil on canvas 76.2 x 64
O.2003.5

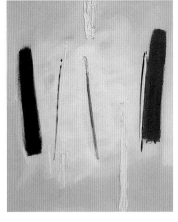

Frost, Terry 1915–2003
Black, White and Blue
oil on canvas 74.5 x 62.8
O.1984.6

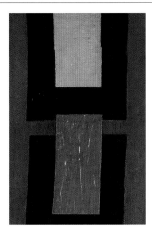

Gear, William 1915–1997
Gray Vertical 1956
oil on canvas 122 x 81
O.2001.9

Gilman, Harold 1876–1919
Nude on a Bed 1911–1912
oil on canvas 62.2 x 51
O.1980.1

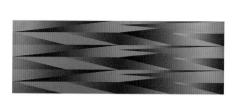

Goddard, Jonathan
Windrush 1971
acrylic on cotton duck 122 x 366
O.1971.2

Gore, Spencer 1878–1914
Spring in North London, 2 Houghton Place
1912
oil on canvas 50.8 x 40.7
O.1983.4

Goyen, Jan van 1596–1656
A View of Arnhem
oil on panel 20.8 x 36.8
O.1984.3

Greenaway, Peter b.1942
Landscape Section 1972
oil, wax & sand on wood 12 x 12
O.2010.1

Hagedorn, Karl 1889–1969
A Wash Stand 1913
oil on canvas 52 x 44.5
O.1990.2

Halswelle, Keeley 1832–1891
Dewey Morning 1882
oil on canvas 34.3 x 59.7
O.1910.11

Hambling, Maggi b.1945
Max as Godot's Vladimir 1981
oil on canvas 167.6 x 121.9
O.1986.1

Hammond, Hermione 1910–2005
Stooks in a Cornfield
oil on board 35.4 x 50.9
O.1999.6

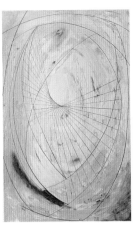

Hepworth, Barbara 1903–1975
Marble Form 1964
oil & pencil on hardboard 77 x 49.8
O.1993.4

Hilton, Roger 1911–1975
March, 1961 1961
oil on canvas 132.2 x 139.6
O.1968.1

Hitchens, Ivon 1893–1979
August Flowers 1943
oil on board 84.2 x 50.8
O.1974.2

Hitchens, Ivon 1893–1979
Green Chestnut with Larch
oil on canvas 65.5 x 99.2
O.2001.6

Hitchens, Ivon 1893–1979
Patchwork Poppies
oil on canvas 50.8 x 102
O.1987.2

Hodgkin, Eliot 1905–1987
Two Hyacinth Bulbs 1966
tempera on board 10.2 x 21.3
O.1992.2

Hodgkin, Howard b.1932
Interior at Oakwood Court 1978–1983
oil on wood 81.3 x 137.2
O.1983.9

Hughes, Ian b.1958
Man is Wolf to Man
oil on canvas 152.4 x 152.4
O.1989.1

Huxley, Paul b.1938
Untitled No.128 1971
acrylic on canvas 195.5 x 195.9
O.1975.4

Facing page: Watts, George Frederic, 1817–1904, *The Good Samaritan*, 1850, Manchester City Galleries (p. 258)

Innes, James Dickson 1887–1914
Collioure 1911
oil on canvas 32.9 x 40.9
O.1999.7

Irwin, Fiona b.1931
Light Depiction 9 1999
oil on canvas 70 x 90
MH2

Italian School
Winter Vegetables 1650–1699
oil on canvas 72 x 97.8
O.1999.8

Jaray, Tess b.1937
Minaret 1984
acrylic on linen 159.8 x 127.4
O.1984.5

Kennington, Thomas Benjamin 1856–1916
Robert Dukinfield Darbishire (1826–1908)
oil on canvas 125.1 x 101.6
O.1908.2

Kennington, Thomas Benjamin 1856–1916
Sir Joseph Whitworth (1803–1887)
oil on canvas 125.1 x 100.3
O.1908.1

Kitaj, R. B. 1932–2007
Trout for Factitious Bait 1965
oil on canvas 152 x 212
O.1976.4

Lambert, George c.1700–1765
Landscape with Farm Buildings 1760
oil on canvas 52.8 x 76.4
O.1982.1

Lancaster, Mark b.1938
Exposure I 1968
oil on canvas 172.7 x 91.3
O.1969.2

Landsley, Andrea
Self Portrait 1991
oil on canvas 256 x 180.5
O.1993.5

Lanyon, Peter 1918–1964
Glide Path 1964
oil & plastic collage on canvas 152.4 x 121.7
O.1978.2

Latham, John 1921–2006
P.(n) 2:5/12 1964
acrylic on canvas 94 x 217
O.1979.3

Lawrence, Thomas 1769–1830
Richard Payne Knight (1750–1824) 1794
oil on canvas 127 x 101.5
O.1975.2

Lawson, Kenneth 1920–2008
Still Life – Timbale des fruits de mer 1943–1944
oil on canvas 25 x 35
O.2011.3

Lawson, Kenneth 1920–2008
Structure in Space
oil on canvas 62 x 90
O.2011.7

Le Brun, Christopher b.1951
Portrait of L. as a Young Man 1984–1985
oil on canvas 198 x 173
O.1985.1 🐝

Leader, Benjamin Williams 1831–1923
English Cottage Homes 1896
oil on canvas 29.6 x 49.9
O.1910.10

Levy, Emmanuel 1900–1986
Olive Flowers
oil on canvas 68.8 x 50.8
O.1997.1

Lewis, John Frederick 1804–1876
Indoor Gossip, Cairo 1873
oil on canvas 30.4 x 20.2
O.1961.1

Lin, Richard b.1933
Painting Relief 1963
aluminium, perspex & oil on canvas
101.8 x 91.6
O.1964.2

Linnell, James Thomas 1826–1905
Springtime 1853
oil on canvas 71.4 x 96.2
O.1896.1

Linnell, John 1792–1882
Harvest Scene
oil on wood 21.4 x 33.3
O.1976.2

Liverseege, Henry 1803–1832
*Edie Ochiltree, Sir Arthur Wardour and
Isabella Wardour in the Storm: An Illustration
to Sir Walter Scott's 'The Antiquary'*
oil on canvas 33.1 x 25.6
O.1905.3

Liverseege, Henry 1803–1832
Falstaff and Bardolph
oil on wood 40.8 x 32.5
O.1905.4

Liverseege, Henry 1803–1832
Little Red Riding Hood
oil on wood 30.6 x 25.2
O.1905.1

Liverseege, Henry 1803–1832
The Recruit
oil on canvas 38 x 49.6
O.1905.2

Liverseege, Henry 1803–1832
The Visionary
oil on wood 32.9 x 24.9
O.1905.5

Lowe, Adam b.1959
The Chalice 1988
oil & wax on canvas 182 x 156.6
O.1992.1

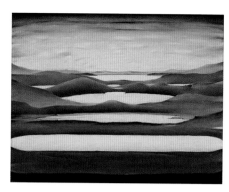

Lowry, Laurence Stephen 1887–1976
Lake Landscape 1950
oil on canvas 71 x 91.5
O.1972.2

Lowry, Laurence Stephen 1887–1976
Ancoats Hospital Outpatients' Hall 1952
oil on canvas 59.3 x 90
O.1975.3

Lowry, Laurence Stephen 1887–1976
A Couple Crossing the Road 1953
oil on canvas 42.4 x 52.6
O.2001.5

Lowry, Laurence Stephen 1887–1976
In a Park 1963
oil on canvas 76.5 x 101.9
O.1974.6

Lowry, Laurence Stephen 1887–1976
Industrial Scene 1965
oil on canvas 56 x 86.3
O.1973.3

Magnus, Rose 1859–1900
Wallflowers
oil on canvas 30.4 x 61.1
O.1898.1

Major, Theodore 1908–1999
Wigan Street
oil on board 52 x 75
PCF5

McKeever, Ian b.1946
Island 4a
acrylic & charcoal on photograph 150 x 103
O.2003.7.1

McLean, John b.1939
Sweet Briar 1980
acrylic on canvas 16 x 12
O.2003.2

Momper the younger, Joos de 1564–1635
Landscape with Travellers
oil on canvas 71 x 78
O.1963.2

Morris, Mali b.1945
Black Iris II 1990
acrylic on canvas 172.3 x 216.8
O.1991.2

Mulready, William 1786–1863
Horses Baiting 1816
oil on wood 40.1 x 33
O.1910.3

Nancollis, Robert b.1947
Department Store 1968
oil on canvas 121.7 x 152.4
O.1968.3

Nash, Paul 1889–1946
Whiteleaf Cross 1931
oil on canvas 53.7 x 76.1
O.1979.2

Nasmyth, Patrick 1787–1831
Richmond on Thames – Morning 1815
oil on canvas 44 x 59
O.1991.3

Nasmyth, Patrick 1787–1831
Richmond upon Thames – Early Evening 1815
oil on canvas 45 x 60
O.1991.4

Nasmyth, Patrick 1787–1831
View near St Albans 1829
oil on wood 30.4 x 40.6
O.1910.2

Neiland, Brendan b.1941
Cross Grid 1981
acrylic on canvas 86.3 x 76.2
O.1982.2

Newsome, Victor b.1935
Corner of the Bathroom 1975
pencil & acrylic on wood 121.9 x 91.4
O.1976.1

Nicholson, Ben 1894–1982
1946 (window in Cornwall) 1946
oil, pencil, charcoal & surface scratching on
canvas 49.5 x 59.7
O.1974.7

Nimr, Amy b.1898
*View of the Farm at Nashart, in the Fayoum,
near Cairo, Egypt*
oil on wood 37 x 77.8
O.1975.7

Paton
James Edge Partington
oil on canvas 125 x 95
PCF9

Philipson, Robin 1916–1992
Rose Windows, Blue 1962
oil on canvas 50 x 127
O.1970.3

Phillips, Peter b.1939
Composition No.8
acrylic on canvas 93 x 113.5
O.1983.7

Phillips, Tom b.1937
Fragment C. P. No.6 (Mappin) 1974
acrylic on canvas 92 x 61
O.1983.3

Piper, John 1903–1992
Abstract Construction 1934
oil, sand & wood on board 51.4 x 61.5
O.1980.2

Piper, John 1903–1992
Approach to Fonthill 1940
oil on linen on board 69.4 x 94.6
O.2001.7

Pissarro, Camille 1830–1903
The Quai du Pothuis at Pontoise after Rain
1876
oil on canvas 46 x 55
O.1989.3

Pissarro, Camille 1830–1903
The Young Maid 1896
oil on canvas 61 x 50
O.1998.2

Pissarro, Lucien 1863–1944
View in the Dart Valley, Devon 1922
oil on canvas 64.9 x 53.4
O.1974.3

Pitchforth, Roland Vivian 1895–1982
The Deanery, Westminster 1941
oil on board 86.4 x 111.6
O.1947.1

Poelenburgh, Cornelis van 1594/1595–1667
Landscape with Mythological Figures
oil on panel 21.5 x 28
O.1961.3

Porter, Michael b.1948
Puffballs in the Undergrowth 1990
PVA & oil on canvas 199.7 x 170
O.1991.1

Porter, Michael b.1948
Puffballs in the Undergrowth 1990
PVA & oil on canvas 199.7 x 170
O.1991.1b

Procktor, Patrick 1936–2003
Single Figure in a Landscape 1963
oil on canvas 192.6 x 198.2
O.1964.3

R., R.
Abstract 1993
oil on canvas 146 x 114
MH1

Rae, Barbara b.1943
Beach Gleaming 1985
acrylic & collage on board 80 x 110
O.1991.5

Ralston, John 1789–1833
Market Stead Lane, Manchester
oil on canvas 65.4 x 92.1
O.1906.2

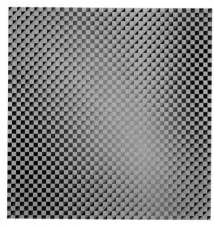

Riley, Bridget b.1931
Search 1966
acrylic on board 89.4 x 89.4
O.1966.2

Riviere, Briton 1840–1920
'Conscience makes cowards of us all', Study for 'Conscience'
oil on canvas 29.7 x 39.8
O.1910.9

Roberts, David 1796–1864
Street in St Lo, Normandy 1845
oil on wood 70 x 51.5
O.1910.8

Roberts, Thomas Sautelle 1764–1826
The Casino at Marino, Dublin
oil on canvas 62.3 x 96.3
O.1963.1

Russell, Bruce John b.1946
Gallowgate 12 1977
acrylic, gel & ink on cotton duck 205.3 x 205.3
O.1979.1

Sadée, Philip Lodewijk Jacob Frederik
1837–1904
Potato Digging 1875
oil on panel 28.4 x 59.1
O.1910.6

Schwartz, Leonard 1923–1988
Nude Study 1965
oil on vellum 49.7 x 37
O.1968.2

Sickert, Walter Richard 1860–1942
The Façade, St Jacques, Dieppe 1899–1900
oil on canvas 53.8 x 45.3
O.1970.1

Sickert, Walter Richard 1860–1942
Cicely Hey 1922–1923
oil on canvas 75.8 x 35.5
O.1996.3

Smith, Jack 1928–2011
Child on a Merry-Go-Round 1956–1958
oil on hardboard 75 x 124
O.1958.2

Smith, Matthew Arnold Bracy 1879–1959
Reclining Nude 1925–1930
oil on canvas 30.8 x 61
O.1982.3

Smith, Matthew Arnold Bracy 1879–1959
Vase of Irises
oil on canvas 75.6 x 63.5
O.1987.3

Spencer, Stanley 1891–1959
Soldiers Washing 1927
oil on canvas 69.4 x 46.1
O.1978.1

Stanhope, John Roddam Spencer 1829–1908
John Montagu Spencer Stanhope 1862
oil on board 17 x 15
O.2009.5

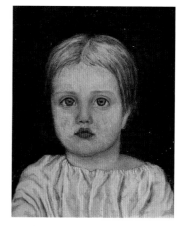

Stanhope, John Roddam Spencer 1829–1908
Mary Gertrude Spencer Stanhope
oil on board 14 x 12
O.2009.6

Facing page: Ayrton, Michael, 1921–1975, *Dressing of the Vine*, c.1940, Manchester City Galleries (p. 22)

Stephenson, Ian 1934–2000
Screened Painting I 1966
oil & enamel on canvas 213.4 x 304.5
O.1975.1

Swimmer, Thomas b.1932
Abstract Town 1959
oil on board 17.2 x 50.8
O.1987.5

Swimmer, Thomas b.1932
Abstract Town and Bridge 1959
oil on board 28.7 x 61
O.1987.4

Teniers II, David 1610–1690
A Village Festival
oil on panel 61.7 x 92.7
O.1984.4

Turner, Joseph Mallord William 1775–1851
View of the Beach at Margate
oil on canvas 46.2 x 61.3
O.1922.1

unknown artist
An Early Vaccination
oil on canvas 124 x 95
PCF8

unknown artist
Charles Hereford
oil on canvas 110 x 86
PCF7

unknown artist
Evening on the Run
oil on canvas 38 x 64
PCF2

unknown artist
Landscape
oil on board 25 x 35
PCF6

unknown artist
Religious Scene
oil on canvas 90 x 125
PCF1

unknown artist
Visit of the Three Kings the Wise and Foolish Virgin
oil on canvas 80.6 x 108.3
O.1908.3

Vaughan, John Keith 1912–1977
Green Bathers 1952
oil on canvas 91.7 x 71.3
O.2003.6

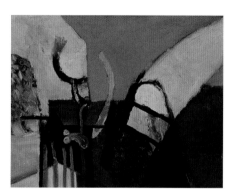

Vaughan, John Keith 1912–1977
Landscape 1953
oil on board 34 x 43.5
O.1974.4

Velde II, Willem van de 1633–1707
Shipping Scene: A Breeze
oil on panel 23.1 x 19.7
O.1984.2

Velde II, Willem van de 1633–1707
Shipping Scene: A Calm
oil on panel 22.9 x 19.5
O.1984.1

Verhaecht, Tobias c.1560–1631
Landscape with the Conversion of Saint Paul
oil on panel 26.2 x 36.8
O.1999.5

Vuillard, Jean Edouard 1868–1940
Paysage
oil on canvas 53.7 x 78.7
O.1974.5

Wadsworth, Edward Alexander 1889–1949
Coquillages 1926
tempera on board 53.5 x 39.5
O.1982.5

Walker, John b.1939
The Shape and the Disgruntled Oxford Philosopher 1979–1980
oil, acrylic & collage on canvas 21.1 x 18.4
O.1983.1

Watts, George Frederic 1817–1904
Love and Death 1877–1887
oil on canvas 248.9 x 116.8
O.1887.1

Webster, Thomas George 1800–1886
Study for 'The Connoisseurs' 1832
oil on panel 19.1 x 26.7
O.1910.7

Weight, Carel Victor Morlais 1908–1997
View from the Artist's Window, Putney 1950
oil on canvas 91.7 x 66.2
O.1974.8

Wood, Christopher 1901–1930
Fishing Boats, Finistère 1929
oil on canvas 53.8 x 65.1
O.1983.5

Wootton, John c.1682–1764
Classical Landscape
oil on canvas 77.2 x 127.8
O.1960.2

Wynter, Bryan 1915–1975
Earth's Riches 1958
oil on canvas 91.2 x 61.1
O.2003.3

Withington Community Hospital

Atwell, Tish
Landscape 1
acrylic on canvas 122 x 122
PCF2

Atwell, Tish
Landscape 2
acrylic on canvas 121 x 182
PCF3

Coulburn, Kathleen & **Lime Art** active since 1973 & **Minehead Resource Centre Painting Group**
Cottages by a Road
oil on board 39 x 29
PCF9

Ellis, Sandra & **Lime Art** active since 1973 & **Platt Lane Planning Group**
Cottages
acrylic on paper 42 x 60
PCF23

Ellis, Sandra & **Lime Art** active since 1973 & **Platt Lane Planning Group**
Flowers in a Vase
acrylic on paper 57 x 40
PCF21

Hemsted, Sheila & **Lime Art** active since 1973 & **Minehead Resource Centre Painting Group**
Poppies in a Field
oil on board 29 x 24
PCF16

Hemsted, Sheila & **Lime Art** active since 1973 & **Minehead Resource Centre Painting Group**
Woodland Path
oil on board 28 x 23
PCF6

Hughes, Alan & **Lime Art** active since 1973 & **Minehead Resource Centre Painting Group**
Boats in a Harbour
oil on board 39 x 29
PCF10

Hughes, Alan & **Lime Art** active since 1973 & **Minehead Resource Centre Painting Group**
Storm
oil on board 24 x 34
PCF11

King, Bert & **Lime Art** active since 1973 & **Minehead Resource Centre Painting Group**
Stonehenge
oil on board 22 x 29
PCF17

Lawson, Kenneth 1920–2008
Rutland Water
oil on board 52 x 89
PCF5

Lime Art active since 1973 & **McDermott, John** & **Minehead Resource Centre Painting Group**
Mountains and Beach
oil on board 23 x 30
PCF15

Lime Art active since 1973 & **Millington, Edna** & **Minehead Resource Centre Painting Group**
Landscape and Flowers
oil on board 24 x 34
PCF12

Lime Art active since 1973 & **Millington, Edna** & **Minehead Resource Centre Painting Group**
Sheep by a Church
oil on board 24 x 29
PCF13

Lime Art active since 1973 & **Minehead Resource Centre Painting Group** & **Prime, Len**
Boats in a Harbour
oil on board 22 x 29
PCF14

Lime Art active since 1973 & **Minehead Resource Centre Painting Group** & **Prime, Len**
Dinner by the Sea
oil on board 24 x 29
PCF18

Lime Art active since 1973 & **Minehead Resource Centre Painting Group** & **Wells, Kay**
Catch a Leaf to get a Wish
oil on board 29 x 39
PCF8

Lime Art active since 1973 & **Minehead Resource Centre Painting Group** & **Wells, Kay**
Playing by a Waterfall
oil on board 29 x 19
PCF7

Lime Art active since 1973 & **Platt Lane Planning Group** & **Smith, Dorothy**
Cottages and Boats
acrylic on paper 40 x 59
PCF24

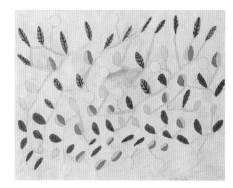

Lime Art active since 1973 & **Platt Lane Planning Group** & **Smith, Dorothy**
Leaf Pattern
acrylic on paper 40.5 x 56.5
PCF22

Lime Art active since 1973 & **Platt Lane Planning Group** & **Smith, Dorothy**
Leaves
acrylic on paper 57 x 40.5
PCF19

Lime Art active since 1973 & **Platt Lane Planning Group** & **Stephenson, Sue**
Leaf Pattern
acrylic on paper & mixed media 56.5 x 40
PCF20

Todd, Anna b.1964
High Tea at the Cricket Match
acrylic on board 214 x 122
PCF4

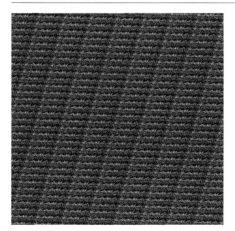

unknown artist
Skye
acrylic on canvas 185 x 145 (E)
PCF1

Paintings Without Reproductions

This section lists all the paintings that have not been included in the main pages of the catalogue. They were excluded as it was not possible to photograph them for this project. Additional information relating to acquisition credit lines or loan details is also included. For this reason the information below is not repeated in the Further Information section.

Central Manchester University Hospitals NHS Foundation Trust

unknown artist *Robert Barnes' Wife,* oil on canvas, PCF21, not available at the time of photography

Manchester City Galleries

Ansdell, Richard 1815–1885, *Traveller Attacked by Wolves,* 1854 oil on canvas, 274 x 377, 1912.49, gift from L. L. Armitage, 1912, not available at the time of photography

Arundel, James 1875–1960, *Landscape,* 1931 oil on panel, 76.2 x 63.3, 1945.35, gift from Mrs Essil Elmslie Rutherston, 1945, not available at the time of photography

Barretta, V. *Lady in a Green Greek Dress,* oil on canvas (?), 1918.427, transferred from the Horsfall Museum Collection, 1918, not available at the time of photography

Barretta, V. *Lady with Writing Tablet,* oil on canvas (?), 1918.426, transferred from the Horsfall Museum Collection, 1918, not available at the time of photography

Bellini, Gentile (attributed to) 1429–1507, *Virgin and Child and Two Saints,* oil on canvas, 1920.2, bequeathed by J. F. Cheetham, 1920, not available at the time of photography

Benjamin, Anthony 1931–2002, *Composition, 1962,* oil & watercolour with black ink, 1963.15, purchased from the artist, 1963, not available at the time of photography

Breakspeare, William Arthur 1855–1914, *Head of a Moor,* oil on canvas, 48.9 x 39.4, 1936.243, bequeathed by Alderman F. W. Millington, 1936, not available at the time of photography

British (English) School *Interior of Chetham's Hospital,* oil (?), 1926.15, purchased from Mrs M. Kershaw, 1926, not available at the time of photography

British (English) School *Portrait of a Man with High Right Hand on a Book,* oil on canvas, 1962.242/1, gift from Miss B. Ball, 1962, not available at the time of photography

British (English) School *Joseph Bellot (1765–1849),* 1800–1810 oil on canvas, 49 x 38, 1969.136, bequeathed by Professor H. Hale Bellot, 1969, not available at the time of photography

British (English) School *View of Garret Hall, Manchester,* c.1800–1825 oil on canvas, 14 x 18, 1962.208, gift from Mr P. K. Tower, 1962, not available at the time of photography

British (English) School *Officer Griffith of the Royal Manchester and Salford Volunteers,* c.1805 oil on canvas, 66.5 x 56.4, 1980.226, purchased at Sotheby's, 1980, not available at the time of photography

Brown, Ford Madox 1821–1893, *Commerce,* 1887 oil on canvas, 400 x 400, 1926.81, gift from Edgar Wood, 1926, not available at the time of photography

Brown, Ford Madox 1821–1893, *Corn,* 1887 oil on canvas, 400 x 400, 1926.82, gift from Edgar Wood, 1926, not available at the time of photography

Brown, Ford Madox 1821–1893, *Iron,* 1887 oil on canvas, 400 x 400, 1926.77, gift from Edgar Wood, 1926, not available at the time of photography

Brown, Ford Madox 1821–1893, *Shipping,* 1887 oil on canvas, 400 x 400, 1926.79, gift from Edgar Wood, 1926, not available at the time of photography

Brown, Ford Madox 1821–1893, *Spinning,* 1887 oil on canvas, 400 x 400, 1926.8, gift from Edgar Wood, 1926, not available at the time of photography

Brown, Ford Madox 1821–1893, *Weaving,* 1887 oil on canvas, 400 x 400, 1926.78, gift from Edgar Wood, 1926, not available at the time of photography

Brown, Ford Madox 1821–1893, *Wool,* 1887 oil on canvas, 400 x 400, 1926.83, gift from Edgar Wood, 1926, not available at the time of photography

Bylandt, Alfred Edouard Agenor van 1829–1890, *Man Driving Cattle,* oil (?), 1918.436, transferred from the Horsfall Museum Collection, 1918, not available at the time of photography

Caille, Léon Émile 1836–1907, *Selling Cupids,* oil (?), 1918.424, transferred from the Horsfall Museum Collection, 1918, not available at the time of photography

Callow, George Dodgson c.1831–1875, *Rocky Coast with Sailing Ships,* 1874 oil on canvas, 20 x 40, 1966.628, gift from Mr F. E. Simpson, 1966, not available at the time of photography

Callow, George Dodgson c.1831–1875, *Rocky Coast with Sailing Ships,* oil on canvas, 20 x 40.1, 1966.627, gift from Mr F. E. Simpson, 1966, not available at the time of photography

Chambers II, George 1830–c.1900, *Ships off the Coast,* 1870 oil on canvas, 20 x 40, 1966.625, gift from Mr F. E. Simpson, 1966, not available at the time of photography

Collins, Cecil 1908–1989, *Northern Bull,* 1950 oil on paper, 38 x 52, 2001.26, bequeathed by Mrs Elisabeth Collins, 2001, not available at the time of photography

Constable, John (attributed to) 1776–1837, *On the River Mole at Dorking,* c.1805–1807 oil on paper, 11.4 x 17.2, 1941.7, purchased from Thomas Agnew and Sons Ltd, 1941, not available at the time of photography

Cook, Richard P. b.1949, *View from the Studio,* 1984 oil on board, 1992.96, gift from Gerald Deslandes, Newton Orion Gallery, 1992, not available at the time of photography

Crozier, William 1930–2011, *Essex Landscape,* 1959 oil on paper, 55.9 x 76.4, 1962.169, purchased from the artist, 1961, not available at the time of photography

Daniels, Alfred b.1924, *Men Drinking,* 1956 oil on hardboard, 38.9 x 53.4, 1968.147, gift from the Leonard Cohen Fund, 1968, not available at the time of photography

Davies, Austin 1926–2012, *The Painter's Wife (Beryl Bainbridge),* oil on hardboard, 91.7 x 71.5, 1954.1122, purchased from the artist, 1954, not available at the time of photography

Donne, J. *The Jungfrau,* oil on paper, 24.8 x 34.3, 1918.894, transferred from the Horsfall Museum Collection, 1918, not available at the time of photography

Dutch School *Boats in a Landscape,* oil on canvas, 1917.248, bequeathed by Mr James Thomas Blair, 1917, not available at the time of photography

Dutch School *Boats in Harbour,* oil on canvas, 1917.179, bequeathed by Mr James Thomas Blair, 1917, not available at the time of photography

Edwards, Edwin 1823–1879, *Oak Forest at Ludlow,* 1866 oil on canvas, 65.4 x 97, 1905.25, gift from Mrs E. Ruth Edwards, 1905, not available at the time of photography

Egyptian School *Head of a Young Woman,* 100–300 tempera on linen, 24.4 x 25.7, 1947.147, bequeathed by George Beatson Blair, 1947, not available at the time of photography

Eitner, Wilhelm Heinrich Ernst 1867–1955, *Monte Crissilano,* oil on canvas, 80.7 x 100, 1944.27, gift from Mrs Oscar Samson, 1944, not available at the time of photography

Epstein, Jacob 1880–1959, *Epping Forest,* c.1930 oil on paper, 45.4 x 57.5, 1941.122, gift from Professor E. J. Dent, 1941, image unavailable due to copyright restrictions

Estall, William Charles 1857–1897, *The Coming Storm,* oil on canvas, 47.1 x 64.7, 1912.54, gift from Frank Hindley Smith, 1912, not available at the time of photography

Daniels, Alfred

Etchells, Frederick 1886–1973, *Painting 1914: Woman at a Mirror,* 1914 oil on canvas, 115.2 x 76.9, 1964.1, gift from the Contemporary Art Society, 1964, image unavailable due to copyright restrictions

Freeman, Frank b.1901, *The Red Teapot,* 1924 oil on canvas, 16 x 11, 1928.81, gift from H. C. Coleman, 1928, not available at the time of photography

Giacometti, Alberto 1901–1966, *Elvezia Michel-Baldini (née Stampa),* 1949 oil on canvas, 74.3 x 38.8, 1952.277, gift from the Contemporary Art Society, 1952, image unavailable due to copyright restrictions

Hadfield, Thomas Raleigh 1836–1918, *A River in a Flat Landscape with Buildings and a Beached Boat (Freddie's Ferry),* oil on canvas, 1966.58, gift from Miss Amy Hadfield, 1966, not available at the time of photography

Hadfield, Thomas Raleigh 1836–1918, *King Street, Manchester,* oil on panel, 12.7 x 21.6, 1961.3, gift from Hawke's Bay and East Coast Art Society, New Zealand and the Art Gallery and Museum of Napier, New Zealand, 1961, not available at the time of photography

Horsfield, Nicholas 1917–2005, *The Yellow House, La Roche Guyon,* 1962 oil on canvas, 76 x 63.5, 1970.2, gift from Miss Margaret Pilkington, 1970, not available at the time of photography

Hughes-Stanton, Herbert Edwin Pelham 1870–1937, *Landscape,* 1892 oil on canvas, 60.9 x 91.6, 1913.29, purchased from Charles Jackson, 1913, not available at the time of photography

Jackson, Frederick William 1859–1918, *Outside the Mosque, Tunis,* oil on canvas, 1918.5, gift from the Jackson Memorial Committee, 1918, not available at the time of photography

Lamb, Henry 1883–1960, *Head of a Boy,* oil on canvas, 50.8 x 40.7, 1940.2, bequeathed by Frank Hindley Smith, 1940, not available at the time of photography

Lanteri, Edouard 1848–1917, *Peasant Girl,* 1858 oil on canvas, 1919.18, gift from Madame Lanteri, 1919, not available at the time of photography

Levy, Emmanuel 1900–1986, *The Meadow,* 1935 oil & pencil on paper, 28.9 x 22.9, 1935.135, purchased from Lewis's Ltd, 1935, not available at the time of photography

Loker, John b.1938, *Extracts from Landscape Three Times,* 1948 acrylic & pencil, 1976.3, purchased from the Angela Flowers Gallery, 1976, not available at the time of photography

Mercier, Charles 1834–after 1893, *Group of Officers, 6th Lancs. Militia,* oil on canvas, 1893.2, gift from Officers Commanding 6th Lancs. Regiment, 1893, not available at the time of photography

Milne, John Maclauchlan 1886–1957, *Artichoke Flowers,* oil on canvas, 73 x 54, 1932.67, gift from the Contemporary Art Society, 1932, not available at the time of photography

Müller, Adèle Rose Bertha c.1868–1948, *Angels (after Fra Angelico)* oil on panel, 1918.43, transferred from the Horsfall Museum Collection, 1918, not available at the time of photography

Müller, Adèle Rose Bertha c.1868–1948, *Angels (after Fra Angelico)* oil (?), 40.6 x 5.1, 1918.431, transferred from the Horsfall Museum Collection, 1918, not available at the time of photography

Müller, Adèle Rose Bertha c.1868–1948, *Marriage of the Parents of the Virgin Mary* (after Fra Angelico) oil (?), 19 x 52.1, 1918.433, transferred from the Horsfall Museum Collection, 1918, not available at the time of photography

Müller, Adèle Rose Bertha c.1868–1948, *The Disciples at Emmaeus* (after Fra Angelico) oil (?), 17.8 x 19, 1918.432, transferred from the Horsfall Museum Collection, 1918, not available at the time of photography

Müller, Adèle Rose Bertha c.1868–1948, *The Resurrection* (after Giotto di Bondone) oil on canvas, 94 x 111.8, 1918.581, transferred from the Horsfall Museum Collection, 1918, not available at the time of photography

Munnings, Alfred James 1878–1959, *The Edge of the Wood,* 1938 oil on canvas, 102.1 x 127.1, 1938.253, purchased from Leicester Galleries, 1938, not available at the time of photography

Nicholson, George *The Green Charrette,* oil on canvas, 1938.26, purchased from the Redfern Gallery, 1938, not available at the time of photography

Percy, William 1820–1893, *Self Portrait,* 1878 oil on canvas, 51.2 x 41, 1904.18, gift from James W. Bentley, 1904, not available at the time of photography

Raphael (after) 1483–1520, *The Madonna of the Goldfinch,* 19th C oil on canvas, 40 x 30, 1918.406, transferred from the Horsfall Museum Collection, 1918, not available at the time of photography

Shields, Frederick James 1833–1911, *Little Lamb, Who Made Thee?,* oil on canvas, 20.5 x 25.4, 1917.301, bequeathed by Leicester Collier, 1917, not available at the time of photography

Sicciolante da Sermonta, Girolamo (circle of) 1521–c.1580, *Saint Mark,* 1538–1580 oil on copper, 22.1 x 17.3, 1979.61, purchased from Capes Dunn & Co., Manchester, 1979, not available at the time of photography

Sicciolante da Sermonta, Girolamo (circle of) 1521–c.1580, *Saint Matthew,* 1538–1580 oil on copper, 22.4 x 17, 1979.6, purchased from Capes Dunn & Co., Manchester, 1979, not available at the time of photography

Southern Netherlandish School *Christ in the House of Mary, Martha and Lazarus,* c.1600 oil on canvas, 101.9 x 120, 1979.613, untraced find, 1979, not available at the time of photography

Steer, Philip Wilson 1860–1942, *Misty Evening, Harwich,* 1913 oil on canvas, 61.1 x 91.5, 1914.21, purchased from the artist, 1914, not available at the time of photography

Thornton, Alfred Henry Robinson 1863–1939, *A Spring Landscape,* 1922 oil on canvas, 51.5 x 61.6, 1925.303, gift from Charles Lambert Rutherston, 1925, not available at the time of photography

unknown artist *Selling Armour,* oil (?), 1918.428, transferred from the Horsfall Museum Collection, 1918, not available at the time of photography

Utrillo, Maurice 1883–1955, *Chapelle à Roscoff,* oil on canvas, 62 x 81.5, 1974.93, bequeathed by Mrs S. R. Macnair, 1974, image unavailable due to copyright restrictions

Valette, Adolphe 1876–1942, *Study for the Irwell,* c.1913 oil on canvas, 16.3 x 8.8, 1991.77, purchased from Capes Dunn & Co., Manchester, 1991, not available at the time of photography

Watts, George Frederic 1817–1904, *The Court of Death,* 1863–1864 oil on canvas, 381 x 259, 1900.23, gift from the artist, 1900, not available at the time of photography

Webb, William Edward 1862–1903, *Douglas Harbour, Isle of Man,* oil on canvas, 35.6 x 30, 1966.626, gift from Mr F. E. Simpson, 1966, not available at the time of photography

White, Ethelbert 1891–1972, *The Mill Farm, Cottishall, Essex,* oil on canvas, 33.7 x 25.1, 1939.17, bequeathed by Dr Jane Walker, CH, LLD, 1939, not available at the time of photography

Wood, Catherine M. 1880–1939, *Church of St Etienne,* 1911 oil on millboard, 32.8 x 24.6, 1939.16, bequeathed by Dr Jane Walker, CH, LLD, 1939, not available at the time of photography

Manchester Jewish Museum

unknown artist *Portrait of an Unknown Man,* oil on canvas, 1985-839, gift, not available at the time of photography

Watson, George Spencer 1869–1934, *Nathan Laski, Chairman of the Manchester Victoria Memorial Jewish Hosiptal,* oil on canvas, MJMP3, not available at the time of photography

Manchester Town Hall

Munns, Henry Turner 1832–1898, *Abel Heywood,* 1889 oil on canvas, 91.5 x 61, THP086001, gift from Dawson News, 1977, not available at the time of photography

unknown artist *Alderman Clark,* 1878 oil on canvas, 270.25 x 189, THP053001, not available at the time of photography

National Football Museum

Keane, Gary *Stunned,* 1966 (?) acrylic on board, 24 x 32, LANGTON 016, purchased from the Langton Collection, image unavailable due to copyright restrictions

The University of Manchester

Pasmore, Victor 1908–1998, *Metamorphosis,* 1968 oil (?), EPS/Ren/001, not available at the time of photography

unknown artist *John Hunter,* oil (?), MH27, not available at the time of photography

unknown artist *Professor John Garside,* oil (?), EPS/Ren/004, not available at the time of photography

unknown artist *Professor R. N. Hazeldine,* oil (?), EPS/Ren/003, not available at the time of photography

unknown artist *Roy Chadwick,* oil (?), EPS/Ren/005, not available at the time of photography

unknown artist *Sir Charles Renold,* oil (?), EPS/Ren/002, not available at the time of photography

Whitworth Art Gallery, The University of Manchester

Agar, Eileen 1899–1991, *The Black Flower,* 1969 oil on canvas, 76.2 x 55.9, O.2001.2, on loan from the University of Manchester, Senior Common Room Association, since before 1994, not available at the time of photography

Alley, Anthea 1927–1993, *Box with Chains,* acrylic & collage on board, 36 x 36, O.1986.2, image unavailable due to copyright restrictions

Bloemen, Jan Frans van 1662–1749, *Classical Landscape with Washerwoman,* oil on canvas, 47 x 37.3, O.1988.2, not available at the time of photography

Bough, Samuel 1822–1878, *On the Avon, Perthshire,* 1856 oil on canvas, 99.7 x 125.1, O.1899.1, not available at the time of photography

British School *The White Abbott,* oil on canvas, 92.7 x 127, O.1954.1, not available at the time of photography

Cohen, Bernard b.1933, *Shepherds,* 1961 oil on canvas, 244.5 x 306.2, O.1964.1, not available at the time of photography

Crane, Walter 1845–1915, *Study of a Greyhound,* c.1880 oil on canvas, O.2011.6, not available at the time of photography

Jones, Thomas 1742–1803, *House at Naples,* 1782 oil on paper, 14.4 x 22, O.1999.1, not available at the time of photography

Leader, Benjamin Williams 1831–1923, *The Cleddau, Pembrokeshire,* 1901 oil on card, 25.6 x 45.6, O.1987.7, not available at the time of photography

McKeever, Ian b.1946, *Island 4b,* acrylic & charcoal on photograph, 150 x 103, O.2003.7.2, not available at the time of photography

Opie, John 1761–1807, *Thomas Girtin,* 1800 oil on canvas, 77 x 64, O.1997.2, not available at the time of photography

Oursler, Tony b.1957, *Hairy Ball Theorem,* 1989 acrylic on paper, 75.9 x 55.8, O.2011.9, image unavailable due to copyright restrictions

Oursler, Tony b.1957, *JLB Relationship,* 2001 acrylic on paper, 73.2 x 58, O.2011.10, image unavailable due to copyright restrictions

Oursler, Tony b.1957, *Freq Zenith,* 2003 acrylic on paper, 73 x 48.4, O.2011.8, image unavailable due to copyright restrictions

Oursler, Tony *Manchester from Hunts Bank,* oil on canvas, 65.4 x 92.7, O.1906.1, image unavailable due to copyright restrictions

Pope *Portrait of a Man,* oil on canvas, 60.4 x 50, O.1987.6, not available at the time of photography

Porter, Michael b.1948, *Beneath a Rotting Tree,* 1991 PVA & oil on canvas, 315 x 170, O.1993.3, not available at the time of photography

Porter, Michael b.1948, *Bindweed,* 1991 PVA & oil on canvas, 315 x 170, O.1993.2, not available at the time of photography

Porter, Michael b.1948, *Silver Birches,* 1991 PVA & oil on canvas, 315 x 170, O.1993.1, not available at the time of photography

Rebeyrolle, Paul 1926–2005, *Landscape,* 1958 oil on canvas, 61.9 x 61.1, O.1962.2, not available at the time of photography

Richardson-Jones, Keith 1925–2005, *Quartered Whites,* acrylic on canvas, 107 x 107, O.1973.1, not available at the time of photography

Rumney, Ralph 1934–2002, *Untitled,* 1995 acrylic & gesso, 146 x 113.6, O.2001.8, not available at the time of photography

Schirmer, Johann Wilhelm 1807–1863, *Cypress Trees in the Gardens of the Villa d'Este,* pencil & oil on paper, 42.2 x 31.8, O.1926.1, not available at the time of photography

Scully, Sean b.1945, *Amber,* 1973 acrylic on cotton duck, 243.8 x 243.8, O.1975.8, not available at the time of photography

Stroud, Peter b.1921, *Shift Out,* 1962 acrylic on board, 12.2 x 41.5, O.1963.4, not available at the time of photography

Ullyart, Edwin James b.1948, *Untitled,* 1970 oil on canvas, 257 x 257, O.1971.3, not available at the time of photography

Wales, Austin *Untitled,* acrylic on canvas, 236.2 x 175.3, O.1973.2, not available at the time of photography

Walker, Ethel 1861–1951, *Spanish Market,* 1920–1922 oil on millboard, 25.1 x 33.4, O.1996.2, not available at the time of photography

Weiser, Garth b.1979, *Grinder,* 2011 copper leaf, acrylic & dimensional fabric on canvas, O.2011.1, not available at the time of photography

Wood, Edgar 1860–1935, *Mediterranean Scene,* oil on board, O.2005.1, not available at the time of photography

Wynter, Bryan 1915–1975, *Images Moving out onto Space I,* 1960–1965 oil (?) & mixed media on canvas (?), 116.8 x 100.3, O.1965.6, not available at the time of photography

Further Information

The paintings listed in this section have additional information relating to one or more of the five categories outlined below. This extra information is only provided where it is applicable and where it exists. Paintings listed in this section follow the same order as in the illustrated pages of the catalogue.

I   The full name of the artist if this was too long to display in the illustrated pages of the catalogue. Such cases are marked in the catalogue with a (…).

II   The full title of the painting if this was too long to display in the illustrated pages of the catalogue. Such cases are marked in the catalogue with a (…).

III   Acquisition information or acquisition credit lines as well as information about loans, copied from the records of the owner collection.

IV   Artist copyright credit lines where the copyright owner has been traced. Exhaustive efforts have been made to locate the copyright owners of all the images included within this catalogue and to meet their requirements. Any omissions or mistakes brought to our attention will be duly attended to and corrected in future publications.

V   The credit line of the lender of the transparency if the transparency has been borrowed. Bridgeman images are available subject to any relevant copyright approvals from the Bridgeman Art Library at www.bridgemanart.com

Central Manchester University Hospitals NHS Foundation Trust

Ashton, Stuart *Manchester Royal Eye Hospital*
Baker, Darren b.1976, *Football Crowd*, gift, © the artist
Burscough, Lucy *Peter Mount*, gift, © the copyright holder
Channon, Fergus b.1979 & Dickinson, Richard, *Seagulls*, commissioned, © the artist
Channon, Fergus b.1979 & Dickinson, Richard, *Seagulls*, commissioned, © the artist
D., E. *Robert Barnes' Daughter and Son*
El-Assaad, Rached b.1945, *Flowers*, gift from the artist, © the artist
El-Assaad, Rached b.1945, *Poppies*, gift, © the artist
Harris, Rolf b.1930, *Snow White and the Seven Dwarfs*, gift, © the copyright holder
Macdonald, Charles b.1943, *People on a Beach*, gift, © the artist
Macdonald, Charles b.1943, *Boats in a Harbour*, gift, © the artist
Macdonald, Charles b.1943, *Red-Roofed Village*, gift, © the artist
Macdonald, Charles b.1943, *Village and a Rocky Shore*, gift, © the artist
Macdonald, Charles b.1943, *Village and Girl in a Red Dress*, gift, © the artist
Macdonald, Charles b.1943, *Village and Mountain*, gift, © the artist
Macdonald, Charles b.1943, *Village, Mountain and Clouds*, gift, © the artist

Macdonald, Geoff b.1950, *English Countryside*, gift, © the artist
Macdonald, Geoff b.1950, *Fife Fishing Village*, gift, © the artist
Macdonald, Geoff b.1950, *Green Door*, gift, © the artist
Macdonald, Geoff b.1950, *Island Cottages*, gift, © the artist
Macdonald, Geoff b.1950, *Tulips*, gift, © the artist
Macdonald, Geoff b.1950, *Where's the Party?*, gift, © the artist
Nash, Martin b.1955, *Icon Pictogram I*, commissioned, © the copyright holder
Nicholson, Alastair b.1956, *M. R. I. Band*, © the artist
Ouless, Walter William (after) 1848–1933, *Philip Goldschmidt*
R., J. *Landscape*, commissioned, © the copyright holder
Scholes, Steven b.1951, *Booth Hall*, © the artist
Shiels, Charles Anthony 1947–2012, *Hospitality, Haven Lane*, commissioned, © the artist's estate
Tate, William 1747–1806, *Charles White (1728–1813), First Surgeon to the Manchester Royal Infirmary (1752–1790)*
unknown artist *Dauntesey Hulme, Esq.*
unknown artist *David Little*
unknown artist *Frank Renaud (d.1904), MD (1848), Consulting Physician (1866)*
unknown artist *Henry Worrall, Treasurer (1786–1792)*
unknown artist *James Massey, First President of the Manchester Royal Infirmary*, gift from William Tate, Esq., 1793

unknown artist *John Windsor, Esq., FRCS, Honorary Consulting Surgeon (1822–1868)*
unknown artist *Richard Thomas Smith, MRCS*
unknown artist *Robert Platt*
unknown artist *Sir Harry Platt*

Chetham's Library

Allen, Joseph 1769–1839, *Reverend John Clowes (1743–1831)*
British (English) School *Elizabeth Leigh (1736–1820)*
British (English) School *John Egerton Killer (1768–1854)*
British (English) School *Martha Taylor*
British (English) School *Alexander Nowell (1507–1602)*, gift from James Illingworth, 1684
British (English) School *Humphrey Chetham (1580–1653)*
British (English) School *John Bradford (1510–1555), the Manchester Martyr*, gift from James Illingworth, 1684
British (English) School *Robert Bolton (1572–1631)*, gift from James Illingworth, 1684
British (English) School *William Whitaker (1548–1595)*, gift from James Illingworth, 1684
British (English) School *Portrait of a Young Man Wearing a Wig*
British (English) School *Reverend John Radcliffe, Chetham's Librarian (1787–1797)*
British (English) School *Portrait of an Elderly Lady*
British (English) School *Reverend William Huntington (1797–1874)*

Hudson, Thomas (circle of) 1701–1779, *Captain John Wagstaffe*
Kneller, Godfrey (circle of) 1646–1723, *Joseph Addison (1672–1719), and Sir Richard Steele (1672–1729)*
Krusemans (follower of) *Silence Wagstaffe (1714–1735), as a Child, with Her Brother*
Mercier, Philippe (circle of) 1689–1760, *Portrait of a Young Gentleman Wearing a Blue Coat*
Pickersgill, Henry William 1782–1875, *William Harrison Ainsworth (1805–1882)*
Romney, George 1734–1802, *Robert Thyer (1709–1781), Chetham's Librarian*
Sellaer, Vincent (attributed to) c.1500–c.1589, *An Allegory with Putti and Satyrs*
unknown artist *Bosdin Leach, Mayor of Manchester*
unknown artist *Portrait of Man with a Red and White Cravat*
unknown artist *Reverend Francis Robert Raines*
Walker, John Hanson 1844–1933, *James Crossley (1800–1883)*
Walker, John Hanson 1844–1933, *Thomas Jones, Chetham's Librarian*
Wimpenny, George Henry 1857–1939, *Chetham's Kitchen*
Wimpenny, George Henry 1857–1939, *Chetham's Reading Room*

Greater Manchester County Record Office

Plaxton, T. *Donald Summerfield, HM Coroner for the City of Manchester*, © the copyright holder
unknown artist *Portrait of an Unknown Child*
unknown artist *St James, New Bury*
Ward, A. A. *Half-Timers*

Greater Manchester Police Museum & Archives

Laycock, James A. *The Moss Side Riots, 1981*, gift, 1983, © the copyright holder
Malone, Tom active 1950–1961, *Chief Superintendant Jack Wilson, Salford City Police*, gift, 2005, © the copyright holder
unknown artist *Police Dog 'Gunner'*, gift, 2005

John Rylands Library, The University of Manchester

Coventry, Gertrude Mary 1886–1964, *Portrait of an Unknown Man*, © the copyright holder
Dugdale, Thomas Cantrell 1880–1952, *Archbishop Temple (1881–1944)*, © Joanna Dunham
Dunnington, Alfred 1860–1928, *The Opening of the Manchester Ship Canal*, gift from Miss Evelyn F. Parry to the Manchester Geographical Society; on long-term loan to the John Rylands Library
Dunnington, Alfred 1860–1928, *The Opening of the Manchester Ship Canal*, gift from Miss Evelyn F. Parry to the Manchester Geographical Society; on

long-term loan to the John Rylands Library

Nowell, Arthur Trevethin 1862–1940, *Arthur Samuel Peake (1865–1929), Chair of Biblical Exegesis (1904–1929)*

Thompson, Jacob 1806–1879, *George John (1758–1834), 2nd Earl Spencer*

unknown artist 'The Grafton Portrait' (Portrait of an Unknown Man), bequeathed by Thomas Kay, 1914

unknown artist *George John (1758–1834), 2nd Earl Spencer*

unknown artist *John Rylands*

unknown artist *Portrait of an Unknown Scholar in Academic Costume*

Manchester City Galleries

Adams, Norman 1927–2005, *Angels around the Cross*, purchased from the artist, 1964, © the artist's estate

Adeney, William Bernard 1878–1966, *The Window*, gift from Charles Lambert Rutherston, 1925, © the copyright holder

Adin, Charles Waldo 1854–1930, *The Verandah*, purchased from The Manchester Academy of Fine Arts, 1924

Adler, Jankel 1895–1949, *Composition*, purchased from the Waddington Galleries, 1960, © DACS 2013

Adnams, Marion Elizabeth 1898–1995, *The Living Tree*, purchased from Stafford Gallery, 1939, © the artist's estate

Adnams, Marion Elizabeth 1898–1995, *L'infante égarée*, purchased from the artist, 1944, © the artist's estate

Adshead, Mary 1904–1995, *The Picnic*, purchased from the Goupil Gallery, 1930, © the artist's estate

Aken, Joseph van c.1699–1749, *A Tea Party*, bequeathed by Mr and Mrs Edgar Assheton Bennett, 1979

Aldridge, John Arthur Malcolm 1905–1983, *River Scene*, gift from the Contemporary Art Society, 1946, © the copyright holder

Aldridge, John Arthur Malcolm 1905–1983, *The Grove Farmyard*, purchased from Leicester Galleries, 1940, © the copyright holder

Allan, Robert Weir 1851–1942, *Fresh from the Sea*, purchased from the artist, 1900

Allan, Ronald 1900–1966, *Sewing*, purchased from the artist, 1930, © the copyright holder

Allan, Ronald 1900–1966, *K. Russell Brady*, purchased from The Manchester Academy of Fine Arts, 1933, © the copyright holder

Allen, Joseph 1769–1839, *Peter Clare*, purchased from Charles F. Jesper, 1927

Allen, Joseph 1769–1839, *Saint Francis at Devotion*, gift from Dr E. J. Sidebotham, 1927

Allen, Joseph 1769–1839, *Dr*

Charles White (1728–1813), bequeathed by Dr David Lloyd Roberts, 1920

Allen, Joseph 1769–1839, *Samuel Ashton of Middleton*, gift from F. Ashton-Gwatkin, 1964

Allen, Joseph 1769–1839, *John Pooley*, gift from Mrs Mary Ormsby, 1962

Allen, Joseph 1769–1839, *Hannah Hatfield*, bequeathed by J. B. Willans, 1957

Allen, Joseph 1769–1839, *Thomas Hatfield*, bequeathed by J. B. Willans, 1957

Allinson, Adrian Paul 1890–1959, *November Fair in Brienz*, gift from the artist, 1937, © the artist's estate

Allinson, Adrian Paul 1890–1959, *Farewell to Mallorca*, purchased from the artist, 1936, © the artist's estate

Allinson, Adrian Paul 1890–1959, *Cotswold Autumn*, purchased from Leicester Galleries, 1936, © the artist's estate

Allsopp, Judith b.1943, *Number Eight*, purchased from the artist, 1968, © the copyright holder

Alma-Tadema, Laura Theresa Epps 1852–1909, *Sweet Industry*, purchased from the New Gallery Exhibition, 1904

Alma-Tadema, Lawrence 1836–1912, *A Roman Flower Market*, bequeathed by John Edward Yates, 1934

Alma-Tadema, Lawrence 1836–1912, *Etruscan Vase Painters*, purchased from The Fine Art Society, 1980

Alma-Tadema, Lawrence 1836–1912, *Silver Favourites*, bequeathed by George Beatson Blair, 1946

Annan, Dorothy 1908–1983, *Christmas, 1944*, gift from Mrs Essil Elmslie Rutherston, 1945, © the copyright holder

Ansaldo, Giovanni Andrea 1584–1638, *Allegory of the Arts*, purchased from P. & D. Colnaghi & Co. Ltd, 1964

Ansdell, Richard 1815–1885, *The Chase*, transferred from the Royal Manchester Institution, 1882

Anthony, Henry Mark 1817–1886, *The Village Church*, purchased from Shepherd Bros, 1904

Archer, James 1823–1904, *La mort d'Arthur*, gift from Miss L. A. Haworth

Archer, James 1823–1904, *Thomas de Quincey (1785–1859)*, purchased from the artist, 1904

Arentsz., Arent 1585/1586–1635, *River Scene with Fishermen in a Rowing Boat in the Foreground*, bequeathed by Mr and Mrs Edgar Assheton Bennett, 1979

Arentsz., Arent 1585/1586–1635, *Winter Scene with Numerous Figures on the Ice*, bequeathed by Mr and Mrs Edgar Assheton Bennett, 1979

Arif Quadri, Saleem b.1949, *Carpet of Contemplation*, gift from the artist, 1993, © the artist

Armstrong, John 1893–1973, *September, 1940*, gift from HM Government, War Artists Advisory Committee, 1947, © the artist's estate/Bridgeman Art Library

Armstrong, John 1893–1973, *Black Pyramids*, gift from Mrs Essil Elmslie Rutherston, 1943, © the artist's estate/Bridgeman Art Library

Armstrong, Thomas 1832–1911, *Manchester and Salford Children*, purchased from The Fine Art Society, 1985

Astley, John (attributed to) 1724–1787, *Thomas Carill Worsley of Platt*, purchased from Bourne Fine Art, 1989

Atkinson, Amy B. 1859–1916, *Bubbles*, purchased, 1907

Aumonier, James 1832–1911, *The Silver Lining of the Cloud*, gift from Frederick Smallman, 1890

Aumonier, James 1832–1911, *When the Tide is Out*, purchased from the 13th Autumn Exhibition, 1895

Aumonier, James 1832–1911, *Landscape with Sheep*, bequeathed by Dr Jane Walker, CH, LLD, 1939

Aved, Jacques-André-Joseph 1702–1766, *A Lady with Embroidery*, purchased from Shepherd Bros, 1904

Avercamp, Barent Petersz. 1612/1613–1679, *River Scene with Fishermen Drawing Nets*, bequeathed by Mr and Mrs Edgar Assheton Bennett, 1979

Ayres, Gillian b.1930, *Mushroom*, purchased from A. C. Sewter, 1973, © the artist

Ayrton, Michael 1921–1975, *Dressing of the Vine*, acquired, 2003, © estate of the artist

Ayrton, Michael 1921–1975, *The Shepherds*, purchased from the Autumn Exhibition, 1951, © estate of the artist

Backhuysen I, Ludolf 1630–1708, *Seascape*, bequeathed by Mr and Mrs Edgar Assheton Bennett, 1979

Backhuysen I, Ludolf 1630–1708, *Coast Scene*, bequeathed by Mr and Mrs Edgar Assheton Bennett, 1979

Bacon, Francis 1909–1992, *Henrietta Moraes on a Blue Couch*, purchased from Ronald K. Greenberg, 1979, © the estate of Francis Bacon. All rights reserved. DACS 2013

Baellieur, Cornelis de 1607–1671, *Martyrdom of Saint Catherine*, purchased from A. Staal, 1931

Baker, Charles Henry Collins 1880–1959, *The Bay*, purchased from Charles Henry Collins Baker, 1925, © the copyright holder

Ball, G. *Clayton Old Hall*, gift from the Recreational Services Department, 1979

Balmford, Hurst 1871–1950, *A Cornish Creek*, purchased from The Manchester Academy of Fine Arts Exhibition, 1939, © the copyright holder

Balston, Thomas 1883–1967, *Geraniums*, gift from the artist,

1938, © the copyright holder

Balston, Thomas 1883–1967, *Young Hollyhocks*, gift from the artist, 1950, © the copyright holder

Bancroft, Elias 1846–1924, *Midday Cheshire*, gift from The Manchester Academy of Fine Arts, 1921

Bancroft, Louisa Mary 1864–1948, *Wallflowers*, purchased from the artist, 1928, © the copyright holder

Bancroft, Louisa Mary 1864–1948, *Old-Fashioned Flowers*, purchased from The Manchester Academy of Fine Arts, 1935, © the copyright holder

Barber, Reginald 1851–1928, *John Cassidy (RBS)*, purchased from the sitter, 1928

Barker, Allen b.1937, *Untitled*, purchased from the artist, 1974, © the artist

Barker, John Joseph 1824–1904, *Landscape with Man and Donkey*, gift from the executors of the will of Mr C. R. Dunkerley, 1951

Barker, Thomas 1769–1847, *Landscape with Cattle*, gift from Norman Spencer, 1906

Barker, Thomas 1769–1847, *Distant View of Malvern*, purchased from Messrs J. Davey and Sons, 1963

Barnard, Frederick 1846–1896, *A Dress Rehearsal*, bequeathed by Mrs C. S. Garnett, 1936

Barnes, Archibald George 1887–1972, *Head of a Boy*, purchased from The Fine Art Society, 1926, © the copyright holder

Barnett, John b.1914, *Old House, Cheltenham*, purchased from The Manchester Academy of Fine Arts, 1956, © the copyright holder

Barns-Graham, Wilhelmina 1912–2004, *Long Brown*, purchased from the Peterloo Gallery, 1967, © by courtesy of the Barns-Graham Charitable Trust

Barret the younger, George c.1767–1842, *The Sketcher*, bequeathed by Dr David Lloyd Roberts, 1920

Barry, Claude Francis 1883–1970, *Date Palms*, bequeathed by Dr Jane Walker, CH, LLD, 1939, © the artist's estate

Barry, James 1741–1806, *The Birth of Pandora*, purchased, 1856

Bateman, James 1893–1959, *Somerset Farm*, bequeathed by Mr Frank Stephens Rosser, 1968, © the copyright holder

Bateman, James 1893–1959, *Cottages in the Cotswold Hills*, bequeathed by Mr Frank Stephens Rosser, 1968, © the copyright holder

Batoni, Pompeo 1708–1787, *Lord Archibald Hamilton*, purchased from Artemis Fine Arts, 1984

Batoni, Pompeo 1708–1787, *Sir Gregory Page-Turner*, purchased at Christie's, 1976

Bauhof, Frederick active 19th C, *A Cattle Market in Pont-Croix, Brittany*, gift from William Pownall, 1911

Bayes, Walter 1869–1956, *Cornlands*, gift from Charles Lambert Rutherston, 1925, © the artist's estate

Bayes, Walter 1869–1956, *Oratio Obliqua*, gift from Howard Bliss, 1926, © the artist's estate

Baynes, Keith 1887–1977, *Flowers in a Blue Glass Jug*, purchased from the Goupil Gallery, 1931, © the artist's estate

Baynes, Keith 1887–1977, *Flowers in a Jug*, gift from Sir Thomas D. Barlow, 1932, © the artist's estate

Baynes, Keith 1887–1977, *Window, Florence*, gift from Charles Lambert Rutherston, 1925, © the artist's estate

Beach, Thomas 1738–1806, *Miss Elizabeth Phelips, Dressed as Diana*, purchased from Horace Buttery, 1949

Bega, Cornelis Pietersz. 1631/1632–1664, *Three Peasants Seated Together*, bequeathed by Mr and Mrs Edgar Assheton Bennett, 1979

Bell, Robert Anning 1863–1933, *The Meeting of the Virgin and Saint Elizabeth*, purchased from Leicester Galleries, 1910

Bell, Vanessa 1879–1961, *Red-Hot Pokers*, gift from Charles Lambert Rutherston, 1925, © 1961 estate of Vanessa Bell, courtesy Henrietta Garnett

Bell, Vanessa 1879–1961, *Still Life with Flowers*, bequeathed by Frank Hindley Smith, 1940, © 1961 estate of Vanessa Bell, courtesy Henrietta Garnett

Bell, Vanessa 1879–1961, *Still Life*, gift from Mrs Essil Elmslie Rutherston, 1928, © 1961 estate of Vanessa Bell, courtesy Henrietta Garnett

Bell, Vanessa 1879–1961, *The Well*, gift from Mr Eric C. Gregory, 1946, © 1961 estate of Vanessa Bell, courtesy Henrietta Garnett

Bellot, William Henry 1811–1895, *Jane Bellot (1772–1811)*, bequeathed by Professor H. Hale Bellot, 1969

Bellot, William Henry 1811–1895, *Frances Bellot (1820–1903)*, bequeathed by Professor H. Hale Bellot, 1969

Bellotto, Bernardo 1722–1780, *The Fortress of Konigstein: Courtyard with the Magdalenenburg*, purchased from the Marquess of Londonderry, 1983

Bellotto, Bernardo 1722–1780, *The Fortress of Konigstein: Courtyard with the Brunnenhaus*, purchased from the Marquess of Londonderry, 1982

Benjamin, Anthony 1931–2002, *Senius*, purchased from A. C. Sewter, 1973, © the artist's estate and The Benjamin Trust

Benois, Nadia 1896–1975, *Quai Anatole, France, La Ciotat*, purchased from the Goupil Gallery, 1930, © the artist's estate

Benois, Nadia 1896–1975,

Kensington Gardens, purchased from Arthur Tooth and Sons Ltd, 1937, © the artist's estate

Bentley, Charles 1808–1854, *Mont St Michel*, gift from Mrs C. J. Pooley, 1927

Berg, Adrian 1929–2011, *Punchbowl Valley Gardens*, purchased from the Piccadilly Gallery, 1991, © estate of Adrian Berg

Bevan, Robert Polhill 1865–1925, *The Farmhouse*, gift from Mr Eric C. Gregory, 1929

Bevan, Robert Polhill 1865–1925, *Horse Dealers (Sale at Ward's Repository No.1)*, purchased from the Mayor Gallery, 1935

Beyeren, Abraham van 1620/1621–1690, *Fishing Boats off the Coast in a Choppy Sea*, bequeathed by Mr and Mrs Edgar Assheton Bennett, 1979

Bidlingmeyer, Jules 1830–1893, *Apples and a Pan*, gift from George Harvard Thomas, 1917

Bidlingmeyer, Jules 1830–1893, *Flowers and Apricots*, gift from George Harvard Thomas, 1917

Birch, Samuel John Lamorna 1869–1955, *December*, purchased from the Royal Academy of Arts, 1905, © the artist's estate

Birch, Samuel John Lamorna 1869–1955, *Lamorna*, purchased from the artist, 1919, © the artist's estate

Bishop, Henry 1868–1939, *Gravesend*, purchased from Leicester Galleries, 1937

Bishop, Henry 1868–1939, *Sicilian Landscape*, purchased from Leicester Galleries, 1937

Bissill, George William 1896–1973, *Hurstbourne, Tarrant*, purchased from the Artists of Today exhibition, 1937, © the copyright holder

Bissill, George William 1896–1973, *Winter Landscape*, gift from the Contemporary Art Society, 1935, © the copyright holder

Blake, William 1757–1827, *Friedrich Gottlieb Klopstock (1724–1803)*, purchased from Thomas Agnew and Sons Ltd, 1885

Blake, William 1757–1827, *Demosthenes (384–322 BC)*, purchased from Thomas Agnew and Sons Ltd, 1885

Blake, William 1757–1827, *Marcus Tullius Cicero (106 BC–43 BC)*, purchased from Thomas Agnew and Sons Ltd, 1885

Blake, William 1757–1827, *Thomas Alphonso Hayley (1780–1800)*, purchased from Thomas Agnew and Sons Ltd, 1885

Blake, William 1757–1827, *Torquato Tasso (1544–1595)*, purchased from Thomas Agnew and Sons Ltd, 1885

Blake, William 1757–1827, *William Cowper (1731–1800)*, purchased from Thomas Agnew and Sons Ltd, 1885

Blake, William 1757–1827,

Alexander Pope (1688–1744), purchased from Thomas Agnew and Sons Ltd, 1885

Blake, William 1757–1827, *Alonso de Ercilla y Zúñiga (1533–1594)*, purchased from Thomas Agnew and Sons Ltd, 1885

Blake, William 1757–1827, *Dante Alighieri (c.1265–1321)*, purchased from Thomas Agnew and Sons Ltd, 1885

Blake, William 1757–1827, *Francois Marie Arouet de Voltaire (1694–1778)*, purchased from Thomas Agnew and Sons Ltd, 1885

Blake, William 1757–1827, *Geoffrey Chaucer (c.1343–1400)*, purchased from Thomas Agnew and Sons Ltd, 1885

Blake, William 1757–1827, *Homer*, purchased from Thomas Agnew and Sons Ltd, 1885

Blake, William 1757–1827, *John Dryden (1631–1700)*, purchased from Thomas Agnew and Sons Ltd, 1885

Blake, William 1757–1827, *Louis vaz de Camoens (c.1524–1580)*, purchased from Thomas Agnew and Sons Ltd, 1885

Blake, William 1757–1827, *Thomas Otway (1652–1685)*, purchased from Thomas Agnew and Sons Ltd, 1885

Blake, William 1757–1827, *Edmund Spenser (c.1552–1599)*, purchased from Thomas Agnew and Sons Ltd, 1885

Blake, William 1757–1827, *John Milton (1608–1674)*, purchased from Thomas Agnew and Sons Ltd, 1885

Blake, William 1757–1827, *William Shakespeare (c.1564–1616)*, purchased from Thomas Agnew and Sons Ltd, 1885

Blanche, Jacques-Emile 1861–1942, *Thomas Hardy (1840–1928)*, purchased from the artist, 1936

Blanche, Jacques-Emile 1861–1942, *Mrs Sickert*, purchased from the artist, 1938

Blanche, Jacques-Emile 1861–1942, *The Coronation of George V*, gift from the artist, 1936

Blanche, Jacques-Emile 1861–1942, *Walter Richard Sickert (1860–1942)*, purchased from Arthur Tooth and Sons Ltd, 1937

Blanche, Jacques-Emile 1861–1942, *Miss Winny MacEwan*, gift from Miss Helen J. MacEwan, 1936

Bland, Emily Beatrice 1864–1951, *Flowers in Sunlight*, gift from the Contemporary Art Society, 1940, © the copyright holder

Bland, Emily Beatrice 1864–1951, *The Bouquet*, purchased from Leicester Galleries, 1920, © the copyright holder

Bloemaert, Abraham c.1566–1651, *The Raising of Lazarus*, purchased from the Trafalgar Galleries, 1980

Bloemaert, Abraham c.1566–1651, *A Man with a Dog in a Landscape*, purchased from the Godolphin

Gallery, 1978

Boccaccino, Boccaccio before 1466–1525, *Madonna and Child*, bequeathed by George Beatson Blair, 1947

Bodley, Josselin 1893–1974, *Landscape*, purchased from Leicester Galleries, 1947, © the copyright holder

Bohm, Max 1868–1923, *Fishermen in a Stormy Sea*, gift from Henry Boddington, 1912

Boks, Marinus 1849–1885, *Landscape with a Farmhouse*, bequeathed by Lady Mary Ann Boyd Dawkins, 1979

Bold, John 1895–1979, *A Suburban Landscape*, gift from Edna Bold, 1980, © the copyright holder

Bold, John 1895–1979, *An Aran Landscape (Inishmore)*, purchased from the artist, 1948, © the copyright holder

Bold, John 1895–1979, *An Aran Village*, purchased from the artist, 1948, © the copyright holder

Bold, John 1895–1979, *Portrait of a Cat*, purchased from the artist, 1958, © the copyright holder

Bold, John 1895–1979, *The Church, Inishmaan*, purchased from The Manchester Academy of Fine Arts, 1955, © the copyright holder

Bomberg, David 1890–1957, *Figure Composition*, purchased from Marlborough Fine Art Ltd, 1967, © the estate of David Bomberg. All rights reserved, DACS 2013

Bomberg, David 1890–1957, *Outside Damascus Gate, Jerusalem*, purchased from Leicester Galleries, 1928, © the estate of David Bomberg. All rights reserved, DACS 2013

Bomberg, David 1890–1957, *Trendrine in Sun, Cornwall*, purchased from Marlborough Fine Art Ltd, 1967, © the estate of David Bomberg. All rights reserved, DACS 2013

Bone, Stephen 1904–1958, *Hungry Hill, County Cork*, purchased from the Artists of Today exhibition, 1937, © estate of Stephen Bone. All rights reserved, DACS 2013

Bone, Stephen 1904–1958, *Francis Dodd, RA*, purchased from the artist, 1936, © estate of Stephen Bone. All rights reserved, DACS 2013

Bonechi, Matteo 1669–1756, *A Concert of Angels*, purchased from the Arcade Gallery, 1966

Bonechi, Matteo 1669–1756, *The Assumption of the Virgin*, purchased from the Arcade Gallery, 1966

Bonington, Richard Parkes 1802–1828, *Pays de Caux: Twilight*, bequeathed by Mr and Mrs Edgar Assheton Bennett, 1979

Bonington, Richard Parkes 1802–1828, *View in Brittany: Bridge, Cottages and Washerwomen*, bequeathed by Mr and Mrs Edgar Assheton Bennett, 1979

Bonnard, Pierre 1867–1947, *Palm Trees at Le Cannet*, purchased from JPL Fine Arts, 1987, © ADAGP, Paris and DACS, London 2013

Bonner, Lonsdale b.1926, *Rocks, North Wales*, purchased from A. C. Sewter, 1973, © the copyright holder

Bonzi, Pietro Paolo c.1576–1636, *Landscape with Erminia and the Shepherds*, purchased at Christie's, 1979

Booth, James William 1867–1953, *Ploughing*, purchased, 1914, © the copyright holder

Booth, James William 1867–1953, *The Quarry*, gift from Lieutenant Colonel Henry Joseph Candlin, 1905, © the copyright holder

Bordon, Paris (attributed to) 1500–1571, *The Holy Family with Saint John the Baptist*, gift from Lieutenant Colonel R. H. Antrobus, 1971

Bosboom, Johannes 1817–1891, *Almshouses at Het Hofje van Nieuwkoop*, bequeathed by Lady Mary Ann Boyd Dawkins, 1979

Bottomley, Alfred active 1859–1863, *A Little Boy* (said to be Alfred Bottomley, Junior), gift from Mrs F. M. Clarke, 1972

Bottomley, Alfred active 1859–1863, *A Little Girl* (formerly thought to be Henrietta Deplidge), gift from Mrs F. M. Clarke, 1972

Bottomley, Alfred active 1859–1863, *Henrietta Deplidge*, gift from Mrs F. M. Clarke, 1972

Bottomley, Alfred active 1859–1863, *Self Portrait*, gift from Mrs F. M. Clarke, 1972

Boucher, François 1703–1770, *Le galant pêcheur*, purchased from David Carritt Ltd, 1981

Boudin, Eugène Louis 1824–1898, *Près de Quimper*, bequeathed by Lord Sidney Bernstein, 1995

Boudin, Eugène Louis 1824–1898, *Trouville Harbour*, bequeathed by George Beatson Blair, 1947

Boudin, Eugène Louis 1824–1898, *Étaples*, purchased from Durand Ruel and Sons, 1908

Boudin, Eugène Louis (style of) 1824–1898, *A Calm*, bequeathed by Mr James Thomas Blair, 1917

Bough, Samuel 1822–1878, *Edinburgh from Leith Roads*, bequeathed by Jesse Haworth, 1937

Bough, Samuel 1822–1878, *A Castle*, purchased from the executors of the will of Alfred Muir, 1902

Bouguereau, William-Adolphe 1825–1905, *Innocence*, bequeathed by Mr James Thomas Blair, 1917

Boydell, John 1839–1913, *The Lledr Valley near Bettws-y-Coed*, gift from Mrs F. G. Whitehead, 1910

Bradley, Basil 1842–1904, *A Red Squirrel Eating a Nut*, transferred from the Horsfall Museum Collection, 1918

Bradley, William 1801–1857, *Sir Benjamin Heywood, Bt*, gift from

the Manchester Education Committee, 1903

Bradley, William 1801–1857, *Charles Swain (1801–1874)*, gift from Mrs Clara Swain Dickens, 1888

Bradley, William 1801–1857, *Eliza Faulkner*, gift from Mrs M. Cort, 1982

Bradley, William 1801–1857, *George Fraser*, gift from the shareholders of Gerorge Fraser, Son and Co. Ltd, 1930

Bradley, William 1801–1857, *Isaac Faulkner*, gift from Mrs M. Cort, 1982

Bradley, William 1801–1857, *Lady with a Dog*, gift from Edwin Hilton, 1979

Bradley, William 1801–1857, *Miss Eliza Calvert*, bequeathed by George Beatson Blair, 1947

Bradley, William 1801–1857, *The English Belle*, bequeathed by Mrs C. S. Garnett, 1936

Bradley, William (attributed to) 1801–1857, *A Lady in a Plumed Hat*, bequeathed by Dr David Lloyd Roberts, 1920

Bradley, William (circle of) 1801–1857, *Man with a Pipe*, purchased from Eastbrook Galleries, 1982

Bradshaw, Brian b.1923, *Reflections (Rose Hill, Bolton)*, purchased from the Crane Gallery, 1954, © the artist

Bradshaw, Brian b.1923, *The Bed*, purchased from the artist, 1957, © the artist

Brangwyn, Frank 1867–1956, *Santa Maria Della Salute*, purchased from Mr D. Croal Thomson, 1920, © the artist's estate/Bridgeman Art Library

Bratby, John Randall 1928–1992, *Self Portrait in a Mirror*, purchased from the Beaux Arts Gallery, 1957, © the artist's estate/Bridgeman Art Library

Bratby, John Randall 1928–1992, *Flower Pots in a Greenhouse*, gift from the Leonard Cohen Fund, 1968, © the artist's estate/ Bridgeman Art Library

Brekelenkam, Quiringh van b. after 1622–d.1669 or after, *Interior with a Lady Choosing Fish*, bequeathed by Mr and Mrs Edgar Assheton Bennett, 1979

Brekelenkam, Quiringh van b. after 1622–d.1669 or after, *A Family Seated Round a Kitchen Fire*, bequeathed by Mr and Mrs Edgar Assheton Bennett, 1979

Brett, Dorothy Eugénie 1883–1977, *Umbrellas*, gift from the Contemporary Art Society, 1996, © the copyright holder

Brett, John 1831–1902, *Seascape*, transferred from the Horsfall Museum Collection, 1918

Brett, John 1831–1902, *The Norman Archipelago (Channel Islands)*, purchased, 1885

Brierley, Argent 1893–1960, *Bank Holiday*, gift from Jean Brierley, 1960, © the copyright holder

Brierley, Argent 1893–1960, *Street in Stogumber (near Minehead, Somerset)*, purchased from the Civil Defence Exhibition, 1942, © the copyright holder

Bright, Henry (attributed to) 1810–1873, *On the River Bank*, purchased from Messrs Brown and Phillips, 1905

British (English) School *Charles Worsley of Platt Hall, Manchester* (previously called 'Raphe Worsley of Platt Hall')*, purchased from Reverend W. C. Hall, 1946

British (English) School *William Chaderton*, purchased from Messers J. Leger and Son, 1923

British (English) School *Portrait of a Gentleman*, bequeathed by Miss Henrietta Close, 1947

British (English) School *Portrait of a Lady Holding a Jewel*, bequeathed by Miss Henrietta Close, 1947

British (English) School *Portrait of a Young Lady with a Plumed Headdress*, bequeathed by Miss Henrietta Close, 1947

British (English) School *Portrait of an Old Lady in a Ruff*, bequeathed by Miss Henrietta Close, 1947

British (English) School *A Girl with a Pearl Headdress*, bequeathed by George Beatson Blair, 1947

British (English) School *Horse and Dog in a Landscape*, gift from Mrs Robert Hatton, 1908

British (English) School *Three Children in a Park*, purchased from C. Marshall Spink, 1950

British (English) School *Portrait of a Lady, Called Mrs Hutchinson of Bristol*, bequeathed by Mr James Thomas Blair, 1917

British (English) School *Deborah Worsley of Platt*, purchased from Bourne Fine Art, 1989

British (English) School *A Gentleman in a Green Jacket*, bequeathed through the National Art Collections Fund, 1968

British (English) School *Portrait of a Lady with a High Headdress*, bequeathed by Sir Edward Marsh, 1953

British (English) School *Two Sisters*, bequeathed by Mrs Louisa Mary Garrett, 1936

British (English) School *A Horse with Groom and Dog in Platt Fields, Manchester*, gift from Mrs Clementia Tindal-Carill-Worsley, 1963

British (English) School *Mrs Thomas Barrow*, bequeathed by Professor H. Hale Bellot, 1969

British (English) School *Thomas Barrow*, bequeathed by Professor H. Hale Bellot, 1969

British (English) School *Thomas Bellot (1766–1826)*, bequeathed by Professor H. Hale Bellot, 1969

British (English) School *On the River Thames (View of St Paul's Cathedral)*, bequeathed by Mr James Thomas Blair, 1917

British (English) School *Pope's House, Twickenham*, bequeathed by Mr James Thomas Blair, 1917

British (English) School *River Scene with Cows and Timber Waggons*, bequeathed by Mrs Mary Worthington, 1905

British (English) School *Venus Rising from the Sea*, gift from Sir Charles E. Swann, 1917

British (English) School *Henry Barton Marsden*, gift from Miss Dorothy Hartley-Pearson, 1964

British (English) School *Mrs Henry Barton Marsden*, gift from Miss Dorothy Hartley-Pearson, 1964

British (English) School *'Hunter' in a Stable*, bequeathed by George Beatson Blair, 1947

British (English) School *Abraham Bellot*, bequeathed by Professor H. Hale Bellot, 1969

British (English) School *John Maddox with a Cat*, gift from the Manx Museum, 1964

British (English) School *Peter Maddox Holding a Bird*, gift from the Manx Museum, 1964

British (English) School *Unidentified Mill Scene*, gift from J. D. Hughes, 1938

British (English) School *Portrait of a Woman Holding a Red Book*, gift from Miss B. Ball, 1962

British (English) School *William Henry Bellot (1811–1859)*, bequeathed by Professor H. Hale Bellot, 1969

British (English) School *Mrs Mary Grimshaw*, gift from Walter and Miss Russell, 1973

British (English) School *Frances Lee Bellot (1820–1903)*, bequeathed by Professor H. Hale Bellot, 1969

British (English) School *Edmund Buckley*, gift from the Manchester Royal Exchange, 1968

British (English) School *Scotland Bridge, Red Bank*, purchased from Mr T. Smith, 1936

British (English) School *Brenda, Countess of Wilton*, gift from the Earl of Wilton, 1979

British (English) School *Boy with Hawk and Dog*, gift from the executors of the will of Mr C. R. Dunkerley, 1951

British (English) School *Lady Gordon* (formerly attributed to John Downman)*, bequeathed by Mr James Thomas Blair, 1917

British (English) School *Murray Gladstone*, gift from the Manchester Royal Exchange, 1968

British (English) School *Portrait of a Lady*, bequeathed by Mr James Thomas Blair, 1917

British (English) School *The House by the Stream*, bequeathed by Dr Jane Walker, CH, LLD, 1939

British (English) School *The 'Wellington Inn'*, gift from Sir William Fletcher Shaw, 1957

British (English) School *Unfinished Study of a Woman*, bequeathed by Wilfred René Wood, 1976

Brockhurst, Gerald Leslie 1890–1978, *Clytie*, purchased from the Chenil Galleries, 1924, ©

Richard Woodward

Brodzky, Horace 1885–1969, *Deserted Mills*, gift from Mrs Essil Elmslie Rutherston, 1928, © the artist's estate

Bromley, William c.1818–1888, *Catherine of Aragon*, bequeathed by Miss Henrietta Louisa Maw, 1910

Brompton, Richard c.1734–1783, *John Horne Tooke (1736–1812)*, purchased from Shepherd Bros, 1913

Brooker, William 1918–1983, *Early Morning*, purchased from Arthur Tooth and Sons Ltd, 1956, © the artist's estate

Brouwer, Adriaen (follower of) 1605/1606–1638, *Tavern Scene with a Large Crowd of Peasants Drinking and Merrymaking*, bequeathed by Mr and Mrs Edgar Assheton Bennett, 1979

Brouwer, Adriaen (style of) 1605/1606–1638, *Peasants Eating Mussels*, bequeathed by Mr and Mrs Edgar Assheton Bennett, 1979

Brown, Ford Madox 1821–1893, *Frederick Henry Snow Pendleton*, purchased from Shepherd Bros, 1913

Brown, Ford Madox 1821–1893, *The Vicar of Wakefield: Dr Primrose and His Daughters*, purchased from James Tregaskis, 1912

Brown, Ford Madox 1821–1893, *Manfred on the Jungfrau*, gift from Frederick William Jackson, 1916

Brown, Ford Madox 1821–1893, *The Prisoner of Chillon*, gift from Harold Rathbone, 1911

Brown, Ford Madox 1821–1893, *Out of Town*, bequeathed by George Beatson Blair, 1947

Brown, Ford Madox 1821–1893, *The Bromley Family*, bequeathed by George Beatson Blair, 1947

Brown, Ford Madox 1821–1893, *Wilhelmus Conquistador (The Body of Harold)*, purchased from M. J. Hampson Thornton, 1907

Brown, Ford Madox 1821–1893, *Study for 'Courtier in Yellow Hood' (Sir John Froissart)*, gift from the National Art Collections Fund, 1931

Brown, Ford Madox 1821–1893, *Two Studies of a Little Girl's Head*, bequeathed by George Beatson Blair, 1947

Brown, Ford Madox 1821–1893, *William Shakespeare (c.1564–1616)*, purchased from Montague Fordham, 1900

Brown, Ford Madox 1821–1893, *Heath Street, Hampstead (Study for Work)*, purchased from Leicester Galleries, 1924

Brown, Ford Madox 1821–1893, *Work*, purchased from T. E. Plint, 1885

Brown, Ford Madox 1821–1893, *Stages of Cruelty*, purchased from Henry Boddington, 1911

Brown, Ford Madox 1821–1893, *The English Boy*, bequeathed by Mr C. P. Scott, 1932

Brown, Ford Madox 1821–1893,

The Traveller, purchased from Mr Charles A. Jackson, 1925

Brown, Ford Madox 1821–1893, *Byron's Dream*, bequeathed by George Beatson Blair, 1947

Brown, Ford Madox 1821–1893, *Cromwell, Protector of the Vaudois*, gift from Lieutenant Colonel Henry Joseph Candlin, 1901

Brown, Ford Madox 1821–1893, *Crabtree Watching the Transit of Venus, 1639*, bequeathed by George Beatson Blair, 1947

Brown, Ford Madox 1821–1893, *Madeline Scott*, gift from the executors of the will of C. P. Scott, 1932

Brown, Ford Madox 1821–1893, *The Establishment of the Flemish Weavers in Manchester, 1363*, bequeathed by George Beatson Blair, 1947

Brown, Ford Madox 1821–1893, *Unfinished Sketch for 'John Kay, Inventor of the Fly Shuttle, 1753'*, bequeathed by George Beatson Blair, 1947

Brown, Ford Madox 1821–1893, *The Proclamation Regarding Weights and Measures, 1556*, bequeathed by George Beatson Blair, 1947

Brown, Frederick 1851–1941, *Marketing*, bequeathed by Mrs Dorothy Una McGrigor Phillips, 1968

Brown, John Alfred Arnesby 1866–1955, *The Drinking Pool*, purchased from the 13th Autumn Exhibition, 1895, © the copyright holder

Brown, Reginald Victor 1897–1940, *The Wye River*, gift from Alderman R. A. D. Carter, 1930

Browning, Amy Katherine 1881–1978, *Seascape*, gift from Forrest Hewit, 1935, © Joanna Dunham

Brown-Morison, Guy Edward 1868–1949, *The Harbour, Pont Aven*, bequeathed by Lady Mary Ann Boyd Dawkins, 1979, © the copyright holder

Brueghel the elder, Jan (follower of) 1568–1625, *Landscape with Figures on a Path in the Foreground and a Castle on a River*, bequeathed by Mr and Mrs Edgar Assheton Bennett, 1979

Brueghel the elder, Jan (follower of) 1568–1625, *Landscape with Windmills*, gift from Mrs Robert Hatton, 1908

Bryce, Alexander Joshua Caleb 1868–1940, *The Last Days of Censorship: Prisoners of War Mails*, gift from Alexander Joshua Caleb Bryce, 1920

Bryce, Alexander Joshua Caleb 1868–1940, *A Room in the Censor's Office: Neutral Trade Mails*, purchased from Alexander Joshua Caleb Bryce, 1920

Bunce, William Harold S. 1920–1995, *Park Farm*, purchased from The Manchester Academy of Fine Arts, 1959, © the copyright holder

Burn, Rodney Joseph 1899–1984, *Snow Scene*, gift from the Contemporary Art Society, 1940, © the artist's estate

Burne-Jones, Edward 1833–1898, *Sibylla Delphica*, purchased from Mrs W. A. Turner, 1886

Burr, John 1831–1893, *The Incorrigible*, bequeathed by Miss Henrietta Louisa Maw, 1910

Butler, Arthur Stanley George 1888–1965, *The Church, Briancon*, bequeathed by Dr Jane Walker, CH, LLD, 1939, © the copyright holder

Butler, Arthur Stanley George 1888–1965, *Flamingoes*, purchased from Arthur Stanley George Butler, 1955, © the copyright holder

Butler, Elizabeth Southerden Thompson 1846–1933, *Balaclava*, gift from Robert Whitehead, 1898

Butterworth, Alice active 1936–1946, *Miss M. B. Moorcroft*, gift from Miss M. B. Moorcroft, 1986, © the copyright holder

Byrne, John b.1940, *Self Portrait*, purchased from William Hardie, Ltd, 1987, © the artist/Bridgeman Art Library

Cadell, Francis Campbell Boileau 1883–1937, *Interior with Figure*, purchased from the Paterson Gallery, 1930

Cadell, Francis Campbell Boileau 1883–1937, *Lady in a Black Hat (Miss Don Wauchope of Edinburgh)*, purchased from Messrs T. and R. Annan, 1955

Caille, Léon Émile 1836–1907, *Chiding*, transferred from the Horsfall Museum Collection, 1918

Caille, Léon Émile 1836–1907, *Prayer*, transferred from the Horsfall Museum Collection, 1918

Caldecott, Randolph 1846–1886, *May Day*

Caldecott, Randolph 1846–1886, *The Girl I Left Behind Me*, purchased from Thomas Agnew and Sons Ltd, 1886

Calderon, Philip Hermogenes 1833–1898, *Study of a Historical Scene Showing Henry VIII and His Courtiers*, gift from Mr F. E. Simpson, 1983

Calderon, Philip Hermogenes 1833–1898, *Margaret*, bequeathed by Mr James Thomas Blair, 1917

Callcott, Augustus Wall 1779–1844, *View of Ghent*, bequeathed by Mrs Mary Worthington, 1905

Callcott, Augustus Wall 1779–1844, *Landscape with Water Mill*, purchased from Thomas Agnew and Sons Ltd, 1898

Callow, William 1812–1908, *The Wartburg; The Place of Luther's Captivity in 1521*, purchased from Shepherd Bros, 1903

Cambier, Juliette 1879–1963, *Flowers, Harmony in Rose*, gift from G. B. Alexander, 1938, © the copyright holder

Cameron, David Young 1865–1945, *Dark Angers*,

purchased from the 21st Autumn Exhibition, 1904, © the artist's estate

Cameron, David Young 1865–1945, *The Hills of Arran*, purchased from the International Society of Sculptors, Painters, etc, 1913, © the artist's estate

Canaletto 1697–1768, *The Church of San Giorgio Maggiore, Venice*, gift from HM Treasury, 1984

Canaletto 1697–1768, *The Church of the Redentore, Venice*, gift from HM Treasury, 1984

Cappelle, Jan van de 1626–1679, *Winter Scene with Thatched Cottages and a Frozen River Spanned by a Wooden Bridge*, bequeathed by Mr and Mrs Edgar Assheton Bennett, 1979

Cappelle, Jan van de 1626–1679, *Shipping Anchored in a Calm Sea*, bequeathed by Mr and Mrs Edgar Assheton Bennett, 1979

Cappelle, Jan van de 1626–1679 & **Dubbels, Hendrik Jacobsz. (follower of)** *Shipping at Anchor off the Shore in a Calm Sea*, bequeathed by Mr and Mrs Edgar Assheton Bennett, 1979

Carabain, Jacques François 1834–1933, *Coast Scene*, transferred from the Horsfall Museum Collection, 1918

Carline, Nancy 1909–2004, *VE Night*, gift from the artist, 1986, © the artist's estate

Carline, Sydney William 1888–1929, *The Walnut Tree*, gift from Mrs Carline, 1929

Carline, Sydney William 1888–1929, *The Eiderdown*, gift from Mrs Carline, 1929

Carlone, Carlo Innocenzo (attributed to) 1686–1775, *A Soldier Entering the Tent of a Queen*, purchased from the Arcade Gallery, 1966

Carmichael, John Wilson 1799–1868, *Shipping on the Thames*, transferred from the Horsfall Museum Collection, 1918

Caroselli, Angelo 1585–1652, *Madonna and Child with the Infant Baptist*, gift from Mrs E. F. Hickman, 1931

Carpenter, Dora active 1870–1883, *Mare and Foal*, transferred from the Horsfall Museum Collection, 1918

Carr, Thomas James 1909–1999, *The Window*, purchased from the Redfern Gallery, 1945, © the artist's estate

Caulfield, Patrick 1936–2005, *Inside a Weekend Cabin*, gift from the Contemporary Art Society, 1972, © the estate of Patrick Caulfield. All rights reserved, DACS 2013

Cavaillès, Jules 1901–1977, *Interior, Music Room*, bequeathed by Miss Dorothy Pilkington, 1974, © ADAGP, Paris and DACS, London 2013

Cave, William Wilfred 1879–1962(?), *Girl's Head (Phyllis Sachs)*, gift from Charles Lambert Rutherston, 1925, © the copyright holder

Cazin, Jean-Charles 1841–1901, *The Barleyfield*, purchased from the French Gallery, 1930

Chaigneau, Jean Ferdinand 1830–1906, *Flock of Sheep*, bequeathed by H. J. Sambrook, 1944

Chaigneau, Jean Ferdinand 1830–1906, *Sheep*, bequeathed by Mr James Thomas Blair, 1917

Challié, Jean Laurent 1880–1943, *Snow in Sunshine*, purchased from the French Gallery, 1928, © the copyright holder

Chalmers, George c.1720–c.1791, *Colonel Archibald Grant*, bequeathed by Miss Laetitia Satterthwaite, 1986

Chalmers, George c.1720–c.1791, *Mrs Anne Grant*, bequeathed by Miss Laetitia Satterthwaite, 1986

Charles, James 1851–1906, *Christening Sunday (South Harting, Sussex)*, purchased from John Maddocks, 1908

Charles, James 1851–1906, *The Knifegrinder*, gift from John Maddocks, 1908

Cheston, Evelyn 1875–1929, *Creech Barrow, Dorset*, purchased from Mr Charles A. Jackson, 1925

Chettle, James Patchell 1871–1944, *The Grain Warehouse*, gift from the Royal Manchester Institution, 1932, © the copyright holder

Chettle, James Patchell 1871–1944, *Sharpness*, purchased from The Manchester Academy of Fine Arts, 1935, © the copyright holder

Chettle, James Patchell 1871–1944, *Early Morning, Poole Harbour*, purchased from The Manchester Academy of Fine Arts, 1938, © the copyright holder

Chettle, James Patchell 1871–1944, *Pulteney Bridge, Bath*, untraced find, 1979, © the copyright holder

Chettle, James Patchell 1871–1944, *Bloody but Unbowed (Portland Street, Manchester)*, purchased from the artist, 1941, © the copyright holder

Chettle, James Patchell 1871–1944, *Derbyshire Farm*, bequeathed by Mr Frank Stephens Rosser, 1957, © the copyright holder

Chettle, James Patchell 1871–1944, *War Memorial, Manchester*, purchased from the artist, 1941, © the copyright holder

Chowne, Gerard 1875–1917, *Polyanthus*, bequeathed by Mr James Thomas Blair, 1917

Chowne, Gerard 1875–1917, *Stocks*, gift from Charles Lambert Rutherston, 1925

Christopherson, John 1921–1996, *Jardin de Luxembourg, Paris*, purchased from the City Art Gallery, 1954, © the copyright holder

Chubb, Ralph Nicholas 1892–1960, *A Berkshire Farm*, gift from the artist, 1954, © the

copyright holder

Citti Ferreira, Lucy b.1914, *Still Life with Lamp*, gift from the artist, 1949, © the copyright holder

Clause, William Lionel 1887–1946, *Marcel and His Sister*, gift from A. E. Anderson, 1928, © the copyright holder

Clause, William Lionel 1887–1946, *Portrait of a Man's Head*, purchased from the artist, 1932, © the copyright holder

Clausen, George 1852–1944, *Portrait of a Girl's Head*, purchased from William Marchant & Co., Goupil Art Gallery, 1922, © Clausen estate

Clausen, George 1852–1944, *Portrait of a Village Woman*, purchased from the Autumn Exhibition, 1906, © Clausen estate

Clausen, George 1852–1944, *Winter Morning*, purchased from Thomas Agnew and Sons Ltd, 1907, © Clausen estate

Clausen, George 1852–1944, *The Old Reaper*, bequeathed by George Beatson Blair, 1947, © Clausen estate

Clough, Prunella 1919–1999, *The Dead Bird*, purchased from Roland, Browse and Delbanco, 1951, © estate of Prunella Clough 2013. All rights reserved, DACS

Clough, Prunella 1919–1999, *Cave*, purchased from Annely Juda Fine Art, 1994, © estate of Prunella Clough 2013. All rights reserved, DACS

Clover, Chris b.1948, *Your Memory Is Your Bible, Your Imagination Your Future*, gift from the artist, 1968, © the artist

Coates, George James 1869–1930, *Memories*, gift from Mrs D. M. Coates, 1935

Codrington, Isabel 1874–1943, *Evening*, gift, 1927, © the copyright holder

Cole, Chisholm 1871–1902, *An Anglesey Common*, gift from Councillor John Royle, 1902

Cole, George 1810–1883, *Showery Weather*, bequeathed by Mr James Thomas Blair, 1917

Cole, George Vicat 1833–1893, *Springtime*, bequeathed by Mr James Thomas Blair, 1917

Cole, George Vicat 1833–1893, *The Heart of Surrey*, purchased from Thomas Agnew and Sons Ltd, 1895

Cole, John Vicat 1903–1975, *In Church Street, Kensington*, gift from the Royal Manchester Institution, 1936, © the copyright holder

Cole, Leslie 1910–1976, *10 H. A. A., Zeebug, Malta*, gift from HM Government, War Artists Advisory Committee, 1947, © the artist's estate

Colkett, Samuel David 1806–1863, *Farmhouse with Pond*, gift from the executors of the will of J. R. Oliver, 1934

Colles, Elizabeth Orme 1869–1943, *Miss M. C. Murray*, gift from the sitter, 1954, © the

copyright holder

Collins, Cecil 1908–1989, *Landscape of the Unknown God*, gift from the Contemporary Art Society, 1966, © Tate, London 2012

Collins, Charles Allston 1828–1873, *The Pedlar*, purchased from Harry H. Martyne, 1896

Collins, William 1788–1847, *The Cottage Door*, bequeathed by John Edward Yates, 1934

Collinson, James 1825–1881, *Answering the Emigrant's Letter*, purchased at Sotheby's, 1966

Collinson, James 1825–1881, *A Son of the Soil*, purchased from Renate Nahum, Leicester Galleries, 2003

Colquhoun, Robert 1914–1962, *Mater Dolorosa*, gift from the Contemporary Art Society, 1962, © the artist's estate/Bridgeman Art Library

Colquhoun, Robert 1914–1962 & **MacBryde, Robert** 1913–1966, *Costume for Donald (in a Palace Scene)*, purchased from the Redfern Gallery, 1952, © the artist's estate/Bridgeman Art Library

Colquhoun, Robert 1914–1962 & **MacBryde, Robert** 1913–1966, *The Goatmen* (costume design for Leonide Massine's ballet 'Donald of the Burthens' of 1951), purchased from the Redfern Gallery, 1952, © the artist's estate/ Bridgeman Art Library

Colquhoun, Robert 1914–1962 & **MacBryde, Robert** 1913–1966, *The Sword Dancer*, purchased from the Redfern Gallery, 1952, © the artist's estate/Bridgeman Art Library

Compard, Émile 1900–1977, *Portrait of a Woman (L'étudiante)*, gift from Sir Thomas D. Barlow, 1936, © ADAGP, Paris and DACS, London 2013

Compton, Edward Theodore 1849–1921, *The Jungfrau*, gift from the Trustees of Samuel Redfern, 1927

Conca, Sebastiano 1680–1764, *The Blessings of Good Government*, purchased from the Arcade Gallery, 1966

Conca, Sebastiano 1680–1764, *The Government of Pope Benedict XIV*, purchased from the Arcade Gallery, 1966

Conder, Charles 1868–1909, *Smoke and Chrysanthemum Flowers*, gift from Charles Lambert Rutherston, 1925

Conder, Charles 1868–1909, *The Moulin Rouge*, gift from Charles Lambert Rutherston, 1925

Conder, Charles 1868–1909, *Dieppe*, gift from Charles Lambert Rutherston, 1925

Conder, Charles 1868–1909, *Self Portrait*, gift from Charles Lambert Rutherston, 1925

Conder, Charles 1868–1909, *On the Beach, Swanage*, gift from Charles Lambert Rutherston, 1925

Conder, Charles 1868–1909, *The Gardener's Daughter*, purchased from Messrs Wallis and Son, 1923

Conder, Charles 1868–1909, *The Red Kimono*, bequeathed by Mr C. P. Scott, 1932

Connard, Philip 1875–1958, *Lady in Pink*, bequeathed by Mr Frank Stephens Rosser, 1968, © the copyright holder

Connard, Philip 1875–1958, *The River Tang*, purchased from Leicester Galleries, 1914, © the copyright holder

Connard, Philip 1875–1958, *British Warships at Constantinople*, purchased from the artist, 1920, © the copyright holder

Constable, John 1776–1837, *View from Hampstead Heath, Looking Towards Harrow*, bequeathed by Mr James Thomas Blair, 1917

Constable, John (after) 1776–1837, *London from Hampstead Heath*, bequeathed by Dr Jane Walker, CH, LLD, 1939

Constable, John (attributed to) 1776–1837, *Early Morning*, purchased from Thomas Agnew and Sons Ltd, 1909

Constable, John (attributed to) 1776–1837, *Cottage in a Cornfield*, bequeathed by Mr James Thomas Blair, 1917

Constable, John (attributed to) 1776–1837, *Moonlight at Brighton*, purchased from Thomas Agnew and Sons Ltd, 1909

Constable, John (follower of) 1776–1837, *A Windy Day*, bequeathed by George Beatson Blair, 1947

Constable, John (follower of) 1776–1837, *Landscape with a Fisherman on a Bridge*, gift from Mr James Gresham, 1917

Constable, John (follower of) 1776–1837, *South Downs*, gift from the National Art Collections Fund, 1931

Conti, Francesco 1681–1760, *The Assumption of the Virgin*, purchased from Thomas Agnew and Sons Ltd, 1983

Cook, Francis Ferdinand Maurice 1907–1978, *Cornish Flooded Claypit*, gift from the artist, 1944, © the artist's estate

Cook, Francis Ferdinand Maurice 1907–1978, *Falls of Inversnaid, Scotland*, gift from the artist, 1944, © the artist's estate

Cook, Francis Ferdinand Maurice 1907–1978, *Trees, Richmond Park, Surrey*, gift from the artist, 1943, © the artist's estate

Cooke, Edward William 1811–1880, *Venetian Lagoons – Sunset*, bequeathed by Mr James Thomas Blair, 1917

Cooke, Edward William 1811–1880, *On the Shore at Scheveling – Low Water*, bequeathed by Mr James Thomas Blair, 1917

Cooper, Byron 1850–1933, *Godrevy Light, Cornwall*, purchased from the artist, 1905

Cooper, John Albert 1894–1943, *Alpine Love*, purchased from the Lefevre Galleries, 1931, © the artist's estate

Cooper, Thomas Sidney 1803–1902, *Heat Showers in August*, gift from Mrs I. C. Rayner, 1921

Cooper, Thomas Sidney 1803–1902, *Cattle by the River Side*, bequeathed by John Edward Yates, 1934

Cooper, Thomas Sidney 1803–1902, *Sheep on the Common*, bequeathed by John Edward Yates, 1934

Cooper, Thomas Sidney 1803–1902, *O'er the Braes of Balquhidder (Perthshire)*, bequeathed by Mrs A. Enriqueta Rylands, 1908

Cooper, Thomas Sidney 1803–1902, *Cattle Crossing a Stream*, bequeathed by Sir Joseph Whitworth, 1896

Cooper, Thomas Sidney 1803–1902, *Cattle Crossing a Stream and a Man Fishing*, bequeathed by Sir Joseph Whitworth, 1896

Copley, John 1875–1950, *Men and Mountains*, purchased from The Manchester Academy of Fine Arts, 1935, © the artist's estate

Copley, John 1875–1950, *A Maiden*, gift from the Royal Manchester Institution, 1940, © the artist's estate

Copley, John 1875–1950, *Chamber Music*, purchased from the artist, 1938, © the artist's estate

Corot, Jean-Baptiste-Camille 1796–1875, *Rider in the Water*, bequeathed by George Beatson Blair, 1947

Corot, Jean-Baptiste-Camille 1796–1875, *Sunset: Figures under Trees*, purchased from L. W. Livesey, 1908

Corsi, Nicolas de 1882–1956, *Morning Mists in Venice*, gift from Alderman E. F. M. Sutton, 1930, © the copyright holder

Cortona, Pietro da (follower of) 1596–1669, *The Finding of Moses*, gift from Thomas Gough, 1904

Cotman, John Sell 1782–1842, *An Old House at St Albans*, purchased from P. & D. Colnaghi & Co. Ltd, 1981

Courbet, Gustave 1819–1877, *Le ruisseau du puits noir*, purchased from Arthur Tooth and Sons Ltd, 1955

Cox the elder, David 1783–1859, *Boys Fishing*, bequeathed by Jesse Haworth, 1937

Cox the elder, David 1783–1859, *Crossing the Ford*, bequeathed by Mr James Thomas Blair, 1917

Cox the elder, David 1783–1859, *Landscape with Man on a Horse*, bequeathed by George Beatson Blair, 1947

Cox the elder, David 1783–1859, *Crossing the Moor*, bequeathed by Mr James Thomas Blair, 1917

Cox the elder, David 1783–1859, *Haymaking near Conway*, gift from Frederick John Nettlefold, 1948

Cox the elder, David 1783–1859, *Dudley Castle*, purchased from Thomas Agnew and Sons Ltd, 1900

Cox the elder, David 1783–1859, *Rhyl Sands*, bequeathed by Mr James Thomas Blair, 1917

Cox the elder, David 1783–1859, *The Gathering of the Flocks*, gift from Edward Behrens, 1902

Coxon, Raymond James 1896–1997, *Henry Moore (1898–1986)*, gift from Charles Lambert Rutherston, 1925, © the artist's estate

Coxon, Raymond James 1896–1997, *Landscape with Barn*, gift from Mr Eric C. Gregory, 1929, © the artist's estate

Coxon, Raymond James 1896–1997, *Knitting*, gift from the guarantors of the London Artists' Association, 1934, © the artist's estate

Coxon, Raymond James 1896–1997, *Linton Village*, gift from Mr Eric C. Gregory, 1946, © the artist's estate

Coxon, Raymond James 1896–1997, *Model Resting*, gift from the Contemporary Art Society, 1931, © the artist's estate

Coxon, Raymond James 1896–1997, *Muker Village, Swaledale*, gift from Mr Eric C. Gregory, 1946, © the artist's estate

Coxon, Raymond James 1896–1997, *Penrhyndeudraeth*, gift from Mrs Hazel King-Farlow, 1936, © the artist's estate

Craig-Martin, Michael b.1941, *Inhale (Yellow)*, purchased from the Gagosian Gallery, 2003, © Michael Craig-Martin. Courtesy Gagosian Gallery

Craxton, John 1922–2009, *Vine Pruner*, purchased from the Crane Gallery, 1954, © estate of John Craxton 2013. All rights reserved, DACS

Crespi, Giuseppe Maria 1665–1747, *A Singer with a Donkey*, purchased from Amos R. Ramsbottom, 1963

Creswick, Thomas 1811–1869, *The Mouth of a River*, bequeathed by Mr James Thomas Blair, 1917

Creswick, Thomas 1811–1869, *The River Tees at Rokeby, Yorkshire*, purchased from Thomas Agnew and Sons Ltd, 1904

Creswick, Thomas 1811–1869, *Coast Scene with Figures*, bequeathed by Mrs Annie Woodhouse, 1940

Creswick, Thomas 1811–1869, *The Weald, Surrey*, gift from Mr James Gresham, 1917

Crome, John 1768–1821, *View near Norwich with Harvesters*, purchased from Thomas Agnew and Sons Ltd, 1900

Crome, John 1768–1821, *Woodland Scene with Sheep (Chapel Fields)*, purchased from Thomas Agnew and Sons Ltd with the assistance of the National Art Collections Fund, 1979

Crome, John 1768–1821, *The Steam Packet*, purchased from Thomas Agnew and Sons Ltd, 1905

Crome, William Henry 1806–1873, *Wooded Landscape with Windmill*, gift from Miss Lillies Pickles, 1914

Crome, William Henry 1806–1873, *Wooded Landscape with Cottage*, gift from Miss Lillies Pickles, 1914

Crowe, Eyre 1824–1910, *The Dinner Hour, Wigan*, purchased from A. E. Knight, 1922

Crozier, Robert 1815–1891, *The Patriot (John Sheldon)*, purchased from Mrs Anne Sheldon, 1909

Culbert, Bill b.1935, *Journey through Landscape, Lacoste to Bonnieux*, purchased from the Society for Education through Art, Pictures for Schools Exhibition, 1964, © the artist

Cundall, Charles Ernest 1890–1971, *The Arena, Assisi*, gift from Charles Lambert Rutherston, 1925, © the artist's estate/Bridgeman Art Library

Cundall, Charles Ernest 1890–1971, *A Chelsea Cup-Tie*, gift from Manchester citizens, 1924, © the artist's estate/Bridgeman Art Library

Cundall, Charles Ernest 1890–1971, *Temeside, Ludlow*, gift from Sir Thomas D. Barlow, 1923, © the artist's estate/Bridgeman Art Library

Cundall, Charles Ernest 1890–1971, *Surrey Hills*, bequeathed by George Beatson Blair, 1947, © the artist's estate/Bridgeman Art Library

Cundall, Charles Ernest 1890–1971, *Pont Neuf, Paris*, purchased from P. & D. Colnaghi & Co. Ltd, 1926, © the artist's estate/Bridgeman Art Library

Cundall, Charles Ernest 1890–1971, *The Demolition of Devonshire House*, gift from Howard Bliss, 1931, © the artist's estate/Bridgeman Art Library

Cundall, Charles Ernest 1890–1971, *Quai des Grands Augustins, Paris*, purchased from the artist, 1927, © the artist's estate/Bridgeman Art Library

Cundall, Charles Ernest 1890–1971, *William Burton, MA, FCS*, gift from Mrs F. C. Ormerod, 1964, © the artist's estate/Bridgeman Art Library

Cundall, Charles Ernest 1890–1971, *Liverpool from the Mersey*, purchased from The Manchester Academy of Fine Arts, 1939, © the artist's estate/Bridgeman Art Library

Cundall, Charles Ernest 1890–1971, *Avro Lancaster Bombers at Woodford*, gift from A. V. Roe and Co. Ltd, 1945, © the artist's estate/Bridgeman Art Library

Cundall, Charles Ernest 1890–1971, *Metropolitan-Vickers Works, Trafford Park*, gift from Metropolitan-Vickers Electrical Co. Ltd, 1945, © the artist's estate/Bridgeman Art Library

Cundall, Charles Ernest 1890–1971, *Fête at St Cloud*, gift from Alderman Frederick Todd, 1925, © the artist's estate/Bridgeman Art Library

Cunningham, Vera 1897–1955, *Exuberant Flower*, gift from the Leonard Cohen Fund, 1968, © the artist's estate

Currie, Ken b.1960, *On the Edge of a City*, purchased from the Raab Gallery, 1988, © the artist/courtesy Flowers Gallery, London

Cuyp, Aelbert 1620–1691, *River Scene with a View of Dordrecht and a Windmill*, bequeathed by Mr and Mrs Edgar Assheton Bennett, 1979

Cuyp, Aelbert (follower of) 1620–1691, *Poultry with a Distant View of Dordrecht*, bequeathed by Mrs Elizabeth Hatton Wood, 1908

Dacre, Susan Isabel 1844–1933, *Lydia Becker*, gift from the National Union of Women's Suffrage, 1920

Dacre, Susan Isabel 1844–1933, *Colonel Volbert*, gift from the artist, 1932

Dacre, Susan Isabel 1844–1933, *Louise*, purchased from the artist, 1923

Dacre, Susan Isabel 1844–1933, *A View in Venice*, gift from Thomas Gough, 1928

Dacre, Susan Isabel 1844–1933, *The Artist's Mother*, gift from the artist, 1932

Dacre, Susan Isabel 1844–1933, *Alderman Sir Thomas Baker*, gift from Henry Boddington, 1911

Dacre, Susan Isabel 1844–1933, *Little Annie Rooney*, gift from The Friends of Manchester City Galleries, 1911

Dacre, Susan Isabel 1844–1933, *Assisi from Perugia*, bequeathed by Mr C. P. Scott, 1932

Dacre, Susan Isabel 1844–1933, *A Girl (Bertha Edgar)*, gift from the sitter, 1931

Dacre, Susan Isabel 1844–1933, *Assisi*, bequeathed by Mr C. P. Scott, 1932

Dacre, Susan Isabel 1844–1933, *Assisi from the City Walls*, gift from Miss Bertha Edgar, 1943

Dacre, Susan Isabel 1844–1933, *Gateway at Siena*, gift from Miss Florence Chapman, 1942

Dacre, Susan Isabel 1844–1933, *Italian Child*, gift from Henry Boddington, 1884

Dacre, Susan Isabel 1844–1933, *Italian Girl with Necklace*, gift from Henry Boddington, 1884

Dacre, Susan Isabel 1844–1933, *Italian Women in Church*, gift from Francis Dodd, 1927

Dacre, Susan Isabel 1844–1933, *Swans*, purchased from the artist, 1927

Dacre, Susan Isabel 1844–1933, *The Walls of Siena*, gift from Miss Florence Chapman, 1942

Daddi, Bernardo (style of) c.1280–1348, *Virgin and Child with the Goldfinch*, purchased from C. Marshall Spink, 1959

Daintrey, Adrian Maurice 1902–1988, *Augustus John (1878–1961)*, gift from Mrs Essil Elmslie Rutherston, 1928, © the artist's estate

Daintrey, Adrian Maurice 1902–1988, *Miss Ann Knox*, gift from Mrs Essil Elmslie Rutherston, 1928, © the artist's estate

Daintrey, Adrian Maurice 1902–1988, *Still Life*, gift from Mrs Essil Elmslie Rutherston, 1928, © the artist's estate

Daintrey, Adrian Maurice 1902–1988, *Wallflowers*, gift from Mrs Powell, 1953, © the artist's estate

Dance-Holland, Nathaniel 1735–1811, *Thomas Dawson, Lord Cremorne*, purchased from Shepherd Bros, 1905

Dance-Holland, Nathaniel (attributed to) 1735–1811, *A Country Gentleman (Charles Burney)*, purchased from Arthur Tooth and Sons Ltd, 1954

Dandridge, Bartholomew 1691–c.1754, *The Ladies Noel*, purchased from C. Marshall Spink, 1957

Daniels, Leonard 1909–1998, *Kirkstall Forge (Steam Hammer)*, gift from HM Government, War Artists Advisory Committee, 1947, © the copyright holder

Danson, George 1799–1881, *Manchester from Belle Vue*, gift from Mrs Derbyshire, 1947

Darwin, Robin 1910–1974, *T. A. Brocklebank*, purchased from Thomas Agnew and Sons Ltd, 1938, © the artist's estate

Darwin, Robin 1910–1974, *Watchmaker's Shop, Downe*, gift from the Royal Manchester Institution, 1946, © the artist's estate

Daubigny, Charles-François 1817–1878, *Avant et après le vote*, bequeathed by Lord Sidney Bernstein, 1995

Daumier, Honoré 1808–1879, *Le wagon de troisième classe*, bequeathed by Lord Sidney Bernstein, 1995

Davie, Alan b.1920, *Red's New Ball Game No.1*, purchased from Gimpel Fils Ltd, 1961, © the artist

Davies, Austin 1926–2012, *Forms on a Horizontal Surface*, purchased from Austin Howard Davies, 1960, © the copyright holder

Davies, James Hey 1844–1930, *Young Poachers*, purchased from The Manchester Academy of Fine Arts, 1888

Davies, James Hey 1844–1930, *Study of an Ash Tree in Summer*, transferred from the Horsfall Museum Collection, 1918

Davies, James Hey 1844–1930, *Study of an Ash Tree in Winter*, transferred from the Horsfall Museum Collection, 1918

Davies, James Hey 1844–1930,

Late Autumn: Irlam Hall, near Manchester, gift from the executor of the will of George Thomas, 1928

Davies, James Hey 1844–1930, *Flint's Farm, Moss Side, Manchester*, gift from W. B. Shaw, 1934

Davies, James Hey 1844–1930, *Stiggins Lock*, gift from George Harvard Thomas, 1917

Davies, Norman Prescott 1862–1915, *Love's Whispers*, bequeathed by Mr James Thomas Blair, 1917

Davis, Henry William Banks 1833–1914, *Noonday Rest*, bequeathed by Mr James Thomas Blair, 1917

Davis, Henry William Banks 1833–1914, *Afternoon on the Cliffs*, bequeathed by Mr James Thomas Blair, 1917

Davis, Joseph Barnard 1861–1943, *A Cotswold Farm*, gift from the executors of the will of the artist, 1943, © the copyright holder

Dawson, Charles Frederick b.1864, *Accrington from My Window*, purchased from The Manchester Academy of Fine Arts, 1934

Dawson, Henry 1811–1878, *On the Trent near Nottingham*, purchased from A. S. Dawson, 1891

de Grey, Roger 1918–1995, *Gasometer, Long Benton*, purchased from the artist, 1955, © the artist's estate

De Karlowska, Stanislawa 1876–1952, *Adamson Road, NW3*, gift from Mrs C. W. Baty, 1968, © the artist's estate/Bridgeman Art Library

De Karlowska, Stanislawa 1876–1952, *At Woodnesborough, Kent*, gift from Mrs C. W. Baty, 1936, © the artist's estate/Bridgeman Art Library

de Maistre, Leroy Leveson Laurent Joseph 1894–1968, *Interior*, purchased from the Mayor Gallery, 1934, © the artist's estate

De Wint, Peter 1784–1849, *Landscape with Willow Tree*, purchased from J. J. Schwarz, 1946

De Wint, Peter 1784–1849, *View over Flat Country*, bequeathed by George Beatson Blair, 1947

Deane, Frederick b.1924, *Edward John Stanley*, purchased from the artist, 1958, © the artist

Degas, Edgar (style of) 1834–1917, *Woman in a Café*, bequeathed by George Beatson Blair, 1947

Derain, André 1880–1954, *Head of a Girl*, purchased from Leicester Galleries, 1947, © ADAGP, Paris and DACS, London 2013

Destrée, Johannes Joseph 1827–1888, *Haarlem from the Dunes*, gift from H. B. Wood, 1935

Detmold, Henry Edward 1854–1924, *Spearing*, gift from Mrs Detmold, 1927

Devas, Anthony 1911–1958, *Mrs Creswick Atkinson*, gift from HM Government, War Artists Advisory

Committee, 1947, © the artist's estate/Bridgeman Art Library

Devas, Nicolette Macnamara 1911–1987, *Juanita in the Morning*, purchased from Messrs Matthiesen Ltd, 1940, © the artist's estate

Devis, Arthur 1712–1787, *A Young Gentleman at a Drawing Table*, purchased from Mr Charles A. Jackson, 1928

Devis, Arthur 1712–1787, *Two Children and a Dog in a Park*, bequeathed by George Beatson Blair, 1947

Dewhurst, Wynford 1864–1941, *The Blue Valley*, gift from Ernest A. Knight, 1918

Dewhurst, Wynford 1864–1941, *The Picnic*, purchased from the artist, 1909

Dickey, Edward Montgomery O'Rorke 1894–1977, *Monte Scalambra from San Vito Romano*, purchased from the artist, 1924, © the copyright holder

Dicksee, Frank 1853–1928, *The Funeral of a Viking*, gift from Arthur Burton, 1928

Dicksee, Frank 1853–1928, *My Lady Fair*, bequeathed by Mr James Thomas Blair, 1917

Dodd, Francis 1874–1949, *Miss Caroline Herford (Mrs Robert Blake)*, gift from Mather Training College Old Students Association, 1928, © the artist's estate

Dodd, Francis 1874–1949, *Henry Lamb (1883–1960)*, gift from the artist, 1940, © the artist's estate

Dodd, Francis 1874–1949, *Signora Lotto*, purchased from the artist, 1910, © the artist's estate

Dodd, Francis 1874–1949, *High Street, Greenwich*, purchased from the artist, 1919, © the artist's estate

Dodd, Francis 1874–1949, *Charles Prestwich Scott (1846–1932)*, bequeathed by Mrs Alice Olga Scott, 1978, © the artist's estate

Dodd, Francis 1874–1949, *Willow in Winter*, purchased from the artist, 1929, © the artist's estate

Dodson, Sarah Paxton Ball 1847–1906, *Budding Elms in April, Mayfield*, gift from R. Ball Dodson, 1920

Dods-Withers, Isobelle Ann 1876–1939, *Old Houses at Espalion*, purchased from the artist, 1911

Dou, Gerrit 1613–1675, *Portrait of a Girl*, bequeathed by Mr and Mrs Edgar Assheton Bennett, 1979

Dow, Thomas Millie 1848–1919, *A Vision of Spring*, purchased from the 20th Autumn Exhibition, 1902

Draper, Herbert James 1864–1920, *Calypso's Isle*, gift from E. N. Galloway, 1919

Draper, Herbert James 1864–1920, *A Water Baby*, purchased from the artist, 1900

Du Plessis, Enslin 1894–1978, *Boats, La Rochelle*, gift from Mr Eric C. Gregory, 1933, © the copyright holder

Du Plessis, Enslin 1894–1978, *Flower Piece*, purchased from the Central Institute of Art and

Design, 1945, © the copyright holder

Dubufe, Claude Marie 1790–1864, *Mrs Hervey Francis de Montmorency and Her Daughter Frances*, gift from the National Art Collections Fund, 1955

Duccio (school of) c.1255–before 1319, *The Crucifixion*, purchased from a private collector, 1984

Dufy, Raoul 1877–1953, *Equestrian Statue of Henri IV, Paris*, bequeathed by Miss Dorothy Pilkington, 1974, © ADAGP, Paris and DACS, London 2013

Dugdale, Thomas Cantrell 1880–1952, *Allenby's White Mice: Feeding the Pack Donkeys: Desert Corps HQ*, purchased from the Exhibition of War Paintings and Drawings, 1920, © Joanna Dunham

Dugdale, Thomas Cantrell 1880–1952, *Night*, purchased from the artist, 1927, © Joanna Dunham

Dugdale, Thomas Cantrell 1880–1952, *William Temple*, gift from fellow-workers and friends of Bishop Temple, 1930, © Joanna Dunham

Dugdale, Thomas Cantrell 1880–1952, *A. S. Mitchell*, gift from the sitter, 1957, © Joanna Dunham

Dugdale, Thomas Cantrell 1880–1952, *Boy with Boats*, purchased from The Manchester Academy of Fine Arts, 1941, © Joanna Dunham

Dugdale, Thomas Cantrell 1880–1952, *A Boy*, bequeathed by Mr Frank Stephens Rosser, 1957, © Joanna Dunham

Dugdale, Thomas Cantrell 1880–1952, *Cecil Rowntree*, gift from the sitter, 1942, © Joanna Dunham

Dugdale, Thomas Cantrell 1880–1952, *Posies*, purchased from The Manchester Academy of Fine Arts, 1912, © Joanna Dunham

Dughet, Gaspard 1615–1675, *Landscape with Shepherds*, purchased from H. N. Bier, 1949

Dunbar, Evelyn Mary 1906–1960, *The Cerebrant*, gift from R. W. Folley, 2005, © the artist's estate

Dunbar, Evelyn Mary 1906–1960, *A 1944 Pastoral: Land Girls Pruning at East Malling*, gift from HM Government, War Artists Advisory Committee, 1947, © the artist's estate

Dunbar, Evelyn Mary 1906–1960, *Potato Sorting, Berwick*, gift from HM Government, War Artists Advisory Committee, 1947, © the artist's estate

Dunbar, Evelyn Mary 1906–1960, *Sprout Picking, Monmouthshire*, gift from HM Government, War Artists Advisory Committee, 1947, © the artist's estate

Dunington, Albert 1860–1941, *Barton Aqueduct*, bequeathed by Mrs C. S. Garnett, 1936

Dunlop, Ronald Ossory 1894–1973, *Tom Balston (1883–1967)*, gift from the sitter,

1950, © the copyright holder

Dunlop, Ronald Ossory 1894–1973, *Still Life*, gift from Mr Eric C. Gregory, 1946, © the copyright holder

Durden, James 1878–1964, *Summer in Cumberland*, purchased from the artist, 1926, © the copyright holder

Dutch School *A Female Saint*, bequeathed by Mr James Thomas Blair, 1917

Dutton, John Frederick Harrison 1872–1909, *Robert Henry Grenville Tatton (Young Man Seated with a Dog)*, untraced find, 1984

Dyck, Anthony van (after) 1599–1641, *Charles I (1600–1649)*, gift from W. Bentley Capper, 1902

Dyck, Anthony van (attributed to) 1599–1641, *The Holy Family*, bequeathed by George Beatson Blair, 1947

Dyck, Anthony van (studio of) 1599–1641, *Saint Sebastian*, transferred from the Royal Manchester Institution, 1882

East, Alfred 1844/1849–1913, *Autumn*, purchased from the artist, 1888

East, Alfred 1844/1849–1913, *The Sleepy River Somme*, purchased from the 15th Annual Exhibition, 1898

Eastlake, Charles Lock 1793–1865, *Christ Blessing Little Children*, gift from James Worthington, 1886

Edgar, James H. active 1857–1870, *Thomas Grosvenor Egerton, 2nd Earl of Wilton*, purchased from D. H. R. Bell, 1973

Edgar, James H. active 1857–1870, *The Mushroom Gatherer*, bequeathed by Miss Florence Harrison, 1971

Edwards, Arthur Sherwood 1887–1960, *Mr and Mrs Robinson at St Ives*, purchased from the artist, 1938, © the copyright holder

Egg, Augustus Leopold 1816–1863, *A Walk on the Beach*, purchased from Thomas Agnew and Sons Ltd, 1947

Eisler, Georg 1928–1998, *London Road Station I*, purchased from the artist, 1988, © Georg and Alice Eisler Foundation/Georg Eisler Archive, Vienna

Ekels the younger, Jan 1759–1793, *Interior with Man Reading*, gift from James Porter, 1935

Eldridge, Mildred E. 1909–1991, *Poplars, Chirk Valley*, bequeathed by Dr Jane Walker, CH, LLD, 1939, © the copyright holder

Ellis, Edwin 1842–1895, *The Haven under the Hill (Anglesey)*, purchased from the 3rd Autumn Exhibition, 1885

Elmslie, Essil R. 1880–1952, *Emma, Covent Garden*, gift from Jeannette Powell, 1953, © the copyright holder

Emslie, Alfred Edward 1848–1918, *Henry Dunckley*, gift from Miss Helena Dunckley, 1905

Erni, Hans b.1909, *Composition No.36*, gift from A. C. Sewter,

1956, © the artist

Ernst, Max 1891–1976, *La ville pétrifiée (The Petrified City)*, purchased from Roland, Browse and Delbanco, 1955, © ADAGP, Paris and DACS, London 2013

Espagnat, Georges d' 1870–1950, *Woman Reading*, purchased from Durand Ruel and Sons, 1908, © ADAGP, Paris and DACS, London 2013

Estall, William Charles 1857–1897, *The Sheepfold*, gift from J. Arthur Bland, 1907

Etty, William 1787–1849, *The Destroying Angel and Daemons of Evil Interrupting the Orgies of the Vicious and Intemperate*, gift from Sir Joseph Whitworth, 1882

Etty, William 1787–1849, *Self Portrait*, gift from Sir Joseph Whitworth, 1882

Etty, William 1787–1849, *The Storm*, transferred from the Royal Manchester Institution, 1882

Etty, William 1787–1849, *The Warrior Arming (Godfrey de Bouillon)*, gift from Sir Joseph Whitworth, 1882

Etty, William 1787–1849, *Venus and Her Doves*, bequeathed by Dr David Lloyd Roberts, 1920

Etty, William 1787–1849, *The Bather 'At the Doubtful Breeze Alarmed'*, gift from Mr James Gresham, 1917

Etty, William 1787–1849, *Andromeda and Perseus*, gift from George Walthew, 1894

Etty, William 1787–1849, *The Honourable Mrs Caroline Norton and Her Sisters*, bequeathed by George Beatson Blair, 1947

Etty, William 1787–1849, *'An Israelite Indeed'*, bequeathed by George Beatson Blair, 1947

Etty, William 1787–1849, *Seated Male Model*, bequeathed by Frank Hindley Smith, 1940

Etty, William 1787–1849, *Study of a Peacock*, gift from Sir Joseph Whitworth, 1882

Etty, William 1787–1849, *The Sirens and Ulysses*, transferred from the Royal Manchester Institution, 1882

Etty, William (follower of) 1787–1849, *Reclining Model*, gift from H. C. Coleman, 1928

Eurich, Richard Ernst 1903–1992, *Lyme Regis*, bequeathed by Dr Jane Walker, CH, LLD, 1939, © the artist's estate/Bridgeman Art Library

Eurich, Richard Ernst 1903–1992, *From the Old Walls, Lyme Regis*, purchased from the Redfern Gallery, 1933, © the artist's estate/Bridgeman Art Library

Eurich, Richard Ernst 1903–1992, *The Blue Barge*, gift from the Contemporary Art Society, 1938, © the artist's estate/Bridgeman Art Library

Eurich, Richard Ernst 1903–1992, *Collier Brig, Falmouth*, purchased from the Redfern Gallery, 1936, © the artist's estate/Bridgeman Art

Library

Eurich, Richard Ernst 1903–1992, *Flowers in a Glass*, purchased from Mr Charles A. Jackson, 1940, © the artist's estate/Bridgeman Art Library

Eurich, Richard Ernst 1903–1992, *The Boats Were Machine-Gunned*, gift from HM Government, War Artists Advisory Committee, 1947, © the artist's estate/Bridgeman Art Library

Evans, Edmund 1826–1905, *Folkstone*, bequeathed by George Beatson Blair, 1947

Evans, Edmund 1826–1905, *Landscape with Cottage and Farmcart*, bequeathed by George Beatson Blair, 1947

Evans, Edmund 1826–1905, *Landscape with Cottage at Sunset*, bequeathed by George Beatson Blair, 1947

Ewald, Clara 1859–1948, *Lake Scene*, bequeathed by Dr Jane Walker, CH, LLD, 1939, © the copyright holder

Faed, Thomas 1826–1900, *Evangeline*, gift from Mr James Gresham, 1917

Faithfull, Leila 1896–1994, *Rosette*, gift from the Contemporary Art Society, 1954, © Leila E. Evans

Faithfull, Leila 1896–1994, *In the Luxembourg Gardens*, purchased from Leicester Galleries, 1940, © Leila E. Evans

Fantin-Latour, Henri 1836–1904, *Self Portrait*, purchased from the French Gallery, 1919

Fantin-Latour, Henri 1836–1904, *Grapes and an Apple*, bequeathed by Dr David Lloyd Roberts, 1920

Fantin-Latour, Henri 1836–1904, *La source*, bequeathed by Dr David Lloyd Roberts, 1920

Fantin-Latour, Henri 1836–1904, *L'amour vainqueur*, purchased from Charles Jackson, 1934

Fantin-Latour, Henri 1836–1904, *Cupid and Venus*, bequeathed by Dr David Lloyd Roberts, 1920

Fantin-Latour, Henri 1836–1904, *The Bathers*, bequeathed by Dr David Lloyd Roberts, 1920

Fantin-Latour, Henri 1836–1904, *Flowers*, transferred from the Royal Manchester Institution, 1882

Fantin-Latour, Henri 1836–1904, *A Woodland Glade*, bequeathed by Dr David Lloyd Roberts, 1920

Fantin-Latour, Henri 1836–1904, *Flowers in a Vase*, bequeathed by Dr David Lloyd Roberts, 1920

Fantin-Latour, Henri 1836–1904, *Peaches and Grapes*, bequeathed by Dr David Lloyd Roberts, 1920

Fantin-Latour, Henri 1836–1904, *Still Life: Roses in a Glass Vase*, bequeathed by Mr and Mrs Edgar Assheton Bennett, 1979

Farleigh, John F. W. C 1900–1965, *Hillmorton Locks*, gift from Charles Lambert Rutherston, 1925, © the copyright holder

Farquharson, David 1839–1907, *Summer's Eve*, purchased from the 13th Autumn Exhibition, 1895

Farquharson, Joseph 1846–1935, *Market on the Nile*, purchased from The Fine Art Society, 1924

Farquharson, Joseph 1846–1935, *When the West with Evening Glows*, bequeathed by John Edward Yates, 1934

Farquharson, Joseph 1846–1935, *'The Sun Had Closed the Winter Day'*, bequeathed by Mr James Thomas Blair, 1917

Farquharson, Joseph 1846–1935, *'The Weary Waste of Snow'*, purchased from Thomas Agnew and Sons Ltd, 1898

Faulkner, Benjamin Rawlinson 1787–1849, *Robert Hindley*, transferred from the Royal Manchester Institution, 1882

Feiler, Paul b.1918, *Gwavas Verticals*, purchased from the Redfern Gallery, 1956, © the artist/Bridgeman Art Library

Fellowes, James c.1690–c.1760, *Arabelle Pennant*, bequeathed by George Beatson Blair, 1947

Fergusson, John Duncan 1874–1961, *Le quartier, Paris*, purchased from Ian MacNicol, 1966, © The Fergusson Gallery, Perth and Kinross Council, Scotland

Feyen, Jacques Eugène 1815–1908, *On the Shore*, bequeathed by Mr James Thomas Blair, 1917

Fielding, Anthony V. C. 1787–1855, *Herstmonceux Castle, Sussex*, bequeathed by Mr James Thomas Blair, 1917

Fielding, Anthony V. C. (attributed to) 1787–1855, *Durham Cathedral*, bequeathed by George Beatson Blair, 1947

Fildes, Luke 1843–1927, *Venetians*, purchased from the 3rd Autumn Exhibition, 1885

Fildes, Luke 1843–1927, *A Devotee*, bequeathed by Mr James Thomas Blair, 1917

Fildes, Luke 1843–1927, *Carina*, bequeathed by Mr James Thomas Blair, 1917

Finlayson, A. S. active from 1940, *Multi-Spindle Drilling Machines on Aero-Engine Work*, gift from the Ford Motor Company Ltd, 1945, © the copyright holder

Fisher, Mark 1841–1923, *Horses by a Lock*, bequeathed by Dr David Lloyd Roberts, 1920

Fisher, Mark 1841–1923, *Fen Meadows with Cattle*, gift from the family of Robert Barclay, 1906

Fisher, Mark 1841–1923, *On the Road to Newport*, bequeathed by Sir Christopher Needham, 1942

Fisher, Mark 1841–1923, *Pond and Willows (Widdington, Essex)*, gift from W. H. Wood, 1924

Fisher, Mark 1841–1923, *Cattle*, gift from Alderman Frederick Todd, 1925

Fisher, Mark 1841–1923, *Cattle in a Meadow*, bequeathed by Dr David Lloyd Roberts, 1920

Fisher, Mark 1841–1923, *Landscape with River and Cattle*, bequeathed by George Beatson

Blair, 1947

Fisher, Mark 1841–1923, *Under the Olives*, bequeathed by George Beatson Blair, 1947

Fitton, James 1899–1982, *Les Girls*, purchased from the artist, 1953, © the artist's estate

Flemish (Antwerp) School *The Judgement of Solomon*, purchased from the Arcade Gallery, 1960

Fletcher, Blandford 1858–1936, *The Old Beech Tree*, gift from Rosamund Fletcher, 1988

Fleuss, Henry Joseph 1811–1888, *Thomas Grosvenor Egerton, 2nd Earl of Wilton*, purchased from Alister Mathews, 1972

Forain, Jean Louis 1852–1931, *Dancers in the Wings*, purchased from Leicester Galleries, 1938

Forbes, Elizabeth Adela Stanhope 1859–1912, *Jean, Jeanne and Jeannette*, purchased at Christie's, 1913

Forbes, Stanhope Alexander 1857–1947, *Farmyard*, acquired, 1979, © the artist's estate/ Bridgeman Art Library

Forbes, Stanhope Alexander 1857–1947, *The Lighthouse (Newlyn, Cornwall)*, purchased from the artist, 1892, © the artist's estate/Bridgeman Art Library

Forbes, Vivian 1891–1937, *German Landscape*, gift from the Contemporary Art Society, 1943

Foster, Myles Birket 1825–1899, *The Brook*, bequeathed by John Edward Yates, 1934

Foster, William Gilbert 1855–1906, *Whispering Eve*, gift from Gilbert Foster, 1916

Fragonard, Jean-Honoré (attributed to) 1732–1806, *Tristano Martinelli (actor)*, gift from the National Art Collections Fund, 1930

Francis, Mark b.1962, *Release*, purchased from Mark Francis, Maureen Paley (Interim Art), 1995, © Mark Francis

Francken II, Frans 1581–1642, *The Seven Works of Mercy*, purchased from Roger Oldham, 1912

Francken II, Hieronymus (attributed to) 1578–1623, *The Adoration of the Shepherds*, gift from Edward Neild, 1912

Fraser, Donald Hamilton 1929–2009, *Composition*, gift from the Contemporary Art Society, 1962, © estate of Donald Hamilton Fraser

Fraye, André 1888–1963, *Old Harbour and Cathedral, Marseilles*, gift from the Contemporary Art Society, 1935, © the copyright holder

French School *Classical Landscape with a Sphinx*, gift from Dorothy Palairet, 1988

French School *Classical Landscape with an Urn*, gift from Dorothy Palairet, 1988

Frere, E. J. active c.1860–c.1870, *Landscape*, bequeathed by Mr Frank Stephens Rosser, 1968

Frère, Pierre Edouard 1819–1886,

Roasting Chestnuts, bequeathed by Dr David Lloyd Roberts, 1920

Freud, Lucian 1922–2011, *Girl with Beret*, purchased from the Hanover Gallery, 1952, © estate of Lucian Freud

Freyse, Albert d.1652, *Allegory of Virtue*, gift from Dr and Mrs Langley, 1953

Frith, William Powell 1819–1909, *Claude Duval*, gift from Mr James Gresham, 1917

Frith, William Powell 1819–1909, *The Squire's Boxing Lesson*, bequeathed by Dr David Lloyd Roberts, 1920

Frith, William Powell 1819–1909, *The Derby Day*, gift from James Gresham, 1896

Frith, William Powell 1819–1909, *Elizabeth I and Courtiers*, bequeathed by Dr David Lloyd Roberts, 1920

Frith, William Powell 1819–1909, *Mme Jourdain Discovers Her Husband at the Dinner Which He Gave to the Belle Marquise and the Count Dorante*, bequeathed by Dr David Lloyd Roberts, 1920

Fry, Roger Eliot 1866–1934, *The Church at Ramatuelle*, bequeathed by Frank Hindley Smith, 1940

Fry, Roger Eliot 1866–1934, *Chiswick House*, gift from Mrs Pamela Diamond, 1958

Fry, Roger Eliot 1866–1934, *Excavations at St Rémy*, gift from Miss S. Margery Fry, 1935

Gabain, Ethel Leontine 1883–1950, *Miss Flora Robson as Lady Audley*, purchased from the artist, 1934, © the artist's estate

Gabain, Ethel Leontine 1883–1950, *The Little Bride*, purchased from The Manchester Academy of Fine Arts Exhibition, 1935, © the artist's estate

Gabain, Ethel Leontine 1883–1950, *The Airman*, purchased from The Manchester Academy of Fine Arts Exhibition, 1940, © the artist's estate

Gabain, Ethel Leontine 1883–1950, *Sybilla*, bequeathed by Mr Frank Stephens Rosser, 1968, © the artist's estate

Gabain, Ethel Leontine 1883–1950, *The Little Hat*, gift from John Copley, 1950, © the artist's estate

Gainsborough, Thomas 1727–1788, *Mrs Prudence Rix*, bequeathed by Bernard William Blakely, 1950

Gainsborough, Thomas 1727–1788, *Portrait of a Young Gentleman*, purchased from Thomas Agnew and Sons Ltd, 1900

Gainsborough, Thomas 1727–1788, *Sir Richard Perryn (1723–1803)*, purchased from Mrs Elliot and Mrs McBride, 1981

Gainsborough, Thomas 1727–1788, *A Peasant Girl Gathering Faggots in a Wood*, purchased from Thomas Agnew and Sons Ltd, 1978

Gainsborough, Thomas

1727–1788, *Landscape with Figures*, purchased from C. Marshall Spink, 1950

Gainsborough, Thomas 1727–1788, *Landscape with Sheep*, gift from Frederick John Nettlefold, 1948

Gardini, Theophile *Spring at Nayland, Suffolk*, bequeathed by Dr Jane Walker, CH, LLD, 1939, © the copyright holder

Garstin, Norman 1847–1926, *The Card Players*, gift from Mrs Garstin, 1927

Gauffier, Louis 1761–1801, *Pygmalion and Galatea*, purchased from Hazlitt, Gooden and Fox Ltd, 1979

Gauguin, Paul 1848–1903, *Harbour Scene, Dieppe*, gift from Mrs P. Duxbury, 1944

Gaulli, Giovanni Battista 1639–1709, *Saint John the Baptist*, purchased from P. & D. Colnaghi & Co. Ltd, 1968

Gear, William 1915–1997, *Study with Blue and Orange*, purchased from the Redfern Gallery, 1960, © the artist's estate

Gere, Charles March 1869–1957, *Vintage in Northern Italy*, gift from Charles Lambert Rutherston, 1925, © the artist's estate

Gere, Margaret 1878–1965, *Mrs Alfred Thornton*, gift from Charles Lambert Rutherston, 1925, © the artist's estate

German School *The Bath of Diana*, bequeathed by Mr James Thomas Blair, 1917

Gertler, Mark 1891–1939, *Still Life*, gift from the Contemporary Art Society, 1928

Gertler, Mark 1891–1939, *Fruit*, gift from Charles Lambert Rutherston, 1925

Gertler, Mark 1891–1939, *After Bathing*, purchased from the Goupil Gallery, 1924

Gheyn II, Jaques de 1565–1629, *Master and Pupil*, purchased from H. N. Bier, 1949

Ghirlandaio, Ridolfo (attributed to) 1483–1561, *The Adoration of the Shepherds*, purchased from Roland, Browse and Delbanco, 1947

Gibbon, James active 1860–1865, *William Forbes Gibbon*, gift from Mrs E. Aitken Walker, 1965

Gibbon, James active 1900–1927, *William Forbes Gibbon*, gift from Mrs E. Aitken Walker, 1966

Gibbon, James active 1900–1927, *Mrs W. C. A. Gibbon*, gift from Mrs E. Aitken Walker, 1965

Gibbon, James active 1900–1927, *Edna Forbes Gibbon (1902–1974)*, gift from Mrs E. Aitken Walker, 1966

Gibbon, James active 1900–1927, *Mrs W. C. A. Gibbon*, gift from Mrs E. Aitken Walker, 1966

Gibbon, James active 1900–1927, *Edna Forbes Gibbon (1902–1974)*, gift from Mrs E. Aitken Walker, 1966

Gibbon, James active 1900–1927,

William Charles Alexander Gibbon, gift from Mrs E. Aitken Walker, 1966

Gilbert, John 1817–1897, *Don Sancho Panza, Governor of Barataria*, gift from the artist, 1893

Gilbert, John 1817–1897, *Gipsies*, gift from the artist, 1893

Gilbert, John 1817–1897, *Breaking up the Encampment*, gift from the artist, 1893

Gilbert, John 1817–1897, *'Onward'*, gift from the artist, 1893

Gilbert, John 1817–1897, *A Venetian Council of War*, gift from the artist, 1893

Gilchrist, Philip Thomson 1865–1956, *Loch-an-Eilan*, gift from Miss M. H. C. Mellis, 1961, © the artist's estate

Gilchrist, Philip Thomson 1865–1956, *A Forgotten Lancashire Port (Sunderland on the Lune)*, gift from Alfred White, 1926, © the artist's estate

Giles, Catherina Dawson 1878–1955, *Snow Scene, Étaples*, gift from Henry Boddington, 1911, © the copyright holder

Gill, Basil 1876–1955, *Buildings by a Stream*, gift from Sir Thomas D. Barlow, 1952, © the copyright holder

Gill, Colin Unwin 1892–1940, *Catherine*, gift from Sir Thomas D. Barlow, 1952

Gilman, Harold 1876–1919, *Interior with Artist's Mother*, gift from the Contemporary Art Society, 1931

Gilman, Harold 1876–1919, *Portrait of a Lady (Miss Fletcher)*, gift from Mr Eric C. Gregory, 1929

Ginesi, Edna 1902–2000, *The Thames at Hammersmith*, gift from Mr Eric C. Gregory, 1946, © the copyright holder

Ginesi, Edna 1902–2000, *Cross Roads in the Village*, gift from Mr Eric C. Gregory, 1929, © the copyright holder

Ginesi, Edna 1902–2000, *Grassington*, gift from Mr Eric C. Gregory, 1946, © the copyright holder

Ginesi, Edna 1902–2000, *Farm Buildings, Burnsall*, gift from Mr Eric C. Gregory, 1946, © the copyright holder

Ginner, Charles 1878–1952, *Flask Walk, Hampstead*, purchased from William Marchant & Co., Goupil Art Gallery, 1922, © the copyright holder

Ginner, Charles 1878–1952, *Bethnal Green Allotment*, gift from HM Government, War Artists Advisory Committee, 1947, © the copyright holder

Ginner, Charles 1878–1952, *Landscape with Farmhouses*, gift from Mr Eric C. Gregory, 1929, © the copyright holder

Ginsborg, Michael b.1943, *Her Day at Sneaker's Creek*, gift from the Contemporary Art Society, 1980, © the artist

Giordano, Luca 1634–1705, *The Cave of Eternity*, purchased from David Barclay Ltd, 1964

Glehn, Wilfrid Gabriel de 1870–1951, *A Study*, purchased from the Goupil Gallery, 1930, © the studio estate of Wilfrid de Glehn is represented by David Messum Fine Art Ltd

Gluckmann, Grigory 1898–1973, *Female Nude*, gift from Mr Eric C. Gregory, 1946, © the copyright holder

Gluckstein, Hannah 1895–1978, *Lilac and Guelder Rose*, gift, 1937, © the artist's estate

Godward, John William 1861–1922, *On the Balcony*, bequeathed by Mr James Thomas Blair, 1917

Godward, John William 1861–1922, *Expectation*, bequeathed by Mr James Thomas Blair, 1917

Godward, John William 1861–1922, *Nude Study*, bequeathed by Mr James Thomas Blair, 1917

Goodall, Frederick 1822–1904, *Poultry*, bequeathed by Sir Joseph Whitworth, 1896

Goodall, Frederick 1822–1904, *The Water of the Nile*, gift from Frederick Smallman, 1893

Gordon, John Watson 1788–1864, *Sir Walter Scott (1771–1832)*, purchased from Thomas Agnew and Sons Ltd, 1903

Gordon, John Watson (after) 1788–1864, *Primaticcio (1504–1570)*

Gore, Frederick John Pym 1913–2009, *Teesdale*, purchased from the Redfern Gallery, 1938, © estate of Frederick Gore. All rights reserved, DACS 2013

Gore, Spencer 1878–1914, *Richmond: Winter*, purchased from Leicester Galleries, 1928

Gosse, Laura Sylvia 1881–1968, *Lilies and Fruit*, purchased from Mr Robert H. Jackson, 1933, © the artist's estate/Bridgeman Art Library

Goubau, Laureys c.1640–after 1670, *A Girl at a Kitchen Window Slicing a Lemon*, bequeathed by Mr and Mrs Edgar Assheton Bennett, 1979

Gower, George c.1540–1596, *Mary Cornwallis*, purchased from C. Marshall Spink, 1953

Gowing, Lawrence 1918–1991, *Miss R. of Dinnington Village*, purchased from Leicester Galleries, 1955, © estate of Sir Lawrence Gowing

Goyen, Jan van 1596–1656, *Landscape with a Cottage and a Barn*, bequeathed by Mr and Mrs Edgar Assheton Bennett, 1979

Goyen, Jan van 1596–1656, *Winter Scene with a Sledge in the Foreground and Figures Gathering Round a Tent on the Ice*, bequeathed by Mr and Mrs Edgar Assheton Bennett, 1979

Graham, Fergus 1900–1968, *Landscape with Farm*, gift from the

Contemporary Art Society, 1931, © the copyright holder

Graham, Fergus 1900–1968, *The Far Journey*, purchased from the Lefevre Galleries, 1935, © the copyright holder

Graham, Peter 1836–1921, *A Spate in the Highlands*, gift from Sir William Cunliffe Brooks, 1901

Graham, Peter 1836–1921, *Highland Cattle, Perthshire*, bequeathed by Mr James Thomas Blair, 1917

Graham, Peter 1836–1921, *The Seabirds' Domain*, bequeathed by Mr James Thomas Blair, 1917

Graham Bell, Frank 1910–1943, *The Café (Café Conte, London)*, gift from the Contemporary Art Society, 1944, © the artist's estate

Grant, Duncan 1885–1978, *Caryatid*, purchased from Wildenstein and Co. Ltd, 1964, © estate of Duncan Grant. All rights reserved, DACS 2013

Grant, Duncan 1885–1978, *Window, South of France*, gift from the Contemporary Art Society, 1930, © estate of Duncan Grant. All rights reserved, DACS 2013

Grant, Duncan 1885–1978, *Boats, St Tropez*, gift from the Contemporary Art Society, 1928, © estate of Duncan Grant. All rights reserved, DACS 2013

Grant, Duncan 1885–1978, *Red Hot Pokers*, gift from Charles Lambert Rutherston, 1925, © estate of Duncan Grant. All rights reserved, DACS 2013

Grant, Francis (attributed to) 1803–1878, *Lord Wilton of the Leicestershire Hunt*, purchased at Sotheby's, 1992

Grant, Ian 1904–1993, *Cheshire Mill*, purchased from Mid-Day Studios, 1947, © the artist's estate

Grant, Ian 1904–1993, *Self Portrait*, purchased from The Manchester Academy of Fine Arts Exhibition, 1940, © the artist's estate

Grant, Ian 1904–1993, *Margo Ingham*, gift from Edward Wolfe, 1979, © the artist's estate

Greaves, Walter 1846–1930, *Chelsea Regatta*, purchased from William Marchant & Co., Goupil Art Gallery, 1922

Grebber, Pieter Fransz. de c.1600–c.1653, *The Nativity*, gift from the children of Albert and Edith Eckersley, 1926

Green, Dora active 1900–1926, *Grapes*, gift from the artist, 1926, © the copyright holder

Green, Madeline 1884–1947, *The Future*, gift from Sir Joseph Duveen, 1927, © the copyright holder

Greenwood, Orlando 1892–1989, *The Keeper*, purchased from C. Marshall Spink, 1925, © the copyright holder

Gresty, Hugh 1899–1958, *Spanish City*, bequeathed by Mrs Elizabeth Gresty, 1965, © the copyright holder

Gresty, Kenneth Harry 1928–2002, *Bolton Landscape*, purchased from the artist, 1955, © the copyright holder

Gribble, Kenneth 1925–1995, *Park Parade, Ashton*, purchased from the artist, 1959, © the copyright holder

Gribbon, Charles Edward 1898–1939, *Stormy Afternoon near Cannes*, gift from Mrs Essil and Miss Jeanette Rutherston, 1944

Grundy, Cuthbert Cartwright 1846–1946, *Old Skelwith Bridge, Ambleside*, gift from the artist, 1912, © the copyright holder

Guardi, Francesco (attributed to) 1712–1793, *An Island in the Lagoon*, bequeathed by Mr and Mrs Edgar Assheton Bennett, 1979

Guardi, Francesco (attributed to) 1712–1793, *Capriccio with a Church Seen through a Portico*, bequeathed by Mr and Mrs Edgar Assheton Bennett, 1979

Guardi, Francesco (attributed to) 1712–1793, *Lagoon Capriccio with a Church*, bequeathed by Mr and Mrs Edgar Assheton Bennett, 1979

Guardi, Francesco (attributed to) 1712–1793, *Lagoon Capriccio with a Church and a Bridge*, bequeathed by Mr and Mrs Edgar Assheton Bennett, 1979

Guardi, Francesco (attributed to) 1712–1793, *Lagoon Capriccio with a Peasant and Cattle*, bequeathed by Mr and Mrs Edgar Assheton Bennett, 1979

Guardi, Francesco (attributed to) 1712–1793, *Lagoon Capriccio with a Ruined Arch*, bequeathed by Mr and Mrs Edgar Assheton Bennett, 1979

Guardi, Francesco (attributed to) 1712–1793, *Piazza San Marco, Venice*, bequeathed by Mr and Mrs Edgar Assheton Bennett, 1979

Guardi, Francesco (attributed to) 1712–1793, *Storm at Sea*, bequeathed by Mr and Mrs Edgar Assheton Bennett, 1979

Guardi, Francesco (attributed to) 1712–1793, *The Bridge over the Brenta at Dolo (the Porta del Dolo)*, bequeathed by Mr and Mrs Edgar Assheton Bennett, 1979

Guardi, Francesco (attributed to) 1712–1793, *The Piazzetta, Venice*, bequeathed by Mr and Mrs Edgar Assheton Bennett, 1979

Guercino (after) 1591–1666, *The Death of Dido*, purchased, 1981

Guerrieri, Giovanni Francesco (attributed to) 1589–1656, *Lot and His Daughters*, transferred from the Royal Manchester Institution, 1882

Guevara, Alvaro 1894–1951, *The Hunter*, bequeathed by Dr Jane Walker, CH, LLD, 1939, © the copyright holder

Gumuchian, Margaret 1928–1996, *Peel Park, Salford*, gift from Mrs Ian Grant, 1962, © the artist's estate

Guthrie, Robin 1902–1971, *Late Snowfall*, gift from the

Contemporary Art Society, 1938, © the artist's estate

Guthrie, Robin 1902–1971, *Wild Wales*, bequeathed by Mr Frank Stephens Rosser, 1968, © the artist's estate

Gwynne-Jones, Allan 1892–1982, *Field near Ruan Minor*, gift from Charles Lambert Rutherston, 1925, © the artist's estate/Bridgeman Art Library

Hacker, Arthur 1858–1919, *Syrinx*, purchased from the Autumn Exhibition, 1892

Hacker, Arthur 1858–1919, *Buttercup Meadow*, gift from Alderman R. A. D. Carter, 1936

Hacker, Arthur 1858–1919, *Peonies*, gift from I. P. Carson, 1921

Hagedorn, Karl 1889–1969, *Clerkenwell Green*, purchased from the artist, 1933, © the copyright holder

Hagedorn, Karl 1889–1969, *The Aloe Farm*, gift from the Royal Manchester Institution, 1936, © the copyright holder

Hagedorn, Karl 1889–1969, *Harbour Scene*, bequeathed by Mr Frank Stephens Rosser, 1957, © the copyright holder

Hague, Joshua Anderson 1850–1916, *June*, purchased from the 16th Autumn Exhibition, 1898

Hague, Joshua Anderson 1850–1916, *Landscape in North Wales*, gift from E. N. Galloway, 1919

Hague, Joshua Anderson 1850–1916, *Springtime*, purchased from the 3rd Autumn Exhibition, 1885

Hague, Joshua Anderson 1850–1916, *The Mill Pool*, gift from Lady Holt, 1931

Haile, Samuel 1909–1948, *Woman and Suspended Man*, gift from Mrs Marianne Haile, 1968, © the copyright holder

Hakim-Dowek, Leslie b.1960, *Flowers of the Mediterranean No.13*, purchased from the artist, 1991, © the artist

Hakim-Dowek, Leslie b.1960, *Flowers of the Mediterranean No.2*, purchased from the artist, 1991, © the artist

Hakim-Dowek, Leslie b.1960, *Vulnerables*, purchased from the artist, 1991, © the artist

Hall, Kenneth 1913–1946, *Two Figures*, gift from Ms L. C. Wertheim, 1951, © the copyright holder

Hals, Frans (follower of) c.1581–1585–1666, *A Fisher Boy*, bequeathed by Mr and Mrs Edgar Assheton Bennett, 1979

Hammersley, James Astbury 1815–1869, *Mountains and Clouds – A Scene from the Top of Loughrigg, Westmoreland*, transferred from the Royal Manchester Institution, 1882

Hannot, Johannes (attributed to) 1633–1685, *Still Life: Fruit and Oysters on a Table*, bequeathed by

Mr and Mrs Edgar Assheton Bennett, 1979

Hardie, Gwen b.1962, *Me in Sea*, gift from the Contemporary Art Society, 1989, © the artist

Hardy, Heywood 1842–1933, *The Disputed Toll*, purchased from Wellington Antiques, 1990

Harlow, George Henry 1787–1819, *The Sisters*, bequeathed by Mr James Thomas Blair, 1917

Harmar, Fairlie 1876–1945, *Sarson Farm, Early Spring*, gift from Sir Thomas D. Barlow, 1923, © the copyright holder

Harmar, Fairlie 1876–1945, *St Giles, Oxford*, bequeathed by Mr Frank Stephens Rosser, 1957, © the copyright holder

Harpignies, Henri-Joseph 1819–1916, *The Winding River*, purchased from Thomas Agnew and Sons Ltd, 1920

Harpignies, Henri-Joseph 1819–1916, *The Castle of Clisson*, purchased from Charles Jackson, 1930

Harris, Albert *Barton Old Aqueduct and Bridge*, purchased from Nelson S. Miles, 1963

Haughton, Benjamin 1865–1924, *A Summer Morning*, gift from Mrs J. M. Haughton, 1927

Hawkins, Dennis 1925–2001, *Bus Pier, Putney*, bequeathed by Thomas Balston, 1968, © the copyright holder

Hawthorne, Elwin 1905–1954, *Church near Blackheath*, gift from the Contemporary Art Society, 1939, © the artist's estate

Hayden, Henri 1883–1970, *Pot a Tabac, Fond Bleu*, bequeathed by Lord Sidney Bernstein, 1995, © ADAGP, Paris and DACS, London 2013

Hayes, Frederick William 1848–1918, *Cnicht, Caernarvonshire*, gift from Gerald R. Hayes, 1921

Hayes, Frederick William 1848–1918, *On the Glaslyn River*, gift from Gerald R. Hayes, 1921

Hayes, George c.1823–1895, *The Visit of Queen Victoria and Prince Albert to Manchester in 1851*, gift from the City Treasurer, 1957

Haynes-Williams, John 1836–1908, *Spanish Dancer*, transferred from the Horsfall Museum Collection, 1918

Heck, Claes Jacobsz. van der (studio of) 1575/1581–1652, *Egmond-ann-Zee*, bequeathed by Mr and Mrs Edgar Assheton Bennett, 1979

Heemskerck, Maerten van 1498–1574, *Margaretha Banken*, purchased from C. Marshall Spink, 1958

Heeremans, Thomas c.1640–1697, *River Scene with a Ruined Tower on the Bank and Figures in Rowing Boats*, bequeathed by Mr and Mrs Edgar Assheton Bennett, 1979

Hemy, Charles Napier 1841–1917, *God's Houses, Maestricht*, gift from Mrs Mary Greg, 1919

Hemy, Charles Napier 1841–1917, *Old Putney Bridge*, purchased from the Autumn Exhibition, 1883

Henderson, Keith 1883–1982, *Loading Gantry for Pluto*, gift from W. T. Glover & Co. Ltd, 1945, © the copyright holder

Henderson, Keith 1883–1982, *A Garden in Cyprus*, gift from the artist, 1971, © the copyright holder

Henderson, Keith 1883–1982, *Cock of the North*, purchased from the artist, 1932, © the copyright holder

Henderson, Keith 1883–1982, *Gas Practice in a Hangar*, gift from HM Government, War Artists Advisory Committee, 1947, © the copyright holder

Henriques, Ethel Quixano 1868–1936, *February*, purchased from The Manchester Academy of Fine Arts Exhibition, 1930

Henriques, Ethel Quixano 1868–1936, *Field Flowers*, purchased from the artist, 1928

Henry, George 1858–1943, *Landscape with Rainbow*, gift from the Scottish Artists' Benevolent Association, 1945, © the copyright holder

Henry, James Levin 1855–1929, *Wensleydale*, gift from William Towle, 1908

Hepworth, Barbara 1903–1975, *Theatre Group No.3*, purchased from Messrs Reid and Lefevre, 1948, © Bowness, Hepworth estate

Herkomer, Hubert von 1849–1914, *Hard Times*, purchased from the artist, 1885

Herman, Josef 1911–2000, *Man Kneeling*, gift from the Leonard Cohen Fund, 1968, © estate of Josef Herman. All rights reserved, DACS 2013

Herman, Josef 1911–2000, *Potato Diggers*, purchased from Roland, Browse and Delbanco, 1954, © estate of Josef Herman. All rights reserved, DACS 2013

Herring I, John Frederick 1795–1865, *The Ascot Cup*, bequeathed by Mr and Mrs Edgar Assheton Bennett, 1979

Herring I, John Frederick 1795–1865, *Seed Time*, bequeathed by George Beatson Blair, 1947

Herring I, John Frederick 1795–1865, *Ducks by a Stream*, bequeathed by John Edward Yates, 1934

Hervier, Louis Adolphe 1818–1879, *A Farmyard*, purchased from Mr Charles A. Jackson, 1919

Hewit, Forrest 1870–1956, *Whangpoo River, Shanghai*, gift from the artist, 1938, © the copyright holder

Hewit, Forrest 1870–1956, *Beech Trees in the New Forest*, gift from the artist, 1930, © the copyright holder

Hewit, Forrest 1870–1956, *Boats at Menaggio*, gift from the artist, 1930, © the copyright holder

Hewland, Elsie Dalton 1901–1979, *Assembling a Hawker Hurricane*, gift from HM Government, War Artists Advisory Committee, 1947, © the copyright holder

Heyden, Jan van der 1637–1712, *A Street in Cologne with the Unfinished Cathedral in the Centre*, bequeathed by Mr and Mrs Edgar Assheton Bennett, 1979

Hicks, George Elgar 1824–1914, *Mother and Child*, bequeathed by Dr David Lloyd Roberts, 1920

Highmore, Joseph 1692–1780, *John Sidney, 6th Earl of Leicester*, purchased from Oscar and Peter Johnson Ltd, Lowdes Lodge Gallery, 1963

Highmore, Joseph 1692–1780, *Miss Taylor*, bequeathed by George Beatson Blair, 1947

Hilder, Richard H. 1813–1852, *Okehampton, Devon*, gift from Frederick John Nettlefold, 1948

Hill, James Stevens 1854–1921, *The Thames at Southwark*, purchased from the artist, 1905

Hillier, Tristram Paul 1905–1983, *Le Havre de Grace*, purchased from Arthur Tooth and Sons Ltd, 1946, © the artist's estate/Bridgeman Art Library

Hillier, Tristram Paul 1905–1983, *The War in Somerset*, purchased from the artist, 1943, © the artist's estate/Bridgeman Art Library

Hilton, Arthur Cyril 1897–1960, *Torsos in a Landscape*, gift from the artist, 1947, © the copyright holder

Hilton, Roger 1911–1975, *Untitled*, purchased from the Peterloo Gallery, 1967, © estate of Roger Hilton. All rights reserved, DACS 2013

Hilton II, William 1786–1839, *Phaeton*, transferred from the Royal Manchester Institution, 1882

Hitchens, Ivon 1893–1979, *Spring Woodland*, gift from the Contemporary Art Society, 1977, © Ivon Hitchens' estate/Jonathan Clark & Co.

Hitchens, Ivon 1893–1979, *Flowers in a Vase*, purchased from the Redfern Gallery, 1944, © Ivon Hitchens' estate/Jonathan Clark & Co.

Hitchens, Ivon 1893–1979, *Lavington Common*, purchased from Leicester Galleries, 1940, © Ivon Hitchens' estate/Jonathan Clark & Co.

Hoare, William (attributed to) 1707–1792, *Frances Rix*, bequeathed by Bernard William Blakely, 1950

Hobbema, Meindert (style of) 1638–1709, *Figures Halted at the Outskirts of a Wood, a Pool at the Right*, bequeathed by Mr and Mrs Edgar Assheton Bennett, 1979

Hockney, David b.1937, *Peter.C*, purchased at Sotheby's, 1985, © David Hockney

Hodges, William 1744–1797, *View of Calcutta*, gift from Sir Thomas D. Barlow, 1949

Hodgkin, Howard b.1932, *The Hopes at Home*, purchased from Kasmin Ltd, 1978, © Howard

Hodgkin

Hodgkins, Frances 1869–1947, *Cheviot Farm*, purchased from Messrs Reid and Lefevre, 1947, © the artist's estate

Hodgson, Louisa 1905–1980, *In Search of Peace*, purchased from the artist, 1936, © the copyright holder

Hogarth, William 1697–1764, *The Pool of Bethesda*, purchased from Mr R. B. Beckett, 1955

Hogarth, William 1697–1764, *Portrait of a Gentleman*, purchased from Mr Charles A. Jackson, 1928

Hoggatt, William 1879–1961, *Cregneish*, purchased from The Manchester Academy of Fine Arts Exhibition, 1937, © the copyright holder

Holden, Cliff b.1919, *Reclining Form 1*, purchased from the Crane Kalman Gallery, 1963, © the artist

Holland, James 1799–1870, *Lisbon from Porto Brandas*, purchased from Thomas Agnew and Sons Ltd, 1906

Holland, James 1799–1870, *Venice*, bequeathed by Mr James Thomas Blair, 1917

Holland, James 1799–1870, *Herne Bay, Kent*, bequeathed by Mr James Thomas Blair, 1917

Holmes, Charles John 1868–1936, *The Mythen, Switzerland*, gift from Charles Lambert Rutherston, 1925

Holmes, Charles John 1868–1936, *Biasca*, purchased from Thomas Agnew and Sons Ltd, 1909

Holmes, Charles John 1868–1936, *Keswick Mountains*, purchased from P. & D. Colnaghi & Co. Ltd, 1928

Holt, Edwin Frederick 1830–1912, *Clayton Hall*, gift from G. R. L. Sullivan, 1972

Hondecoeter, Melchior de (style of) 1636–1695, *Domestic Fowls and a Man*, gift from George Spiegelberg, 1910

Hone I, Nathaniel 1718–1784, *Self Portrait*, purchased from Thomas Agnew and Sons Ltd, 1928

Hooch, Pieter de 1629–1684, *Interior with a Gentleman and Two Ladies Conversing*, bequeathed by Mr and Mrs Edgar Assheton Bennett, 1979

Hooch, Pieter de (follower of) 1629–1684, *Interior with a Lady Seated, a Dog on Her Lap*, bequeathed by Mr and Mrs Edgar Assheton Bennett, 1979

Hoogstraten, Samuel van 1627–1678, *A Young Man Reaching for His Cap*, purchased from Lady Ravenscale, 1973

Hook, James Clarke 1819–1907, *The Defeat of Shylock*, bequeathed by Sir Joseph Whitworth, 1896

Hook, James Clarke 1819–1907, *From under the Sea*, purchased at Christie's, 1891

Hook, James Clarke 1819–1907, *Crabbers*, purchased from Thomas Agnew and Sons Ltd, 1904

Hooper, John Horace 1851–1906, *Early Morning Scene in Surrey*, gift

from T. Frank Southam, 1930

Hornel, Edward Atkinson 1864–1933, *Tom-Tom Players, Ceylon*, purchased from the artist, 1908

Horsley, John Callcott 1817–1903, *Coming Down to Dinner*, bequeathed by Henry Lee, 1905

Houbraken, Arnold 1660–1719, *Susannah and the Elders*, gift from Mrs E. F. Hickman, 1931

How, Julia Beatrice 1867–1932, *L'ombrelle bleu*, acquired, 1977

Howard, Ghislaine b.1953, *Newly Born Babe*, purchased from the artist, 1993, © the artist

Hoyland, Henry George 1895–1948, *Interval*, gift from the artist, 1939, © the artist's estate

Hoyland, John 1934–2011, *14.6.64*, purchased from Marlborough Fine Art Ltd, 1964, © Estate of John Hoyland. All rights reserved, DACS 2013

Hudson, Thomas 1701–1779, *John Sharp, Archdeacon of Durham*, gift from Thomas Thornhill Shann, 1901

Hughes, Arthur 1832–1915, *Ophelia*, purchased from J. Hingston, 1955

Hughes, Malcolm Edward 1920–1997, *Performers*, purchased from the Crane Gallery, 1950, © the artist's estate

Hughes-Stanton, Herbert Edwin Pelham 1870–1937, *Mons*, purchased from The Fine Art Society, 1919

Hunt, William Holman 1827–1910, *The Hireling Shepherd*, purchased from Tom Leathart, 1896

Hunt, William Holman 1827–1910, *The Light of the World*, purchased from M. Knoedler & Co., 1912

Hunt, William Holman 1827–1910, *The Scapegoat*, purchased from Thomas Agnew and Sons Ltd, 1906

Hunt, William Holman 1827–1910, *The Lantern-Maker's Courtship*, gift from Mr James Gresham, 1917

Hunt, William Holman 1827–1910, *The Shadow of Death*, gift from Thomas Agnew and Sons Ltd, 1883

Hunt, William Holman 1827–1910, *Study of a Head*, purchased from Leicester Galleries, 1920

Hunt, William Holman 1827–1910, *The Lady of Shalott*, bequeathed by John Edward Yates, 1934

Hunter, Colin 1841–1904, *The Herring Market at Sea (on Loch Fyne, Argyll)*, purchased from the Autumn Exhibition, 1884

Hunter, George Leslie 1879–1931, *Still Life*, purchased from the Lefevre Galleries, 1936

Hunter, Robert c.1715/1720–c.1803, *Mrs Margaret Bolton*, bequeathed by Miss Laetitia Satterthwaite, 1986

Hunter, Robert c.1715/1720–c.1803, *Theophilus Bolton*, bequeathed by Miss Laetitia Satterthwaite, 1986

Hunter, Robert c.1715/1720–c.1803, *Mrs Anna Maria Neynoe*, bequeathed by Miss Laetitia Satterthwaite, 1986

Hunter, Robert c.1715/1720–c.1803, *Mrs Laetitia Christina Sheridan*, bequeathed by Miss Laetitia Satterthwaite, 1986

Hurt, Louis Bosworth 1856–1929, *Scotch Cattle and Mist*, bequeathed by Mr James Thomas Blair, 1917

Huysum, Jan van 1682–1749, *Still Life: Flowers and Fruit*, bequeathed by Mr and Mrs Edgar Assheton Bennett, 1979

Ibbetson, Julius Caesar 1759–1817, *Ludlow Castle from Whitcliffe, Shropshire*, purchased from Leggatt Bros, 1928

Ibbetson, Julius Caesar 1759–1817, *Cave in St Catherine's Rock, Tenby, Pembrokeshire*, purchased from Shepherd Bros, 1902

Ibbetson, Julius Caesar 1759–1817, *The Gathering Storm*, gift from H. B. Wood, 1934

Ibbetson, Julius Caesar 1759–1817, *View of Llantrisant, Glamorganshire, from the Westward*, purchased from Shepherd Bros, 1903

Ihlee, Rudolf 1883–1968, *The Well*, gift from Charles Lambert Rutherston, 1925, © the copyright holder

Innes, James Dickson 1887–1914, *Bala Lake*, purchased from Arthur Tooth and Sons Ltd, 1934

Innes, James Dickson 1887–1914, *The Ring*, purchased from Mr Robert H. Jackson, 1934

Isabey, Eugène 1803–1886, *The Smithy*, purchased from Mr Charles A. Jackson, 1915

Italian School *Classical Landscape with a River*, gift from Lieutenant Colonel R. H. Antrobus, 1971

Italian School *Landscape with Abraham and Isaac*, gift from Paul King, 1931

Jackson, Frederick William 1859–1918, *A Flowery Bank*, gift from Mr Ian Pringle, 1979

Jackson, Frederick William 1859–1918, *Bread and Cheese*, gift from the Jackson Memorial Committee, 1918

Jackson, Frederick William 1859–1918, *Poplars, Montreuil-sur-Mer*, gift from the Jackson Memorial Committee, 1918

Jackson, Frederick William 1859–1918, *Runswick Bay*, bequeathed by George Beatson Blair, 1947

Jackson, Frederick William 1859–1918, *Shadows on the Snow*, gift from the Jackson Memorial Committee, 1918

Jackson, Frederick William 1859–1918, *The Back of Hinderwell*, gift from the Jackson Memorial Committee, 1918

Jackson, Frederick William

1859–1918, *The Path to Ellerby*, gift from the Jackson Memorial Committee, 1918

Jackson, Frederick William 1859–1918, *The Stream*, bequeathed by George Beatson Blair, 1947

Jackson, John 1778–1831, *Thomas Stothard (1755–1834), RA*, purchased from Shepherd Bros., 1909

Jacomb-Hood, George Percy 1857–1929, *Victor Cavendish Bentinck*, gift from Mrs H. K. Jacomb-Hood, 1935

Jacquet, Gustave Jean 1846–1909, *Head of a Girl*, bequeathed by John Edward Yates, 1934

Jacquet, Gustave Jean 1846–1909, *Meditation*, bequeathed by Mr James Thomas Blair, 1917

James, David 1834–1892, *The Tide Coming in, Gurnard's Head, Cornwall*, acquired, 1979

Jamesone, George c.1588–1644, *James Hamilton, 2nd Marquess of Hamilton* (after Daniel Mytens), bequeathed by George Beatson Blair, 1947

Janes, Norman 1892–1980, *Hampstead Ponds*, purchased from The Manchester Academy of Fine Arts Exhibition, 1939, © the artist's estate

Janssens van Ceulen, Cornelis 1593–1661, *Portrait of a Man* (believed to be Robert Tatton), purchased from the Parish of Ashton on Mersey, 2001

Jarman, Derek 1942–1994, *Queer*, purchased from Richard Salmon Ltd, 1992, © the estate of Derek Jarman

John, Augustus Edwin 1878–1961, *Signorina Estella*, purchased from the Goupil Gallery, 1923, © the artist's estate/Bridgeman Art Library

John, Augustus Edwin 1878–1961, *Merikli*, gift from Charles Lambert Rutherston, 1925, © the artist's estate/Bridgeman Art Library

John, Augustus Edwin 1878–1961, *Ardor*, gift from Charles Lambert Rutherston, 1925, © the artist's estate/Bridgeman Art Library

John, Augustus Edwin 1878–1961, *William Butler Yeats*, purchased from Leicester Galleries, 1928, © the artist's estate/Bridgeman Art Library

John, Augustus Edwin 1878–1961, *Dorelia in a Landscape*, purchased from Arthur Tooth and Sons Ltd, 1934, © the artist's estate/ Bridgeman Art Library

John, Augustus Edwin 1878–1961, *A Boy*, purchased from the Grosvenor Gallery, 1922, © the artist's estate/Bridgeman Art Library

John, Augustus Edwin 1878–1961, *Head of a Spanish Gypsy*, bequeathed by Miss Olive Pickstone, 1973, © the artist's estate/Bridgeman Art Library

John, Augustus Edwin 1878–1961, *Lady with a Mantilla*, bequeathed by George Beatson Blair, 1947, ©

the artist's estate/Bridgeman Art Library

John, Gwen 1876–1939, *The Student*, gift from Charles Lambert Rutherston, 1925

John, Gwen 1876–1939, *Interior*, gift from Charles Lambert Rutherston, 1925

John, Gwen 1876–1939, *The Letter*, gift from Charles Lambert Rutherston, 1925

John, Gwen 1876–1939, *Flowers*, gift from Mrs Essil Elmslie Rutherston, 1928

Jones, Charles 1836–1902, *Sheep in Snow*, transferred from the Horsfall Museum Collection, 1918

Jones, David 1895–1974, *Out Tide*, purchased from the Redfern Gallery, 1949, © trustees of the David Jones estate

Jongkind, Johan Barthold 1819–1891, *Le Boulevard Jourdan, Paris*, bequeathed by Lord Sidney Bernstein, 1995

Jopling, Louise 1843–1933, *Self Portrait*, gift from Percy G. Trendell, 1934

Jopling, Louise 1843–1933, *The Painter's Son*, gift from Mrs Joan Jopling, 1935

Kalf, Willem 1619–1693, *Still Life: Fruit, Goblet and Salver*, bequeathed by Mr and Mrs Edgar Assheton Bennett, 1979

Kauffmann, Angelica 1741–1807, *Ellis Cornelia Knight*, purchased from Thomas Agnew and Sons Ltd, 1901

Kelly, Gerald Festus 1879–1972, *Bishop James Edward Cowell Welldon*, gift from the Bishop Welldon Portrait Fund Committee, 1921, © the copyright holder

Kennedy, Charles Napier 1852–1898, *A Fair-Haired Slave Who Made Himself a King*, purchased from the artist, 1888

Key, Geoffrey b.1941, *Albert Square, Manchester*, purchased from Geoffrey Key, 1979, © the artist

Kidner, Michael 1917–2009, *Red, Yellow and Blue*, purchased from the artist, 1965, © the artist's estate/ courtesy Flowers Gallery, London

Kidner, Michael 1917–2009, *Untitled Sketch*, purchased from the artist, 1965, © the artist's estate/ courtesy Flowers Gallery, London

Kiesel, Conrad 1846–1921, *Marguerites*, bequeathed by Mr James Thomas Blair, 1917

Kilburne, George Goodwin 1839–1924, *On the Staircase*, bequeathed by Mr James Thomas Blair, 1917

King, Henry John Yeend 1855–1924, *Landscape*, bequeathed by Marcus S. Bles, 1932

King-Farlow, Hazel 1903–1995, *Unicorn*, purchased from the Cooling Galleries, 1937, © the artist's estate

King-Farlow, Hazel 1903–1995, *The Harbour*, gift from Hugo Guiler, 1939, © the artist's estate

King-Farlow, Hazel 1903–1995,

Powder Mill House, gift from the artist, 1939, © the artist's estate

Kingsley, Harry 1914–1998, *The Green Fence, Hulme*, gift from Harry Kingsley, 1965, © the copyright holder

Kirk, Eve 1900–1969, *Aix-en-Provence*, purchased from Arthur Tooth and Sons Ltd, 1938, © the copyright holder

Kirk, Janet 1884–1966, *Cranes*, purchased from The Manchester Academy of Fine Arts Exhibition, 1937, © the copyright holder

Klinghoffer, Clara 1900–1970, *Giuseppina*, purchased from the New English Art Club Exhibition, 1934, © the copyright holder

Kneller, Godfrey (follower of) 1646–1723, *James II (1633–1701)*, purchased from A. M. McNeill, 1961

Knight, Harold 1874–1961, *Sewing*, purchased from Leicester Galleries, 1925, © reproduced with permission of the estate of Dame Laura Knight, DBE, RA, 2012. All rights reserved

Knight, John William Buxton 1842/1843–1908, *Hop Garden*, bequeathed by George Beatson Blair, 1947

Knight, John William Buxton 1842/1843–1908, *The Hoppers*, gift from Ernest A. Knight, 1909

Knight, John William Buxton 1842/1843–1908, *Midday*, purchased from Leicester Galleries, 1908

Knight, John William Buxton 1842/1843–1908, *Evening*, bequeathed by Lady Mary Ann Boyd Dawkins, 1979

Knight, John William Buxton 1842/1843–1908, *The Mill, Basingstoke, Hampshire*, bequeathed by Lady Mary Ann Boyd Dawkins, 1979

Knight, John William Buxton 1842/1843–1908, *Tidal Breeze, Gosport, Hampshire*, purchased from Mr Charles A. Jackson, 1909

Knight, Joseph 1837–1909, *Lifting Mist*, purchased from the Autumn Exhibition, 1884

Knight, Joseph 1870–1952, *Chinese Pottery*, gift from the Royal Manchester Institution, 1932, © the copyright holder

Knight, Joseph 1837–1909, *A Welsh Hillside, 1883*, bequeathed by Miss H. W. Winterbottom, 1936

Knight, Laura 1877–1970, *Carnaval*, purchased from the Alpine Club Gallery, 1922, © reproduced with permission of the estate of Dame Laura Knight, DBE, RA, 2012. All rights reserved

Knox, Jack b.1936, *Studio 11.1.64*, purchased from the artist, 1965, © the artist

Knüpfer, Benes 1848–1910, *Arthur Wasse*, gift from the Trafalgar Galleries, 1983

Kohn, Elias active 1916–1968, *French Landscape*, gift from the Leonard Cohen Fund, 1968, © the copyright holder

Kohn, Elias active 1916–1968, *Israeli Landscape*, gift from the Leonard Cohen Fund, 1968, © the copyright holder

Kondracki, Henry b.1953, *Easter Evening*, purchased from the William Jackson Gallery, 1992, © the artist

Kondracki, Henry b.1953, *Sunday Night at the London Palladium (The Silent Ventriloquist)*, purchased from the William Jackson Gallery, 1993, © the artist

Koninck, Philips de 1619–1688, *Flat Landscape with a View to Distant Hills*, bequeathed by Mr and Mrs Edgar Assheton Bennett, 1979

Koninck, Philips de 1619–1688, *A Woman with a Glass of Wine and a Man Looking at Her*, bequeathed by Mr and Mrs Edgar Assheton Bennett, 1979

Kramer, Jacob 1892–1962, *Mrs Florence Moser*, gift from Charles Lambert Rutherston, 1925, © estate of John David Roberts. By courtesy of the William Roberts Society

Kynaston, Arthur 1876–1919, *A Moonlight Idyll*, gift from Thomas Gough, 1928

La Fosse, Charles de 1636–1716, *Apollo and Phaeton with the Seasons*, purchased from the Arcade Gallery, 1964

La Thangue, Henry Herbert 1859–1929, *Gathering Plums*, purchased from the artist, 1901

La Thangue, Henry Herbert 1859–1929, *A Provençal Fountain*, bequeathed by Mrs K. La Thangue, 1941

Lake, Gertrude 1858–1928, *Market Day, Concarneau*, purchased from Mr R. Bateman, 1923

Lamb, Henry 1883–1960, *The Lady with Lizards*, gift from the Contemporary Art Society, 1954, © estate of Henry Lamb

Lamb, Henry 1883–1960, *Francis Jones*, gift from Francis Jones, 1961, © estate of Henry Lamb

Lamb, Henry 1883–1960, *Advance Dressing Station on the Struma, 1916*, purchased from the artist, 1921, © estate of Henry Lamb

Lamb, Henry 1883–1960, *David John*, purchased from Mr Charles A. Jackson, 1947, © estate of Henry Lamb

Lamb, Henry 1883–1960, *Darsie Japp and Family*, gift from G. B. Alexander, 1928, © estate of Henry Lamb

Lamb, Henry 1883–1960, *The Yellow Jumper*, gift from Mrs W. B. Dalton and Miss E. M. Plummer, 1931, © estate of Henry Lamb

Lamb, Henry 1883–1960, *An Officer of the Foreign Legion*, gift from HM Government, War Artists Advisory Committee, 1947, © estate of Henry Lamb

Lamb, Henry 1883–1960, *Lawrence Haward (1878–1957)*, gift from friends, 1945, © estate of Henry Lamb

Lamb, Henry 1883–1960, *Teas*, gift

from HM Government, War Artists Advisory Committee, 1947, © estate of Henry Lamb

Lamb, Henry 1883–1960, *Margaret Ashton*, gift from Manchester University Women's Union, 1979, © estate of Henry Lamb

Lambert, George c.1700–1765, *Classical Landscape*, purchased from C. Marshall Spink, 1960

Lander, John Saint-Helier 1869–1944, *HRH Edward, Prince of Wales*, gift from the 'Illustrated London News', 1924, © the copyright holder

Landseer, Edwin Henry 1802–1873, *On the Tilt, Perthshire*, bequeathed by Dr David Lloyd Roberts, 1920

Landseer, Edwin Henry 1802–1873, *Bolton Abbey, Yorkshire*, bequeathed by Dr David Lloyd Roberts, 1920

Landseer, Edwin Henry 1802–1873, *The Desert*, gift from Sir William Bart Agnew, 1902

Lanyon, Peter 1918–1964, *Silent Coast*, purchased from Gimpel Fils Collection, 1978, © Sheila Lanyon. All rights reserved, DACS 2013

Lanyon, Peter 1918–1964, *Built up Coast*, purchased from Mrs Sheila Lanyon, 1978, © Sheila Lanyon. All rights reserved, DACS 2013

Larcher, Dorothy 1884–1952, *White Centaureas*, purchased from the Manchester Society of Modern Painters and Society of Wood Engravers, 1945, © Craft Study Centre, University for the Creative Arts

Larcher, Dorothy 1884–1952, *Black and White Pansies*, purchased from the artist, 1941, © Craft Study Centre, University for the Creative Arts

Lascaux, Elie 1888–1969, *Les vignes sous la neige*, bequeathed by Miss Dorothy Pilkington, 1974, © ADAGP, Paris and DACS, London 2013

László, Philip Alexius de 1869–1937, *Sir Thomas Gardner Horridge (1857–1938)*, bequeathed by Lady Horridge, 1942

Lavery, Hazel 1880–1935, *George Bernard Shaw (1856–1950)*, purchased from Leicester Galleries, 1942

Lavery, John 1856–1941, *Violet and Gold (L'Entente Cordiale)*, purchased from Thomas Agnew and Sons Ltd, 1906

Lavery, John 1856–1941, *The Lady in White*, bequeathed by George Beatson Blair, 1947

Lawrence, Thomas 1769–1830, *James Curtis*, purchased from Thomas Agnew and Sons Ltd, 1953

Lawrence, Thomas (after) 1769–1830, *Sir Robert Peel (1750–1830), 1st Bt*, gift from the Manchester Royal Exchange, 1968

Lawrence, Thomas (follower of) 1769–1830, *Colonel Thomas Stanley*, gift from the Manchester Royal Exchange, 1968

Lawson, Cecil Gordon 1851–1882,

'Twixt Sun and Moon, purchased at Christie's, 1907

Lawson, Cecil Gordon 1851–1882, *The Minister's Garden*, purchased from Grosvenor Galleries, 1883

Lawson, Cecil Gordon 1851–1882, *Landscape*, purchased from Charles Jackson, 1948

Le Jeune, Henry 1819–1904, *Children with a Toy Boat*, bequeathed by Sir Joseph Whitworth, 1896

Le Jeune, Henry 1819–1904, *The Timid Bather*, bequeathed by John Edward Yates, 1934

Le Sidaner, Henri Eugène 1862–1939, *Courtyard from a Window*, purchased from the Goupil Gallery, 1929

Leader, Benjamin Williams 1831–1923, *Stepping Stones*, bequeathed by John Edward Yates, 1934

Leader, Benjamin Williams 1831–1923, *February Fill Dyke*, bequeathed by John Edward Yates, 1934

Leader, Benjamin Williams 1831–1923, *Stratford-on-Avon Church and Lock*, gift from the family of Emil Reiss, 1913

Leader, Benjamin Williams 1831–1923, *The Building of the Manchester Ship Canal*, purchased at Christie's, 1991

Leader, Benjamin Williams 1831–1923, *Shere Church, Surrey*, bequeathed by John Edward Yates, 1934

Leader, Benjamin Williams 1831–1923, *Green Pastures and Still Waters*, bequeathed by Mr James Thomas Blair, 1917

Leader, Benjamin Williams 1831–1923, *Sunset on the Severn*, bequeathed by Mr James Thomas Blair, 1917

Leader, Benjamin Williams 1831–1923, *At Evening Time It Shall Be Light*, bequeathed by John Edward Yates, 1934

Leader, Benjamin Williams 1831–1923, *On the Severn below Worcester*, bequeathed by Mr James Thomas Blair, 1917

Leader, Benjamin Williams 1831–1923, *The Breezy Morn*, bequeathed by Herbert Morgan, 1935

Leader, Benjamin Williams 1831–1923, *Goring Church on the Thames*, bequeathed by Mr James Thomas Blair, 1917

Leader, Benjamin Williams 1831–1923, *Evening's Last Gleam*, bequeathed by Mr James Thomas Blair, 1917

Leapman, Edwina b.1931, *Untitled 1989*, gift from the Contemporary Art Society, 1992, © the artist

Lear, Edward 1812–1888, *View in the Campagna, Rome (with a River)*, gift from Dorothy Palairet, 1988

Lear, Edward 1812–1888, *View in the Campagna, Rome (with Ruins)*, gift from Dorothy Palairet, 1988

Lee, Sydney 1866–1949, *Malham*

Cove, gift from the artist, 1929, © the copyright holder

Lee, Sydney 1866–1949, *The Top of the Pass*, purchased from the Royal Academy of Arts, 1924, © the copyright holder

Leech, Beatrice Mary Seccombe 1880–1945, *Rome, from The Pincio, Piazza Del Popolo, 1933*, purchased from The Manchester Academy of Fine Arts, 1934, © the copyright holder

Lee-Hankey, William 1869–1952, *Fish Market, Dieppe*, gift from Mrs Duxbury, 1944, © the copyright holder

Leeming, Matthew Rodway 1875–1956, *William Batho*, gift from Mrs Hilda Thompson, 1985, © the copyright holder

Lees, Derwent 1885–1931, *The Blue Pool*, purchased from the Redfern Gallery, 1930

Lees, Derwent 1885–1931, *Lyndra by the Pool*, purchased from Mr Robert H. Jackson, 1937

Lees, Derwent 1885–1931, *A Woodland Idyll*, purchased from Mr Robert H. Jackson, 1933

Léger, Fernand 1881–1955, *Painting*, purchased from the Zwemmer Gallery, 1949, © ADAGP, Paris and DACS, London 2013

Legros, Alphonse 1837–1911, *Study of a Head*, gift from the artist, 1879

Legros, Alphonse 1837–1911, *Study of a Head*, transferred from the Royal Manchester Institution, 1882

Legros, Alphonse 1837–1911, *Head of an Old Man*, gift from Guy Knowles, 1933

Legros, Alphonse 1837–1911, *Saint Jerome*, transferred from the Royal Manchester Institution, 1882

Legros, Alphonse 1837–1911, *Study of a Head*, transferred from the Royal Manchester Institution, 1882

Leighton, Edmund Blair 1852–1922, *Waiting for the Coach*, bequeathed by Mr James Thomas Blair, 1917

Leighton, Edmund Blair 1852–1922, *'Off'*, bequeathed by Mr James Thomas Blair, 1917

Leighton, Edmund Blair 1852–1922, *On the Threshold*, bequeathed by Mr James Thomas Blair, 1917

Leighton, Edmund Blair 1852–1922, *Adieu*, bequeathed by Mr James Thomas Blair, 1917

Leighton, Frederic 1830–1896, *A Roman Peasant Girl*, bequeathed by Mr James Thomas Blair, 1917

Leighton, Frederic 1830–1896, *The Isle of Chios*, gift from Mrs Beatrix Heelis, 1933

Leighton, Frederic 1830–1896, *The Temple of Philae*, bequeathed by John Edward Yates, 1934

Leighton, Frederic 1830–1896, *The Last Watch of Hero*, purchased from the artist, 1887

Leighton, Frederic 1830–1896,

Captive Andromache, purchased from the artist, 1889

Lely, Peter 1618–1680, *Sir John Cotton and His Family*, purchased from P. & D. Colnaghi & Co. Ltd, 1966

Lely, Peter (attributed to) 1618–1680, *Lady Whitmore*, purchased from Messrs Shepherd Bros, 1901

Lely, Peter (follower of) 1618–1680, *Raphe Worsley of Platt Hall, Manchester*, purchased from Air Commodore Geoffrey Tindall-Carill-Worsley, 1976

Lely, Peter (follower of) 1618–1680, *Sir William Godolphin*, bequeathed by Mr James Thomas Blair, 1917

Lely, Peter (follower of) 1618–1680, *A Lady Holding a Rose*, gift from A. B. Ireland, 1952

Leslie, George Dunlop 1835–1921, *The Language of Flowers*, purchased from Thomas Agnew and Sons Ltd, 1900

Lessore, Thérèse 1884–1945, *Victoria Park – 'Let's Go Home Sis!'*, gift from the 'Sickert Trust', 1946, © Henry and John Lessore

Lessore, Thérèse 1884–1945, *My Little Piccaninny*, gift from the Contemporary Art Society, 1977, © Henry and John Lessore

Levy, Emmanuel 1900–1986, *Ursula in a Red Scarf*, purchased from the artist, 1953, © the copyright holder

Lewis, Edward Morland 1903–1943, *Beach Scene*, purchased from Messrs Wildenstein & Co., 1938, © the artist's estate

Lewis, John active 1736–1776, *Miss Anne Bolton*, bequeathed by Miss Laetitia Satterthwaite, 1986

Lewis, John Frederick 1804–1876, *The Coffee Bearer*, purchased from Thomas Agnew and Sons Ltd, 1976

Lewis, Neville 1895–1972, *A Barotse Woman*, purchased from the Goupil Gallery, 1929, © the copyright holder

Lewis, Wyndham 1882–1957, *Self Portrait*, gift from Charles Lambert Rutherston, 1925, © by kind permission of the Wyndham Lewis Memorial Trust (a registered charity)

Lhermitte, Léon-Augustin 1844–1925, *A Flood*, bequeathed by George Beatson Blair, 1947

Liedts, Abraham c.1604–1668, *A Lady with Gloves*, bequeathed by George Beatson Blair, 1947

Lingelbach, Johannes 1622–1674, *A Party of Falconers outside the Gates of a Château*, bequeathed by Mr and Mrs Edgar Assheton Bennett, 1979

Linnell, John 1792–1882, *Hampstead Heath*, bequeathed by Mr James Thomas Blair, 1947

Linnell, John 1792–1882, *Mid-Day Rest*, bequeathed by John Edward Yates, 1934

Linnell, John 1792–1882, *Leith Hill, Surrey*, purchased from Thomas Agnew and Sons Ltd, 1900

Liverseege, Henry 1803–1832, *The Betrothed*, purchased from Samuel Hoyle, 1912

Liverseege, Henry 1803–1832, *Sir Piercie Shafton and Mysie Happer*, purchased from Charles Jackson, 1912

Liverseege, Henry 1803–1832, *The Grave Diggers*, purchased from W. J. Newton Butler, 1903

Liverseege, Henry 1803–1832, *A Touch of the Spasms*, purchased from Charles Jackson, 1912

Liverseege, Henry 1803–1832, *Shakespearian Scene*, gift from the Patrons & Associates of Manchester City Art Gallery (PAMCAG), 1983

Liverseege, Henry 1803–1832, *The Conversation* (sketch for 'The Story of My Life'), gift from PAMCAG, 1983

Loiseau, Gustave 1865–1935, *The Seine near Port-Marly*, purchased from Durand Ruel and Sons, 1908

Lomax, John Arthur 1857–1923, *News of the Army*, bequeathed by Mr James Thomas Blair, 1917

Lomax, John Arthur 1857–1923, *'Old birds are not caught by chaff'*, bequeathed by Mr James Thomas Blair, 1917

Lorrain, Claude 1604–1682, *The Adoration of the Golden Calf*, purchased from Walter Morrison Picture Settlement, 1981

Lowry, Laurence Stephen 1887–1976, *An Accident*, purchased from the Six Manchester Art Clubs Exhibition, 1930, © the estate of L. S. Lowry. All rights reserved, DACS 2013

Lowry, Laurence Stephen 1887–1976, *Coming Home from the Mill*, bequeathed by George Spiegelberg, 1962, © the estate of L. S. Lowry. All rights reserved, DACS 2013

Lowry, Laurence Stephen 1887–1976, *An Organ Grinder*, purchased from The Manchester Academy of Fine Arts, 1936, © the estate of L. S. Lowry. All rights reserved, DACS 2013

Lowry, Laurence Stephen 1887–1976, *Laying a Foundation Stone*, gift from the Royal Manchester Institution, 1940, © the estate of L. S. Lowry. All rights reserved, DACS 2013

Lowry, Laurence Stephen 1887–1976, *St John's Church, Manchester*, purchased from Reverend Geoffrey S. Bennett, 1987, © the estate of L. S. Lowry. All rights reserved, DACS 2013

Lowry, Laurence Stephen 1887–1976, *An Island*, purchased from Mid-Day Studios, 1948, © the estate of L. S. Lowry. All rights reserved, DACS 2013

Lowry, Laurence Stephen 1887–1976, *Waiting for the Shop to Open*, purchased from Mid-Day Studios, 1948, © the estate of L. S. Lowry. All rights reserved, DACS 2013

Lowry, Laurence Stephen

1887–1976, *St Augustine's Church, Manchester*, gift from HM Government, War Artists Advisory Committee, 1947, © the estate of L. S. Lowry. All rights reserved, DACS 2013

Lowry, Laurence Stephen 1887–1976, *Street in Pendlebury*, bequeathed by Lord Sidney Bernstein, 1995, © the estate of L. S. Lowry. All rights reserved, DACS 2013

Lowry, Laurence Stephen 1887–1976, *The Mid-Day Studios*, purchased from Pat M. Owens, 2005, © the estate of L. S. Lowry. All rights reserved, DACS 2013

Lowry, Laurence Stephen 1887–1976, *Piccadilly Gardens*, gift from Leonard Cohen & Henry's Stores Ltd, 1956, © the estate of L. S. Lowry. All rights reserved, DACS 2013

Lucas, Caroline Byng c.1886–1967, *A Bouquet of Wild Flowers*, purchased from Leicester Galleries, 1939, © the copyright holder

Luxmoore, Myra E. 1851–1919, *The Very Reverend Edward C. Maclure*, gift from the daughters of the sitter, 1906

Luyten-Behnisch, Jadwiga 1873–1963, *Plums*, purchased from the artist, 1928, © the copyright holder

Lynch, Albert 1851–1912, *Head of a Girl*, bequeathed by Mr James Thomas Blair, 1917

Macallum, John Thomas Hamilton 1841–1896, *Dipping for Sprats*, purchased from Mrs Effie H. Macallum, 1899

Macbeth, Robert Walker 1848–1910, *Osier Peeling on the Cam*, bequeathed by Mrs Annie Woodhouse, 1940

MacBryde, Robert 1913–1966, *Woman with Cantaloupe*, gift from the Contemporary Art Society, 1950, © the copyright holder

MacBryde, Robert 1913–1966, *Still Life with Fish Head*, purchased from Messrs Reid and Lefevre, 1947, © the copyright holder

MacCallum, Andrew 1821–1902, *The River of Life: Birth*, gift from Mrs Thomas Worthington, 1933

MacCallum, Andrew 1821–1902, *The River of Life: Death*, gift from Mrs Thomas Worthington, 1933

MacCallum, Andrew 1821–1902, *The River of Life: Decline*, gift from Mrs Thomas Worthington, 1933

MacCallum, Andrew 1821–1902, *The River of Life: Manhood*, gift from Mrs Thomas Worthington, 1933

MacCallum, Andrew 1821–1902, *The River of Life: Youth*, gift from Mrs Thomas Worthington, 1933

MacCallum, Andrew 1821–1902, *Oak Trees in Sherwood Forest*, transferred from the Horsfall Museum Collection, 1918

MacColl, Dugald Sutherland 1859–1948, *Augustus John at Ambleteuse, 1907*, purchased from the New English Art Club, 1943, ©

the artist's estate

MacDougall, William Brown 1869–1936, *Water Frolic, Barton Broad*, gift from Mrs Margaret MacDougall and Mrs Agnes Watson, 1936

MacKinnon, Sine 1901–1996, *The 'Concepcion' in the Harbour, St Tropez*, gift from G. D. Hornblower, 1946, © the copyright holder

MacKinnon, Sine 1901–1996, *Flowers against the Sea*, purchased from Arthur Tooth and Sons Ltd, 1940, © the copyright holder

MacKinnon, Sine 1901–1996, *Fishing Boat*, purchased from the Artists of Today exhibition, 1937, © the copyright holder

Maclise, Daniel 1806–1870, *The Origin of the Harp*, gift from Mr James Gresham, 1917

Maclise, Daniel 1806–1870, *A Winter Night's Tale*, bequeathed by Mrs A. Enriqueta Rylands, 1908

Macnee, Daniel 1806–1882, *William Gibb, JP*, gift from the Manchester Royal Exchange, 1968

MacWhirter, John 1839–1911, *Constantinople and the Golden Horn from Eyoub*, gift from Frederick Smallman, 1908

MacWhirter, John 1839–1911, *The Lady of the Woods*, bequeathed by Jesse Haworth, 1937

MacWhirter, John 1839–1911, *Autumn in the Highlands*, bequeathed by John Edward Yates, 1934

Magnus, Emma 1856–1936, *Refreshments*, purchased from the artist, 1926

Magnus, Rose 1859–1900, *A Bunch of Thistles*, gift from the executors of Emma Magnus, 1936

Maidment, Thomas 1871–1952, *The Old Harbour, St Ives*, purchased from the Artists of Today exhibition, 1937, © the copyright holder

Major, Theodore 1908–1999, *Head Study*, purchased from Mid-Day Studios, 1948, © the artist's estate

Manson, James Bolivar 1879–1945, *Summer Flowers*, gift from Charles Lambert Rutherston, 1925, © the artist's estate

Manson, James Bolivar 1879–1945, *Antibes*, purchased from Messrs Wallis and Son, 1929, © the artist's estate

Manson, James Bolivar 1879–1945, *Lucien Pissarro*, purchased from the artist, 1941, © the artist's estate

Marchand, Jean Hippolyte 1883–1941, *French Village*, bequeathed by Frank Hindley Smith, 1940

Marchand, Jean Hippolyte 1883–1941, *Olive Trees, Vence*, gift from Charles Lambert Rutherston, 1925

Marchand, Jean Hippolyte 1883–1941, *Portrait of a Lady*, gift from Mrs Archibald, 1937

Marchand, Jean Hippolyte 1883–1941, *The Lady in Brown*, gift

from Charles Lambert Rutherston, 1925

Marcoussis, Louis 1878/1883–1941, *Still Life*, purchased from Roland, Browse and Delbanco, 1951

Maris, Jacob Henricus 1837–1899, *In the Garden*, purchased from Mr Charles A. Jackson, 1911

Maris, Jacob Henricus 1837–1899, *The Gathering Storm*, gift from the National Art Collections Fund, 1927

Maris, Willem 1844–1910, *Cows at Pasture*, bequeathed by George Beatson Blair, 1947

Marks, Edmund active 1837–1875, *Deal Beach*, gift from Mrs L. Campbell Clay, 1907

Marks, Edmund active 1837–1875, *On Brighton Beach*, gift from Mrs L. Campbell Clay, 1907

Marks, Henry Stacy 1829–1898, *South African Crowned Cranes*, gift, 1920

Marlow, William 1740–1813, *Matlock, Derbyshire*, purchased from Thomas Agnew and Sons Ltd, 1938

Marlow, William 1740–1813, *View in Lyons*, purchased from G. P. Dudley Wallis, 1932

Martin, Benito Quinquela 1890–1977, *Morning Sun, Buenos Aires*, gift from Sir Joseph Duveen, 1931, © the copyright holder

Martineau, Robert Braithwaite 1826–1869, *A Lady with a Gold Chain and Earrings*, purchased from Fulda Galleries, 1985

Martineau, Robert Braithwaite 1826–1869, *Study for a Woman of San Germano*, bequeathed by Miss Helen Martineau, 1951

Martineau, Robert Braithwaite 1826–1869, *The Artist's Wife in a Red Cape*, bequeathed by Miss Helen Martineau, 1951

Mason, Arnold 1885–1963, *Head of a Girl*, gift from Sir Thomas D. Barlow, 1940, © the artist's estate

Mason, Bateson 1910–1977, *Landscape*, gift from Mrs Hazel King-Farlow, 1936, © the copyright holder

Mason, Bateson 1910–1977, *Great Gable and Wastwater*, gift from Mrs Hazel King-Farlow, 1938, © the copyright holder

Mason, George Heming 1818–1872, *Landscape – Derbyshire*, purchased at Christie's, 1908

Mason, George Heming 1818–1872, *Only a Shower*, purchased from Thomas Agnew and Sons Ltd, 1911

Master of Frankfurt 1460–c.1533, *Saint Catherine and Saint Barbara with Donors* (diptych), purchased from the National Art Collections Fund, 1957

Master of the Magdalen Legend c.1483–c.1530, *Virgin and Child*, gift from Henry Boddington, 1911

Matteo di Giovanni (school of) c.1430–1495, *The Crucifixion*, purchased from Leo Franklyn, 1951

Maufra, Maxime 1861–1918, *Springtime at Lavardin (Touraine)*, gift from Durand Ruel and Sons, 1908

Mayer, William Edgar 1910–2002, *Square Forms*, purchased from the artist, 1959, © the copyright holder

Mayor, William Frederick 1865–1916, *Paris Plage*, purchased from Mrs Mayor, 1934

Maze, Paul Lucien 1887–1979, *Villefranche*, bequeathed by Dr Jane Walker, CH, LLD, 1939, © the artist's estate

McCannell, Ursula Vivian b.1923, *Self Portrait*, gift from the Contemporary Art Society, 1942, © the artist

McEvoy, Ambrose 1878–1927, *Silver and Grey*, purchased from the Chenil Galleries, 1925

McEvoy, Ambrose 1878–1927, *Miss Teddy Gerrard*, bequeathed by George Beatson Blair, 1947

McEvoy, Ambrose 1878–1927, *Head of a Girl*, bequeathed by George Beatson Blair, 1947

McFadyen, Jock b.1950, *Waiting for the Cortina Boys*, purchased from Blond Fine Art, 1986, © the artist

McFadyen, Jock b.1950, *New York, New York*, acquired, 2002, © the artist

McFadyen, Jock b.1950, *Canal* (diptych, left panel), purchased from the William Jackson Gallery, 1991, © the artist

McFadyen, Jock b.1950, *Canal* (diptych, right panel), purchased from the William Jackson Gallery, 1991, © the artist

McGlynn, Terry 1903–1973, *Ponte Tresa, Lugano, Switzerland*, purchased from the artist, 1954, © the copyright holder

McGlynn, Terry 1903–1973, *Interior with Two Figures, No.2*, 1966, purchased from the artist, 1966, © the copyright holder

McGlynn, Terry 1903–1973, *Chartres*, purchased from the artist, 1954, © the copyright holder

McGlynn, Terry 1903–1973, *Place de Furstenberg, Paris*, purchased from the artist, 1956, © the copyright holder

McKenna, Stephen b.1939, *Still Life of the Sea*, gift from the Contemporary Art Society, 1986, © the artist

Measham, Henry 1844–1922, *The Artist's Mother*, gift from Richard Redfern, 1907

Medley, Robert 1905–1994, *An ARP Demonstration*, gift from HM Government, War Artists Advisory Committee, 1947, © the estate of Robert Medley, courtesy of James Hyman Gallery, London

Medley, Robert 1905–1994, *Gate Duty*, gift from HM Government, War Artists Advisory Committee, 1947, © the estate of Robert Medley, courtesy of James Hyman Gallery, London

Meissonier, Jean Louis Ernest 1815–1891, *A General Officer*,

bequeathed by Mr and Mrs Edgar Assheton Bennett, 1979

Meissonier, Jean Louis Ernest 1815–1891, *Advance Guard of an Army*, bequeathed by Mr and Mrs Edgar Assheton Bennett, 1979

Melcarth, Edward 1914–1973, *Dinner Time*, gift from Mrs Hazel King-Farlow, 1938, © the copyright holder

Melland, Sylvia 1906–1993, *Outpatients, Manchester Royal Infirmary*, gift from David Melland, 1997, © the copyright holder

Melland, Sylvia 1906–1993, *Back Street, Manchester*, gift from David Melland, 1997, © the copyright holder

Melland, Sylvia 1906–1993, *Martello Tower*, gift from David Melland, 1997, © the copyright holder

Melland, Sylvia 1906–1993, *Military Canal*, gift from David Melland, 1997, © the copyright holder

Mengin, Auguste Charles 1853–1933, *Sappho*, gift from Thomas James Lloyd, 1884

Mengs, Anton Raphael 1728–1779, *Saint Eusebius Carried to Heaven*, purchased from the Alfred Brod Gallery, 1966

Meredith, William 1851–1916, *Homewards, Conway Marsh*, purchased from the Autumn Exhibition, 1884

Messent, Charles 1911–1977, *Road through a French Village*, gift from Mrs Charles Messent, 1976, © the copyright holder

Methuen, Paul Ayshford 1886–1974, *Helford River, 1944, with Training Ship*, gift from HM Government, War Artists Advisory Committee, 1947, © trustees of the Corsham estate

Metsu, Gabriel (after) 1629–1667, *A Woman Seated Smoking a Pipe* (copy of an original), bequeathed by Mr and Mrs Edgar Assheton Bennett, 1979

Michau, Theobald 1676–1765, *Farmyard Scene: Reaping*, bequeathed by Mr and Mrs Edgar Assheton Bennett, 1979

Michau, Theobald 1676–1765, *Farmyard Scene: The Vintage*, bequeathed by Mr and Mrs Edgar Assheton Bennett, 1979

Michel, Georges 1763–1843, *Landscape*, purchased from Leicester Galleries, 1958

Middleditch, Edward 1923–1987, *Sheffield Weir*, purchased from the artist, 1955, © the estate of Edward Middleditch, courtesy James Hyman Gallery, London

Miereveld, Michiel Jansz. van 1567–1641, *Portrait of a Lady, Aged 58*, bequeathed by George Beatson Blair, 1947

Miereveld, Michiel Jansz. van (after) 1567–1641, *Lubbert Gerritsz.*, bequeathed by Mrs M. E. Gaskell, 1914

Mieris, Willem van 1662–1747, *A*

Lady Seated Holding a Small Dog, bequeathed by Mr and Mrs Edgar Assheton Bennett, 1979

Mieris, Willem van 1662–1747, *Interior with a Cavalier and Lady*, bequeathed by Mr and Mrs Edgar Assheton Bennett, 1979

Millais, John Everett 1829–1896, *The Death of Romeo and Juliet*, bequeathed by George Beatson Blair, 1947

Millais, John Everett 1829–1896, *Wandering Thoughts*, purchased from Mr Charles A. Jackson, 1913

Millais, John Everett 1829–1896, *Autumn Leaves*, purchased from James Leathart, 1892

Millais, John Everett 1829–1896, *Only a Lock of Hair*, gift from Mr James Gresham, 1917

Millais, John Everett 1829–1896, *Stella*, purchased at Christie's, 1908

Millais, John Everett 1829–1896, *A Flood*, purchased from Thomas Agnew and Sons Ltd, 1891

Millais, John Everett 1829–1896, *Victory O Lord*, purchased from the executors of the will of Mrs James Reiss, 1894

Millais, John Everett 1829–1896, *Winter Fuel*, gift from Gibbon Bayley Worthington, 1897

Millais, John Everett 1829–1896, *Mrs Leopold Reiss*, gift from Mrs Everard Hopkins, 1932

Millais, John Everett 1829–1896, *James Fraser*, transferred from the Town Hall, 1979

Millais, John Everett 1829–1896, *Glen Birnam*, bequeathed by Mrs A. Enriqueta Rylands, 1908

Miller, William Ongley 1883–1960, *The Artist's Daughter*, purchased from The Manchester Academy of Fine Arts Exhibition, 1930, © the copyright holder

Millet, Jean-François (style of) 1814–1875, *Peasant Girl*, purchased from Mr Charles A. Jackson, 1919

Milne, Malcolm Midwood 1887–1954, *Autumn Flowers*, purchased from The Manchester Academy of Fine Arts Exhibition, 1937, © the copyright holder

Milne, Malcolm Midwood 1887–1954, *The Hundred Flowers*, gift from W. A. Propert, 1938, © the copyright holder

Mitchell, John Campbell 1862–1922, *At the Close of Day*, bequeathed by Lady Mary Ann Boyd Dawkins, 1979

Modigliani, Amedeo 1884–1920, *Portrait of an Unknown Model*, bequeathed by Lord Sidney Bernstein, 1995

Molenaer, Jan Miense c.1610–1668, *Interior with Peasants and School Children*, bequeathed by Mr and Mrs Edgar Assheton Bennett, 1979

Molenaer, Klaes c.1630–1676, *Skating Scene: Figures on the Ice near the Walls of a Town*, bequeathed by Mr and Mrs Edgar Assheton Bennett, 1979

Monks, John Christopher b.1954, *The Chandelier*, purchased from

the Paton Gallery, 1991, © the artist

Monnington, Walter Thomas 1902–1976, *The Holy Family* (unfinished), gift from the Contemporary Art Society, 1954, © the artist's estate

Monnington, Walter Thomas 1902–1976, *Battle Area, 15,000ft*, gift from HM Government, War Artists Advisory Committee, 1947, © the artist's estate

Monti, Francesco 1685–1768, *Moses and the Daughters of Jethro*, gift from Dr Mercier Gamble, 1928

Monticelli, Adolphe Joseph Thomas 1824–1886, *A Woodland Glade*, purchased from Mr Charles A. Jackson, 1910

Monticelli, Adolphe Joseph Thomas 1824–1886, *Ladies on a Terrace*, purchased from E. J. van Wisselingh and Co., 1931

Mooney, Edward Hartley 1877–1938, *Still Life*, gift from Victor P. Whittaker, 2010

Mooney, Edward Hartley 1877–1938, *Still Life*, purchased from the Anthenaeum Graphic Club Exhibition, 1920

Mooney, Edward Hartley 1877–1938, *Anemones*, purchased from the artist, 1925

Moore, Albert Joseph 1841–1893, *A Reader*, bequeathed by John Edward Yates, 1934

Moore, Albert Joseph 1841–1893, *Birds of the Air*, bequeathed by John Edward Yates, 1934

Moore, Albert Joseph 1841–1893, *A Garland*, gift from Mr James Gresham, 1917

Moore, Albert Joseph 1841–1893, *A Footpath*, bequeathed by Mr James Thomas Blair, 1917

Moore, Albert Joseph 1841–1893, *An Idyll*, bequeathed by Mr James Thomas Blair, 1917

Moore, Alfred Harvey 1843–1905, *The Thames off Yantlett Creek, Kent*, gift from Mrs L. Campbell Clay, 1907

Moore, Henry 1831–1895, *Cattle Fording a Stream*, transferred from the Horsfall Museum Collection, 1918

Moore, Henry 1831–1895, *Mount's Bay: Early Morning – Summer*, purchased from Thomas Agnew and Sons Ltd, 1886

Moore, Henry 1831–1895, *Arran (Across Kilbrannan Sound)*, bequeathed by Mrs Annie Woodhouse, 1940

Moret, Henry 1856–1913, *Fishing Boats at Douelan*, gift from Durand Ruel and Sons, 1908

Morgenstern, Christian Ernst Bernhard 1805–1867, *Bavarian Highlands*, bequeathed by Henry F. Kessler, 1927

Morland, George 1763–1804, *A Farrier's Shop*, transferred from the Royal Manchester Institution, 1882

Morland, Henry Robert c.1716–1797, *Portrait of an Officer of the Foot Guards*, purchased from Mr Charles A. Jackson, 1928

Morris, Cedric Lockwood 1889–1982 *(George) Loraine Conran (1912–1986)*, gift from friends, 1976, © trustees of the Cedric Lockwood Morris Estate/ Foundation

Morris, Charles Greville 1861–1922, *Marshland*, gift from Mr Walter Hill, 1909

Morris, Philip Richard 1836–1902, *Daniel Adamson*, gift from Lady Alice A. Leigh, 1900

Morris, Philip Richard 1836–1902, *The 'Nancy Lee' of Great Yarmouth*, purchased from the Autumn Exhibition, 1883

Morris, William Bright 1844–1912, *Near the Village of Crécy, France*, purchased from the artist, 1890

Morris, William Bright 1844–1912, *Spanish Beggars*, gift from Mrs Isaac H. Morris, 1898

Morrocco, Alberto 1917–1998, *Bathing Tent and Boat*, bequeathed by Mrs Diane Maud Stirling-King through the National Art Collections Fund, 2003, © the artist's estate

Mostyn, Thomas Edwin 1864–1930, *James Thomas Blair (1863–1917)*, gift from G. B. and A. Campbell-Blair, 1918

Mostyn, Thomas Edwin 1864–1930, *J. K. Bythell*, gift from the family of the sitter, 1916

Mostyn, Thomas Edwin 1864–1930, *Peace*, purchased from the artist, 1911

Mostyn, Thomas Edwin 1864–1930, *Romance*, purchased from the artist, 1911

Motesiczky, Marie-Louise von 1906–1996, *Henriette M.*, purchased from the artist, 1995, © Marie-Louise von Motesiczky Trust

Moynihan, Rodrigo 1910–1990, *The Garden Wall*, gift from the Contemporary Art Society, 1941, © the artist's estate

Moynihan, Rodrigo 1910–1990, *The Artist's Mother*, gift from the Contemporary Art Society, 1977, © the artist's estate

Muckley, William Jabez 1829–1905, *Grapes*, bequeathed by Mrs C. S. Garnett, 1936

Muckley, William Jabez 1829–1905, *Roses*, gift from James Chadwick, 1888

Mudd, James 1821–1906, *Mountainous Landscape*, bequeathed by Miss Vivienne Grundy, 2004

Mudd, James 1821–1906, *River Scene*, bequeathed by Miss Vivienne Grundy, 2004

Muirhead, David 1867–1930, *Night Shadows*, gift from Charles Lambert Rutherston, 1925

Müller, Adèle Rose Bertha c.1868–1948, *The Annunciation (after Lippo Lippi)*, transferred from the Horsfall Museum Collection, 1918, © the copyright holder

Müller, Adèle Rose Bertha c.1868–1948, *Angels (after Fra Angelico)*, transferred from the Horsfall Museum Collection, 1918, © the copyright holder

Müller, William James 1812–1845, *Landscape: Cottage, Trees, a Stream and Distant Hills*, gift from Mr and Mrs G. Sanville, 1964

Müller, William James 1812–1845, *A Rock Tomb, Lycia*, purchased from Mr T. F. Wright, 1896

Müller, William James 1812–1845, *An Encampment in the Desert*, purchased from Thomas Agnew and Sons Ltd, 1897

Müller, William James 1812–1845, *Burial Ground, Smyrna*, purchased from Shepherd Bros, 1907

Müller, William James 1812–1845, *The Approaching Storm*, bequeathed by Mr James Thomas Blair, 1917

Müller, William James 1812–1845, *Hauling Timber*, gift from the family of John Cooke Hilton, 1927

Mulready, William 1786–1863, *Study for 'The Careless Messenger Detected'*, bequeathed by Dr David Lloyd Roberts, 1920

Munsch, Josef 1832–1896, *The Antiquaries*, transferred from the Horsfall Museum Collection, 1918

Mura, Francesco de 1696–1782, *The Death of Virginia*, purchased from P. & D. Colnaghi & Co. Ltd, 1971

Mura, Frank 1863–1913, *In West Mersea: Essex*, purchased from The Fine Art Society, 1924, © the copyright holder

Mura, Frank 1863–1913, *Hayricks*, purchased from Mr Charles A. Jackson, 1914, © the copyright holder

Mura, Frank 1863–1913, *Village Scene*, purchased from Mr Charles A. Jackson, 1919, © the copyright holder

Murray, David 1849–1933, *'Britannia's' Anchor (on the River Dart)*, purchased from the artist, 1888

Murray, David 1849–1933, *Old Shoreham*, gift from the executors of the will of the artist, 1939

Murray, George b.c.1935, *Robot, 1966*, gift from the Moyan Gallery, 1967, © the copyright holder

Murry, Richard 1902–1984, *Crater*, gift from HM Government, War Artists Advisory Committee, 1947, © the copyright holder

Myers, William H. 1890–1924, *The Model*, purchased from Mr R. Bateman, 1924

Nash, John Northcote 1893–1977, *Winter Scene, Buckinghamshire*, gift from Charles Lambert Rutherston, 1925, © the artist's estate/ Bridgeman Art Library

Nash, John Northcote 1893–1977, *Jug of Flowers*, purchased from the Goupil Gallery, 1930, © the artist's estate/Bridgeman Art Library

Nash, John Northcote 1893–1977, *The Road up to Whiteleaf, Buckinghamshire*, purchased from the Artists of Today exhibition,

1937, © the artist's estate/ Bridgeman Art Library

Nash, Paul 1889–1946, *Sandling Park, Kent*, gift from Charles Lambert Rutherston, 1925, © Tate

Nash, Paul 1889–1946, *Nocturnal Landscape*, purchased from Mrs Margaret Nash, 1948, © Tate

Nash, Paul 1889–1946, *Wounded, Passchendaele*, purchased from the Exhibition of War Paintings and Drawings, 1920, © Tate

Nash, Thomas Saunders 1891–1968, *Bathers, 1926*, gift from Thomas Balston, 1950, © the artist's estate

Nash, Thomas Saunders 1891–1968, *Oranges and Lemons*, bequeathed by Dr Jane Walker, CH, LLD, 1939, © the artist's estate

Nash, Thomas Saunders 1891–1968, *The Farmyard*, gift from Thomas Balston, 1950, © the artist's estate

Nash, Thomas Saunders 1891–1968, *Fowls*, bequeathed by Dr Jane Walker, CH, LLD, 1939, © the artist's estate

Nash, Thomas Saunders 1891–1968, *The Woodgatherers*, gift from Thomas Balston, 1950, © the artist's estate

Nash, Thomas Saunders 1891–1968, *The Sermon on the Mount*, bequeathed by Dr Jane Walker, CH, LLD, 1939, © the artist's estate

Nasmyth, Alexander 1758–1840, *View of the Ponte Molle, on the Sylvan Side of Rome*, purchased from Mrs Mary Miller, 1902

Nasmyth, Alexander 1758–1840, *River Landscape with Ruined Castle*, gift from the daughters of Reverend William Gaskell, 1884

Nasmyth, Patrick 1787–1831, *Wooded Landscape with Distant View*, gift from the executors of the will of J. R. Oliver, 1934

Nasmyth, Patrick 1787–1831, *Near Dulwich*, gift from Mr James Gresham, 1917

Nasmyth, Patrick 1787–1831, *Landscape with Haystacks*, bequeathed by John Edward Yates, 1934

Nasmyth, Patrick 1787–1831, *Landscape with Sheep and a Shepherd*, bequeathed by George Beatson Blair, 1947

Nasmyth, Patrick 1787–1831, *Sonning on the Thames*, gift from M. K. Burrows, 1953

Naylor, Martin b.1944, *Fortress 8*, purchased from the Rowan Gallery, 1975, © the copyright holder

Naylor, Martin b.1944, *Lover Variation 3*, gift from the Contemporary Art Society, 1992, © the copyright holder

Neer, Aert van der imitator of 1603–1677, *Skating Scene: Figures on a River Flowing through a Village*, bequeathed by Mr and Mrs Edgar Assheton Bennett, 1979

Neiland, Brendan b.1941, *Juxtaposed Buildings*, purchased from the artist, 1974, © the artist

Neiland, Brendan b.1941, *Quadrate 1987*, gift from the Contemporary Art Society, 1989, © the artist

Nelson, Geoffrey C. b.1887, *The Church, Port Vendres*, purchased from the Paterson Gallery, 1929, © the copyright holder

Netherlandish School *A Lady Seated Holding a Small Dog*, bequeathed by Mr and Mrs Edgar Assheton Bennett, 1979

Nevinson, Christopher 1889–1946, *The Railway Bridge, Charenton*, gift, 1912, © the artist's estate/Bridgeman Art Library

Nevinson, Christopher 1889–1946, *Searchlights*, gift from Councillor Alfred P. Simon, 1920, © the artist's estate/Bridgeman Art Library

Nevinson, Christopher 1889–1946, *A Front Line near St Quentin*, gift from Charles Lambert Rutherston, 1925, © the artist's estate/Bridgeman Art Library

Nevinson, Christopher 1889–1946, *Any Wintry Afternoon in England*, gift, 2008, © the artist's estate/Bridgeman Art Library

Nevinson, Christopher 1889–1946, *Barges on the Thames*, gift from Howard Bliss, 1931, © the artist's estate/Bridgeman Art Library

Nevinson, Christopher 1889–1946, *Motor Lorries*, gift from Charles Lambert Rutherston, 1925, © the artist's estate/Bridgeman Art Library

Newsome, Victor b.1935, *A Corner of the Bathroom*, gift from the Contemporary Art Society, 1975, © the artist

Newton, Herbert H. 1881–1959, *Track of Forest Brook*, gift from Mr and Mrs Mathias, 1953, © the copyright holder

Nicholls, Bertram 1883–1974, *Picturesque Steyning*, gift from Alderman R. A. D. Carter, 1917, © the copyright holder

Nicholls, Bertram 1883–1974, *Villeneuve-les-Avignons*, purchased from The Manchester Academy of Fine Arts Exhibition, 1926, © the copyright holder

Nicholls, Bertram 1883–1974, *Maidstone Revisited*, bequeathed by Frank Voyce, 1974, © the copyright holder

Nicholls, Margaret S. active 1908–1932, *Flower Piece*, purchased from the artist, 1930, © the copyright holder

Nicholson, Ben 1894–1982, *1931 (St Ives Bay): sea with boats)*, gift from the Contemporary Art Society, 1950

Nicholson, Ben 1894–1982, *1932 (Au Chat Botté)*, purchased from Messrs Reid and Lefevre, 1948

Nicholson, Ben 1894–1982, *1946 (composition, still life)*, purchased from Messrs Reid and Lefevre, 1947

Nicholson, Ben 1894–1982, *1950 (still life)*, gift from the Contemporary Art Society and private subscribers, 1951

Nicholson, Ben 1894–1982, *1971 (Piero)*, gift from HM Treasury, 1986

Nicholson, William 1872–1949, *The Landlord*, purchased from Charles Jackson, 1919, © Elizabeth Banks

Nicholson, William 1872–1949, *Walter Greaves (1846–1930)*, purchased from the Goupil Gallery, 1925, © Elizabeth Banks

Nicholson, Winifred 1893–1981, *Primulas*, gift from Mrs Essil Elmslie Rutherston, 1928, © trustees of Winifred Nicholson

Nicholson, Winifred 1893–1981, *Boothby Bank*, purchased from the Lefevre Galleries, 1946, © trustees of Winifred Nicholson

Nixon, Job 1891–1938, *Place Saint-André des Arts, Paris*, purchased from the New English Art Club, 1930

North, John William 1842–1924, *The Flower and the Leaf*, gift from Mrs Stocke, 1918

North, John William 1842–1924, *Springtime*, purchased at Christie's, 1908

Northcote, James 1746–1831, *Othello, the Moor of Venice*, transferred from the Royal Manchester Institution, 1882

Oakes, John Wright 1820–1887, *Glen Muick, Aberdeenshire*, purchased from the Autumn Exhibition, 1887

Ochtervelt, Jacob 1634–1682, *The Doctor's Visit*, bequeathed by Mr and Mrs Edgar Assheton Bennett, 1979

Ochtervelt, Jacob 1634–1682, *The Sleeping Cavalier*, bequeathed by Mr and Mrs Edgar Assheton Bennett, 1979

Ochtervelt, Jacob 1634–1682, *The Embracing Cavalier*, bequeathed by Mr and Mrs Edgar Assheton Bennett, 1979

Ochtervelt, Jacob 1634–1682, *Merry Company*, purchased from Thomas Agnew and Sons Ltd, 1926

Oguiss, Takanori 1901–1986, *Paris Landscape*, gift from Mr Eric C. Gregory, 1946, © ADAGP, Paris and DACS, London 2013

Oliver, Peter 1927–2006, *Blue Beach*, gift from the Leonard Cohen Fund, 1965, © the artist's estate

Oliver, William 1823–1901, *The Duenna*, bequeathed by Mr James Thomas Blair, 1917

Oliver, William (attributed to) 1804–1853, *At the Opera*, bequeathed by Frank R. Craston, 1939

Ollivary, Annette b.1926, *Après l'école*, bequeathed by Lord Sidney Bernstein, 1995, © the copyright holder

Ollivary, Annette b.1926, *Scène de famille*, bequeathed by Lord Sidney Bernstein, 1995, © the copyright holder

O'Malley, Tony 1913–2003, *Graffiti, 1963*, purchased from A. C. Sewter, 1973, © the artist's estate

Ommeganck, Balthazar Paul 1755–1826, *Pastoral Landscape*, gift from Lieutenant Colonel R. H. Antrobus, 1971

Oppenheimer, Charles 1875–1961, *Kirkcudbright: Evening*, purchased from the artist, 1923, © the copyright holder

Oppenheimer, Charles 1875–1961, *Evening: Lake of Lucerne*, purchased from the artist, 1923, © the copyright holder

Oppenheimer, Charles 1875–1961, *The Old Tolbooth, Kirkcudbright*, purchased from The Manchester Academy of Fine Arts, 1941, © the copyright holder

Oppenheimer, Charles 1875–1961, *Last of the Snow*, bequeathed by George Beatson Blair, 1947, © the copyright holder

Orchardson, William Quiller 1832–1910, *Mrs John Pettie*, purchased from Thomas Agnew and Sons Ltd, 1926

Orchardson, William Quiller 1832–1910, *Mrs Robert Mackay*, gift from Dr Thomas Fentem, 1935

Orchardson, William Quiller 1832–1910, *Her Idol*, purchased from Messrs Wallis and Son, 1910

Orpen, William 1878–1931, *James Staats Forbes*, purchased from C. Marshall Spink, 1926

Orpen, William 1878–1931, *Homage to Manet*, purchased from the artist, 1910

Os, Jan van 1744–1808, *Still Life: Flowers and Fruit*, bequeathed by Mr and Mrs Edgar Assheton Bennett, 1979

Os, Jan van 1744–1808, *Still Life: Flowers and Fruit*, bequeathed by Mr and Mrs Edgar Assheton Bennett, 1979

Oss, Tom W. Van 1901–1941, *Foggy Afternoon, Boulevard St Michel, Paris*, gift from the Contemporary Art Society, 1940

Ostade, Adriaen van 1610–1685, *Two Peasants Smoking*, bequeathed by Mr and Mrs Edgar Assheton Bennett, 1979

Ostade, Adriaen van (follower of) 1610–1685, *Interior of a Barn with Two Peasants Fighting*, bequeathed by Mr and Mrs Edgar Assheton Bennett, 1979

Ostade, Adriaen van (follower of) 1610–1685, *An Itinerant Musician Playing the Hurdy-Gurdy to a Group of Children Outside an Inn Door*, bequeathed by Mr and Mrs Edgar Assheton Bennett, 1979

Ostade, Isack van 1621–1649, *Winter Scene, with Figures on a Frozen River in front of a Walled Town*, bequeathed by Mr and Mrs Edgar Assheton Bennett, 1979

Ostade, Isack van 1621–1649, *Interior of a Barn with an Old Woman at a Distaff*, bequeathed by Mr and Mrs Edgar Assheton Bennett, 1979

Ostade, Isack van 1621–1649, *Scene on the Shore at Scheveningen*, bequeathed by Mrs Elizabeth Hatton Wood, 1908

Ouless, Walter William 1848–1933, *Alderman Philip Goldschmidt*, gift from fellow citizens of the sitter, 1888

Owen, Joseph active 1926–1933, *At Bettws-y-Coed, North Wales*, purchased from the artist, 1927, © the copyright holder

Palmer, Jean b.1961, *Head*, purchased from the artist, 1992, © the artist

Palmer, Jean b.1961, *Self Portrait*, purchased from the artist, 1992, © the artist

Palmer, Samuel 1805–1881, *The Bright Cloud*, purchased from Thomas Agnew and Sons Ltd, 1976

Panini, Giovanni Paolo (follower of) 1691–1765, *Roman Ruins with Figures*, gift from Manchester Education Committee, 1903

Park, John Anthony 1880–1962, *Shipping, Venice*, purchased from The Manchester Academy of Fine Arts Exhibition, 1935, © the artist's estate

Park, John Anthony 1880–1962, *Spring in Mallorca*, purchased from The Manchester Academy of Fine Arts Exhibition, 1937, © the artist's estate

Park, John Anthony 1880–1962, *Snowfalls in Essex*, purchased from The Manchester Academy of Fine Arts Exhibition, 1939, © the artist's estate

Park, John Anthony 1880–1962, *This England*, bequeathed by Mr Frank Stephens Rosser, 1957, © the artist's estate

Parker, Brynhild 1907–1987, *The White Hat*, purchased from the Lefevre Galleries, 1935, © the copyright holder

Parlby, Samuel *The Bridgewater Canal from Dr White's Bridge, Looking towards Manchester*, purchased from H. Fisher, 1928

Parry, Joseph 1756–1826, *Eccles Wakes: Racing for the Smock*, purchased from Messrs Haworth and Sons, 1927

Parry, Joseph 1756–1826, *The Village Fair*, purchased from Messrs Haworth and Sons, 1927

Parry, Joseph 1756–1826, *Eccles Wakes*, purchased from Messrts Haworth and Sons, 1927

Parry, Joseph 1756–1826, *Eccles Wakes: Ale-House Interior*, purchased from Messrs Haworth and Sons, 1927

Partington, John Herbert Evelyn 1843–1899, *Dr Joseph Gouge Greenwood*, gift from Miss E. S. Greenwood, 1912

Partington, John Herbert Evelyn 1843–1899, *William Alfred Turner*, purchased from the artist, 1886

Pasini, Alberto 1826–1899, *A Cavalcade of Arabs*, transferred from the Horsfall Museum Collection, 1918

Pasmore, Victor 1908–1998, *Parisian Café*, gift from the Contemporary Art Society, 1941, © Victor Pasmore estate

Pasmore, Victor 1908–1998, *Red Development No.5*, purchased from Marlborough Fine Art Ltd, 1964, © Victor Pasmore estate

Passarotti, Bartolomeo (attributed to) 1529–1592, *Domenico Giuliani and His Servant*, purchased from P. & D. Colnaghi & Co. Ltd, 1959

Paterson, Emily Murray 1855–1934, *Still Life*, gift from the family of the artist, 1934

Paterson, James 1854–1932, *Honfleur*, gift from Mrs H. K. Jacomb-Hood, 1941

Patrick, James McIntosh 1907–1998, *The Ettrick Shepherd*, purchased from the artist, 1937, © the artist's estate/Bridgeman Art Library

Peake, Mervyn 1911–1968, *The Glassblower*, gift from HM Government, War Artists Advisory Committee, 1947, © the artist's estate

Peake, Robert (after) c.1551–1619, *A Procession of Elizabeth I*, bequeathed by George Beatson Blair, 1947

Pearce, Charles Maresco 1874–1964, *Conspiracy, Café Verrey*, gift from Charles Lambert Rutherston, 1925, © the copyright holder

Pearce, Charles Maresco 1874–1964, *Corner of Café Verrey*, gift from Charles Lambert Rutherston, 1925, © the copyright holder

Pears, Charles 1873–1958, *Camouflaged Merchant Steamer Aground*, purchased from the Exhibition of War Paintings and Drawings, 1920, © the artist's estate

Peeters I, Bonaventura 1614–1652, *A Yacht in a Choppy Sea*, bequeathed by Mr and Mrs Edgar Assheton Bennett, 1979

Penteshin, Ivan Milyevich b.1927, *February Blue*, gift from the USSR-GB Society, 1981, © the copyright holder

Peploe, Samuel John 1871–1935, *The Aloe Tree*, purchased from the Lefevre Galleries, 1929

Peploe, Samuel John 1871–1935, *Rocks at Iona*, gift from the Contemporary Art Society, 1944

Peppercorn, Arthur Douglas 1847–1924, *Corn Ricks*, purchased from the 16th Autumn Exhibition, 1898

Peppercorn, Arthur Douglas 1847–1924, *Path by the River Ripley*, gift from Alderman Frederick Todd, 1925

Peppercorn, Arthur Douglas 1847–1924, *Seascape*, gift from Alderman Frederick Todd, 1925

Peppercorn, Arthur Douglas 1847–1924, *The Yacht*, gift from Councillor Frederick Todd, 1913

Percy, William 1820–1893, *Edwin Waugh*, gift from Thomas Read

Wilkinson, 1884

Perrault, Léon Bazile 1832–1908, *Meditation*, gift from John Cottrill, 1911

Perugini, Charles Edward 1839–1918, *Girl Reading*, bequeathed by Mr James Thomas Blair, 1917

Perugino (follower of) c.1450–1523, *The Adoration of the Magi*, bequeathed through the National Art Collections Fund, 1947

Perugino (follower of) c.1450–1523, *The Annunciation*, bequeathed through the National Art Collections Fund, 1947

Perugino (follower of) c.1450–1523, *The Nativity with Saint Bridget*, bequeathed through the National Art Collections Fund, 1947

Perugino (follower of) c.1450–1523, *The Presentation in the Temple*, bequeathed through the National Art Collections Fund, 1947

Peters, Matthew William 1742–1814, *Portrait of a Child*, bequeathed by George Beatson Blair, 1947

Pether, Abraham 1756–1812, *St Albans Abbey, Hertfordshire*, bequeathed by George Beatson Blair, 1947

Pether, Abraham 1756–1812, *Thirlmere, Cumberland*, gift from Edward Rogerson, 1909

Pettie, John 1839–1893, *A Song without Words*, purchased from Thomas Agnew and Sons Ltd, 1904

Pettie, John 1839–1893, *The Duke of Monmouth's Interview with James II*, purchased from Thomas Agnew and Sons Ltd, 1899

Philippeau, Karel Frans 1825–1897, *Playing Cards*, transferred from the Horsfall Museum Collection, 1918

Philippeau, Karel Frans 1825–1897, *Spinning: Italian Scene*, transferred from the Horsfall Museum Collection, 1918

Philpot, Glyn Warren 1884–1937, *A Street Accident*, purchased from the artist, 1925

Pickersgill, Frederick Richard 1820–1900, *Mercury Instructing the Nymphs in Dancing*, bequeathed by Sir Joseph Whitworth, 1896

Pickersgill, Frederick Richard 1820–1900, *Samson Betrayed*, transferred from the Royal Manchester Institution, 1882

Pickersgill, Frederick Richard 1820–1900, *A Little Gondelay*, bequeathed by Miss Sophia Armitt, 1909

Piot, Antoine 1869–1934, *An Italian Lady*, transferred from the Horsfall Museum Collection, 1918

Piper, John 1903–1992, *Autumn at Stourhead*, gift from the Contemporary Art Society, 1948, © the artist's estate

Piper, John 1903–1992, *Coventry Cathedral, 15 November, 1940*, gift from HM Government, War

Artists Advisory Committee, 1947, © the artist's estate

Piper, John 1903–1992, *Ruined Cottage, Tomen y Mur, North Wales*, purchased from the Redfern Gallery, 1950, © the artist's estate

Pissarro, Camille 1830–1903, *Rue de Voisins*, purchased from Miss Enid M. Holden, 1969

Pissarro, Camille 1830–1903, *Pont de la Clef in Bruges, Belgium*, gift from Mrs E. L. Pissarro, 1946

Pissarro, Félix 1874–1897, *The Bonfire*, gift from Mrs E. L. Pissarro, 1951

Pissarro, Lucien 1863–1944, *The Hills from Cadborough, Sunset*, gift from Charles Lambert Rutherston, 1925, © the artist's estate

Pissarro, Lucien 1863–1944, *Wild Boar Fell, Brough*, gift from Charles Lambert Rutherston, 1925, © the artist's estate

Pissarro, Lucien 1863–1944, *Fishpond Bottom*, purchased from Charles Jackson, 1928, © the artist's estate

Pissarro, Lucien 1863–1944, *Willows, Fishpond, Dorset*, gift from the National Art Collections Fund, 1916, © the artist's estate

Pissarro, Lucien 1863–1944, *Crockers Lane, Coldharbour*, gift from Charles Lambert Rutherston, 1925, © the artist's estate

Pissarro, Lucien 1863–1944, *The Dorking Road, Coldharbour, in Snow*, gift from Charles Lambert Rutherston, 1925, © the artist's estate

Pissarro, Lucien 1863–1944, *November Sunset on the Thames, Kew*, gift from Charles Lambert Rutherston, 1925, © the artist's estate

Pissarro, Lucien 1863–1944, *Dartmouth*, gift from Mrs E. L. Pissarro, 1946, © the artist's estate

Pissarro, Lucien 1863–1944, *Kingswear through the Mist*, gift from Charles Lambert Rutherston, 1925, © the artist's estate

Pissarro, Lucien 1863–1944, *On the Dart*, bequeathed by Dr Jane Walker, CH, LLD, 1939, © the artist's estate

Pissarro, Lucien 1863–1944, *The Dart from Week's Hill*, gift from Mrs E. L. Pissarro, 1951, © the artist's estate

Pissarro, Lucien 1863–1944, *La Pierre d'Avignon, Le Lavandou*, gift from Charles Lambert Rutherston, 1925, © the artist's estate

Pissarro, Lucien 1863–1944, *Quai de Seine*, gift from Mrs Essil Elmslie Rutherston, 1944, © the artist's estate

Pissarro, Lucien 1863–1944, *Rue Jean Aicard, Bormes*, gift from Mrs E. L. Pissarro, 1951, © the artist's estate

Pissarro, Orovida Camille 1893–1968, *Zebras Drinking*, gift from Miss Margaret Pilkington, 1970, © trustees of the estate of Orovida Pissarro

Pitchforth, Roland Vivian

1895–1982, *Burnsall*, gift from Mr Eric C. Gregory, 1946, © the artist's estate

Pitchforth, Roland Vivian 1895–1982, *Old Stone Waller*, gift from Mr Eric C. Gregory, 1946, © the artist's estate

Pitchforth, Roland Vivian 1895–1982, *Bainbridge*, gift from Mr Eric C. Gregory, 1946, © the artist's estate

Pitchforth, Roland Vivian 1895–1982, *Cottage, Bainbridge*, gift from Mr Eric C. Gregory, 1946, © the artist's estate

Pitchforth, Roland Vivian 1895–1982, *Still Life*, gift from Mr Eric C. Gregory, 1946, © the artist's estate

Pitchforth, Roland Vivian 1895–1982, *Still Life*, gift from Mr Eric C. Gregory, 1946, © the artist's estate

Pitchforth, Roland Vivian 1895–1982, *Little Ships on Patrol*, gift from HM Government, War Artists Advisory Committee, 1947, © the artist's estate

Pitchforth, Roland Vivian 1895–1982, *Hebden, Yorkshire*, gift from the guarantors of the London Artists' Association, 1934, © the artist's estate

Poel, Egbert Lievensz. van der 1621–1664, *Skating Scene with a Tent and Numerous Figures on a Wide River*, bequeathed by Mr and Mrs Edgar Assheton Bennett, 1979

Polunin, Elizabeth Violet 1878–1950, *Anna Pavlova*, purchased from Stafford Gallery, 1939, © the artist's estate

Poole, Paul Falconer 1807–1879, *Rustic Scene*, bequeathed by Sir Joseph Whitworth, 1896

Poole, Paul Falconer 1807–1879, *The Goths in Italy*, purchased at Christie's, 1891

Porter, Frederick James 1883–1944, *Snow in Hanover Square, London*, gift from Charles Lambert Rutherston, 1925, © the copyright holder

Porter, Frederick James 1883–1944, *Landscape with River*, bequeathed by Frank Hindley Smith, 1940, © the copyright holder

Porter, Frederick James 1883–1944, *Roses*, gift from Mr Eric C. Gregory, 1946, © the copyright holder

Porter, Frederick James 1883–1944, *Winter Morning*, gift from the guarantors of the London Artists' Association, 1934, © the copyright holder

Portway, Douglas 1922–1993, *London*, purchased from Drian Galleries, 1964, © the artist's estate

Potter, Mary 1900–1981, *Hampshire Farm*, purchased from the artist, 1941, © estate of Mary Potter. All rights reserved, DACS 2013

Potter, Mary 1900–1981, *Night and Day (recto)*, purchased from the New Art Centre, 1987, © estate of

Mary Potter. All rights reserved, DACS 2013

Potter, Mary 1900–1981, *Night and Day (verso)*, purchased from the New Art Centre, 1987, © estate of Mary Potter. All rights reserved, DACS 2013

Potter, Mary 1900–1981, *Still Life*, gift from Sir Thomas D. Barlow, 1941, © estate of Mary Potter. All rights reserved, DACS 2013

Potter, Paulus 1625–1654, *Evening Landscape with Cattle and Peasants Dancing to the Sound of a Pipe*, bequeathed by Mr and Mrs Edgar Assheton Bennett, 1979

Pourbus the elder, Frans 1545–1581, *Portrait of an Old Man (possibly Hubertus Langetus)*, purchased from Roland, Browse and Delbanco, 1950

Poynter, Edward John 1836–1919, *The Ides of March*, purchased from the artist, 1883

Poynter, Edward John 1836–1919, *Diana and Endymion*, gift from Mr James Gresham, 1917

Poynter, Edward John 1836–1919, *The Vision of Endymion*, purchased from The Fine Art Society, 1904

Poynter, Edward John 1836–1919, *Study for 'The Ides of March'*, purchased at Christie's, 1993

Praag, Arnold van b.1926, *Old Soldier*, purchased from the Society for Education through Art, Pictures for Schools Exhibition, 1964, © the artist

Priestman, Bertram 1868–1951, *The Great Green Hills of Yorkshire*, purchased from the artist, 1913, © the copyright holder

Prinsep, Valentine Cameron 1838–1904, *At the Golden Gate*, gift from W. A. Turner, 1883

Prinsep, Valentine Cameron 1838–1904, *Cinderella*, bequeathed by Mrs A. Enriqueta Rylands, 1908

Prinsep, Valentine Cameron 1838–1904, *The Queen was in the Parlour, Eating Bread and Honey*, purchased from the Redfern Gallery, 1938

Pritchett, Edward active c.1828–1879, *St Mark's, Venice*, purchased from Shepherd Bros, 1902

Prout, Margaret Fisher 1875–1963, *Mays Farm (recto)*, bequeathed by Mr Frank Stephens Rosser, 1957, © the copyright holder

Prout, Margaret Fisher 1875–1963, *Mays Farm (verso)*, © the copyright holder

Pryde, James Ferrier 1866–1941, *The Arch*, gift from the National Art Collections Fund, 1927

Pym, Roland Vivian 1920–2006, *Italian Girls*, purchased from Stafford Gallery, 1939, © the copyright holder

Pyne, James Baker 1800–1870, *Boppard on the Rhine*, bequeathed by Mr James Thomas Blair, 1917

Raeburn, Henry (attributed to) 1756–1823, *Alexander Gordon, 4th Duke of Gordon*, purchased from

Thomas Agnew and Sons Ltd, 1902

Raeburn, Henry (attributed to) 1756–1823, *Mrs Shafto Clarke and Her Daughter*, bequeathed by Mr James Thomas Blair, 1917

Raeburn, Henry (attributed to) 1756–1823, *Alexander Campbell of Hillyards*, bequeathed by Mr James Thomas Blair, 1917

Ramsay, Patricia 1886–1974, *Tiger Lilies*, purchased from Mrs Marchant, 1934, © the artist's estate

Ranken, William Bruce Ellis 1881–1941, *Ernest Thesiger*, gift from the sitter, 1942

Rankley, Alfred 1819–1872, *Music Hath Charms*, bequeathed by Miss Florence Harrison, 1971

Ratcliffe, William Whitehead 1870–1955, *Winter Scene, Sweden*, gift from Mr Eric C. Gregory, 1946, © the artist's estate

Ratcliffe, William Whitehead 1870–1955, *Still Life by the Fire*, purchased from The Fine Art Society, 2011, © the artist's estate

Ratcliffe, William Whitehead 1870–1955, *Swedish Farm*, gift from S. K. Ratcliffe, 1955, © the artist's estate

Rawson, James active 1855–1863, *Apples, Grapes and Strawberries*, bequeathed by Dr David Lloyd Roberts, 1920

Redpath, Anne 1895–1965, *Table Top*, purchased from the artist, 1962, © the artist's estate/ Bridgeman Art Library

Reekie, William Maxwell 1869–1948, *A Convoy in the Mediterranean, April 1918*, gift from the artist, 1920, © the copyright holder

Reekie, William Maxwell 1869–1948, *Llaneillian*, gift from the artist, 1930, © the copyright holder

Reekie, William Maxwell 1869–1948, *Maclellan's Castle*, purchased from The Manchester Academy of Fine Arts Exhibition, 1937, © the copyright holder

Reid, Flora Macdonald 1860–c.1940, *A Doubtful Customer*, purchased from the 20th Autumn Exhibition, 1902

Reid, Flora Macdonald 1860–c.1940, *A Cornish Fishwife*, purchased from the 21st Autumn Exhibition, 1904

Reid, George 1841–1913, *The Reverend Alexander McLaren*, gift, 1896

Reid, George 1841–1913, *Alderman Sir James Hoy*, gift from the sitter, 1903

Reid, George 1841–1913, *James Moorhouse*, gift from Miss Edith E. Sale, 1924

Reid, John Robertson 1851–1926, *The Mermaid's Arrival*, purchased at Christie's, 1913

Reni, Guido 1575–1642, *Saint Catherine*, purchased from Messrs Thomas Agnew and Sons Ltd, 1974

Renoir, Pierre-Auguste 1841–1919, *Seated Woman*, bequeathed by

George Beatson Blair, 1947

Renoir, Pierre-Auguste 1841–1919, *Seated Nude*, gift from the trustees of the will of Lady Marks of Broughton, 1972

Reynolds, Alan b.1926, *Moonlight*, purchased from Leicester Galleries, 1957, © the artist

Reynolds, Joshua 1723–1792, *Charles, 9th Lord Cathcart*, purchased from Major General, The Earl Cathcart, 1981

Reynolds, Joshua 1723–1792, *Jane Hamilton, Wife of 9th Lord Cathcart, and Her Daughter Jane, Later Duchess of Atholl*, purchased from Major General, The Earl Cathcart, 1981

Reynolds, Joshua 1723–1792, *Lady Anstruther*, purchased from Thomas Agnew and Sons Ltd, 1898

Reynolds, Joshua 1723–1792, *Admiral Lord Hood*, purchased from Thomas Agnew and Sons Ltd, 1898

Ricci, Marco (attributed to) 1676–1730, *A Storm at Sea*, purchased from Gallery Lasson, 1966

Ricci, Sebastiano (school of) 1659–1734, *Mercury, Herse and Aglauros*, gift from the National Art Collections Fund, 1954

Richards, Albert 1919–1945, *Royal Engineers' Dump*, gift from HM Government, War Artists Advisory Committee, 1947, © the copyright holder

Richardson, Edward Harrison 1881–1952, *Albert Square, Manchester*, purchased from Mr J. V. Knott, 1980, © the copyright holder

Richardson the elder, Jonathan (attributed to) 1664–1745, *Portrait of a Gentleman in Red Velvet*, gift from the Royal Manchester Institution, 1973

Richmond, William Blake 1842–1921, *Near Viareggio, Where Shelley's Body Was Found*, gift from the sons of the artist, 1924

Richter, Herbert Davis 1874–1955, *An Artist's Home*, purchased from the artist, 1927, © the copyright holder

Ricketts, Charles S. 1866–1931, *The Trojan Women*, gift from Mr and Mrs Henry Winslow, 1948

Ricketts, Charles S. 1866–1931, *Faust and the Centaur*, gift from Mr Robert H. Jackson, 1933

Ricketts, Charles S. 1866–1931, *Montezuma*, purchased from the Grosvenor Gallery, 1915

Rietschoof, Jan Claesz. 1652–1719, *Massed Shipping Anchored in the Foreground: A View of Rotterdam Beyond*, bequeathed by Mr and Mrs Edgar Assheton Bennett, 1979

Riley, Bridget b.1931, *Zephyr*, purchased from the Rowan Gallery, 1977, © the artist

Riley, Cecil b.1917, *St Cross Road, Oxford*, bequeathed by Mr Frank Stephens Rosser, 1943, © the artist

Ritchie, Hannah active 1926–1932, *Meije, Upper Savoy*, purchased

from the Modern Painters Exhibition, 1930, © the copyright holder

Riviere, Briton 1840–1920, *Calves in a Meadow*, bequeathed by Dr David Lloyd Roberts, 1920

Riviere, Briton 1840–1920, *His Only Friend*, bequeathed by Jesse Haworth, 1937

Riviere, Briton 1840–1920, *The Last of the Garrison*, purchased from Thomas Agnew and Sons Ltd, 1898

Riviere, Briton 1840–1920, *'In Manus Tuas, Domine'*, gift from Arthur A. Haworth and Brothers, 1902

Riviere, Briton 1840–1920, *Daniel's Answer to the King*, bequeathed by Jesse Haworth, 1937

Riviere, Briton 1840–1920, *Dead Hector*, gift from Mr James Gresham, 1917

Roberts, David 1796–1864, *The Lady Chapel, Church of St Pierre, Caen*, purchased from Thomas Agnew and Sons Ltd, 1904

Roberts, David 1796–1864, *The High Altar of the Church of SS Giovanni e Paolo at Venice*, bequeathed by Dr David Lloyd Roberts, 1920

Roberts, Lancelot Percival 1883–1950, *A Lancashire Lass*, purchased from the artist, 1929, © the copyright holder

Roberts, William Patrick 1895–1980, *Sarah*, gift from the Contemporary Art Society, 1931, © estate of John David Roberts. By courtesy of The William Roberts Society

Roberts, William Patrick 1895–1980, *A Woman (Sarah)*, gift from Mrs Essil Elmslie Rutherston, 1928, © estate of John David Roberts. By courtesy of The William Roberts Society

Robertson, John Ewart 1820–1879, *James Hatton*, bequeathed by Mrs Elizabeth Hatton Wood, 1908

Robinson, Bob b.1951, *Going to the Wall*, purchased from the artist, 1986, © the artist

Roden, William Thomas 1817–1892, *John Henry Newman*, bequeathed by R. H. Wood, 1908

Rodgers, Roy b.1935, *Composition with Sunflowers*, purchased from the Pictures for Schools exhibition, 1966, © the copyright holder

Roelofs, Willem 1822–1897, *Ferme sous les arbres*, bequeathed by Lady Mary Ann Boyd Dawkins, 1979

Romiti, Gino 1881–1967, *An Old Tuscan Road*, gift from Alderman E. F. M. Sutton, 1930, © the copyright holder

Romney, George 1734–1802, *Mrs Margaret Ainslie*, bequeathed by Mr James Thomas Blair, 1917

Romney, George 1734–1802, *Captain William Peere Williams*, purchased from C. Marshall Spink, 1950

Ronaldson, Thomas Martine 1881–1942, *Summer*, purchased

from the artist, 1929

Rooker, Michael Angelo 1746–1801, *Westgate, Winchester*, gift from Frederick John Nettlefold, 1948

Rosoman, Leonard Henry 1913–2012, *Auxiliary Fireman Leonard Rosoman, Cheapside*, gift from HM Government, War Artists Advisory Committee, 1947, © the artist's estate

Rossetti, Dante Gabriel 1828–1882, *The Bower Meadow*, purchased at Christie's, 1909

Rossetti, Dante Gabriel 1828–1882, *Joli Coeur*, bequeathed by Miss Annie E. F. Horniman, 1937

Rossetti, Dante Gabriel 1828–1882, *Astarte Syriaca*, purchased from Mr Clarence E. Fry, 1891

Rothenstein, William 1872–1945, *Le grand if vert*, gift from Charles Lambert Rutherston, 1925, © the artist's estate/Bridgeman Art Library

Rothenstein, William 1872–1945, *Alice by the Fireside*, gift from Charles Lambert Rutherston, 1925, © the artist's estate/Bridgeman Art Library

Rothenstein, William 1872–1945, *In the Morning Room*, gift from Charles Lambert Rutherston, 1925, © the artist's estate/Bridgeman Art Library

Rothenstein, William 1872–1945, *The Church of St Seine L'Abbaye*, bequeathed by Dr Jane Walker, CH, LLD, 1939, © the artist's estate/Bridgeman Art Library

Rothenstein, William 1872–1945, *Reading the Book of Esther*, gift from Charles Lambert Rutherston, 1925, © the artist's estate/Bridgeman Art Library

Rothenstein, William 1872–1945, *Nature's Ramparts*, gift from Charles Lambert Rutherston, 1925, © the artist's estate/Bridgeman Art Library

Rothenstein, William 1872–1945, *Eli the Thatcher*, bequeathed by Dr Jane Walker, CH, LLD, 1939, © the artist's estate/Bridgeman Art Library

Rothenstein, William 1872–1945, *Tree in Winter*, bequeathed by Dr Jane Walker, CH, LLD, 1939, © the artist's estate/Bridgeman Art Library

Rothenstein, William 1872–1945, *Self Portrait*, purchased from Thomas Agnew and Sons Ltd, 1935, © the artist's estate/Bridgeman Art Library

Rothenstein, William 1872–1945, *The Beech Wood*, gift from Charles Lambert Rutherston, 1925, © the artist's estate/Bridgeman Art Library

Rothenstein, William 1872–1945, *Sir Arthur Dixon*, gift from HM Government, War Artists Advisory Committee, 1947, © the artist's estate/Bridgeman Art Library

Rothenstein, William 1872–1945,

At the Window, gift from Charles Lambert Rutherston, 1925, © the artist's estate/Bridgeman Art Library

Rothenstein, William 1872–1945, *Flower, Fruit and Thorn Piece*, gift from Charles Lambert Rutherston, 1925, © the artist's estate/Bridgeman Art Library

Rothenstein, William 1872–1945, *Ignacio Zuloaga as a Torero*, gift from Charles Lambert Rutherston, 1925, © the artist's estate/Bridgeman Art Library

Rothenstein, William 1872–1945, *Iles' Farm, Winter*, gift from Charles Lambert Rutherston, 1925, © the artist's estate/Bridgeman Art Library

Rothenstein, William 1872–1945, *Princess Betty*, gift from Charles Lambert Rutherston, 1925, © the artist's estate/Bridgeman Art Library

Rothenstein, William 1872–1945, *Rachel Queen*, gift from Charles Lambert Rutherston, 1925, © the artist's estate/Bridgeman Art Library

Rothenstein, William 1872–1945, *St Martin's Summer*, gift from Charles Lambert Rutherston, 1925, © the artist's estate/Bridgeman Art Library

Rothenstein, William 1872–1945, *The Church at Bourlon*, purchased from the Exhibition of War Paintings and Drawings, 1920, © the artist's estate/Bridgeman Art Library

Rotius, Jan Albertsz. 1624–1666, *Portrait of a Boy with a Dog*, bequeathed by Miss Catherine Scott, 1930

Roworth, Edward 1880–1964, *W. Maxwell Reekie*, gift from the trustees of the estate of the sitter, 1988, © the copyright holder

Royle, Herbert F. 1870–1958, *Haymakers*, gift from Si Charles Behrens, 1916, © the artist's estate

Rubin, Reuven 1893–1974, *Bethlehem*, gift from Lieutenant Colonel C. Beddington, 1938, © Rubin Museum, Tel Aviv

Ruisdael, Jacob van 1628/1629–1682, *Landscape with a Woman and Child Walking along a Wooded Country Lane*, bequeathed by Mr and Mrs Edgar Assheton Bennett, 1979

Ruisdael, Jacob van 1628/1629–1682, *A Storm off the Dutch Coast*, gift from the National Art Collections Fund, 1955

Rutherford, Harry 1903–1985, *Penzance*, purchased from the artist, 1930, © the artist's estate

Rutherford, Harry 1903–1985, *Suburban Summer*, gift from the Royal Manchester Institution, 1936, © the artist's estate

Rutherford, Harry 1903–1985, *Sennen Cove*, purchased from the artist, 1957, © the artist's estate

Rutherston, Albert 1881–1953, *The Chicken Market, Bourbonnais*, gift from Charles Lambert

Rutherston, 1925, © the grandchildren of the artist, Max, Selina and Jane Rutherston

Ruysdael, Salomon van c.1602–1670, *River Scene with Sailing Boats Unloading at the Shore*, bequeathed by Mr and Mrs Edgar Assheton Bennett, 1979

Ruysdael, Salomon van c.1602–1670, *Winter Scene with Sledges and Skaters on a River*, bequeathed by Mr and Mrs Edgar Assheton Bennett, 1979

Ryan, Adrian 1920–1998, *Daffodils and Tulips*, purchased from Arthur Tooth and Sons Ltd, 1954, © estate of Adrian Ryan

Rysbrack, Pieter Andreas c.1684–1690–1748, *Dead Game*, gift from Mrs Robert Hatton, 1908

Sadler, Walter Dendy 1854–1923, *In the Camp of the Amalekites*, purchased from the Autumn Exhibition, 1889

Salanson, Eugénie Marie 1864–1892, *Head of a Girl*, bequeathed by Mr James Thomas Blair, 1917

Salanson, Eugénie Marie 1864–1892, *La Francine de Grandville*, bequeathed by Mr James Thomas Blair, 1917

Sandys, Frederick 1829–1904, *Vivien*, purchased from E. Mitchell Crosse, 1925

Sant, James 1820–1916, *A Thorn amidst the Roses*, purchased from the Autumn Exhibition, 1887

Santoro, Rubens 1859–1942, *A Siesta in Sunshine*, transferred from the Horsfall Museum Collection, 1918

Santoro, Rubens 1859–1942, *Basket Makers in Naples*, transferred from the Horsfall Museum Collection, 1918

Sargent, Frederick 1837–1899 & **Saunders, H. L.** d.1899, *Interior of the Manchester Royal Exchange*, gift from the Manchester Royal Exchange, 1968

Sargent, John Singer 1856–1925, *Albanian Olive Gatherers*, gift from Dr A. Schuster, 1910

Sargent, John Singer 1856–1925, *An Italian Sailor*, purchased from Charles Jackson, 1910

Sargent, John Singer 1856–1925, *Mrs Duxbury and Daughter*, gift from the sitter, 1945

Satchwell, Eric b.1926, *Playing Fields*, purchased from Gibb's Bookshop, 1954, © the copyright holder

Sayers, Reuben Thomas William 1815–1888, *The Water Lily*, transferred from the Royal Manchester Institution, 1882

Scheffer, Ary 1795–1858, *The Holy Women at the Sepulchre*, gift from Lord Ashton of Hyde, 1924

Schooten, Floris Gerritsz. van c.1585–after 1655, *Still Life: Fruit, Bread and a Goblet on a Table*, bequeathed by Mr and Mrs Edgar Assheton Bennett, 1979

Schreyer, Christian Adolphe 1828–1899, *Abandoned*, purchased from the Marton Hall sale, 1888

Schwabe, Randolph 1885–1948, *Head of an Old Woman*, gift from Charles Lambert Rutherston, 1925, © the artist's estate

Schweitzer, Adolf Gustav 1847–1914, *The Old Diligence in Winter*, transferred from the Horsfall Museum Collection, 1918

Scott, William Bell (after) 1811–1890, *Peter Vischer (1487–1528)*

Scully, Sean b.1945, *Drawing No.4*, purchased from the Rowan Gallery, 1975, © the artist

Seabrooke, Elliott 1886–1950, *Wallflowers*, gift from Mrs P. Seabrooke, 1976, © the copyright holder

Seabrooke, Elliott 1886–1950, *Lock House, Heybridge Basin*, purchased from Mrs P. Seabrooke, 1976, © the copyright holder

Seabrooke, Elliott 1886–1950, *Aix-en-Provence*, purchased from Mrs P. Seabrooke, 1976, © the copyright holder

Seeman, Isaac d.1751, *George Lloyd*, purchased from Old Post House Antiques, 1982

Semenowsky, Emile Eisman 1857–1911, *Autumn*, bequeathed by Mr James Thomas Blair, 1917

Severdonck, Franz van 1809–1889, *Domestic Fowl in a Landscape*, gift from C. A. Clarke, 1938

Shackleton, William 1872–1933, *The Sailor's Funeral*, gift from Charles Lambert Rutherston, 1925

Shackleton, William 1872–1933, *Bed Time*, gift from Mrs May Shackleton, 1938

Shackleton, William 1872–1933, *Grass of Parnassus*, gift from Mrs May Shackleton, 1938

Shannon, Charles Haslewood 1863–1937, *The Mill Pond*, purchased from the artist, 1909

Shannon, Charles Haslewood 1863–1937, *Toilet Scene I*, gift from Henry Winslow, 1948

Shannon, Charles Haslewood 1863–1937, *Toilet Scene II*, gift from Henry Winslow, 1948

Sharp, Dorothea 1874–1955, *The Yellow Balloon*, purchased from the artist, 1938, © the copyright holder

Shaw, Peter 1926–1982, *Kinder Scout*, purchased from the artist, 1973, © the copyright holder

Shayer, William 1787–1879, *Landscape with Cattle by a Stream*, gift from Mr James Gresham, 1917

Shee, Martin Archer 1769–1850, *Major General Sir Barry Close, Bt*, purchased from C. Marshall Spink, 1955

Sheffield Junior, George 1839–1892, *A Hundred Years Ago*, purchased from the Autumn Exhibition, 1890

Shephard, Rupert 1909–1992, *Hedgerow*, gift from Mrs Essil Elmslie Rutherston, 1946, © the artist's estate

Shepherd, Juliana Charlotte c.1832–1898, *Thoughts of the Future*, bequeathed by the artist, 1899

Shields, Frederick James 1833–1911, *William Blake's Room*, bequeathed by Leicester Collier, 1917

Shields, Frederick James 1833–1911, *The Annunciation*, bequeathed by Leicester Collier, 1917

Shields, Frederick James 1833–1911, *The Wild Sea's Engulfing Maw (The Gouliot Caves, Sark)*, bequeathed by Leicester Collier, 1917

Shields, Frederick James 1833–1911, *Hamlet and the Ghost*, bequeathed by Leicester Collier, 1917

Shields, Frederick James 1833–1911, *Edwin Gibbs*, gift from the Manchester and Salford Sunday Ragged School Union, 1903

Shields, Frederick James 1833–1911, *Kiss Me, Baby*, bequeathed by Leicester Collier, 1917

Shields, Frederick James 1833–1911, *The Good Shepherd*, purchased, 1913

Shields, Frederick James 1833–1911, *The Widow's Son*, bequeathed by Leicester Collier, 1917

Shields, Frederick James 1833–1911, *Touch Me Not*, bequeathed by Leicester Collier, 1917

Sickert, Walter Richard 1860–1942, *The Grey Dress*, bequeathed by George Beatson Blair, 1947

Sickert, Walter Richard 1860–1942, *Dieppe*, bequeathed by George Beatson Blair, 1947

Sickert, Walter Richard 1860–1942, *Charles Bradlaugh at the Bar of the House of Commons*, gift from the National Secular Society, Manchester Branch, 1911

Sickert, Walter Richard 1860–1942, *Mamma Mia Poveretta*, purchased from the artist, 1911

Sickert, Walter Richard 1860–1942, *Jack the Ripper's Bedroom*, bequeathed by Mrs Mary Cicely Tatlock, 1980

Sickert, Walter Richard 1860–1942, *The Blue Hat*, gift from Charles Lambert Rutherston, 1925

Sickert, Walter Richard 1860–1942, *Hubby and Marie*, gift from Charles Lambert Rutherston, 1925

Sickert, Walter Richard 1860–1942, *Interior with Nude*, gift from Charles Lambert Rutherston, 1925

Sickert, Walter Richard 1860–1942, *Paradise Row, Bath*, gift from Charles Lambert Rutherston, 1925

Sickert, Walter Richard 1860–1942, *Victor Lecour*, bequeathed by George Beatson Blair, 1947

Sickert, Walter Richard 1860–1942, *O nuit d'amour*, purchased at Christie's, 1988

Sickert, Walter Richard 1860–1942, *Cicely Hey*, bequeathed by Mrs Mary Cicely Tatlock, 1980

Sickert, Walter Richard 1860–1942, *Le Grand Duquesne, Dieppe*, purchased from the Lefevre Galleries, 1935

Sickert, Walter Richard 1860–1942, *The Mirror*, gift from Charles Lambert Rutherston, 1925

Sickert, Walter Richard (attributed to) 1860–1942, *Les Modistes*, purchased from C. A. Jackson, 1928

Siefert, Arthur b.1858, *Devotion*, bequeathed by Mr James Thomas Blair, 1917

Simcock, Jack 1929–2012, *Hay Shed and Head I*, gift from the Leonard Cohen Fund, 1965, © the artist's estate

Simon, J. 1861–1945, *Israeli Scene with Figures*, gift from the Leonard Cohen Fund, 1968, © the copyright holder

Sisley, Alfred 1839–1899, *A Normandy Farm*, purchased from Mr Charles A. Jackson, 1927

Smallfield, Frederick 1829–1915, *Early Lovers*, purchased at Christie's, 1903

Smart, Edgar Rowley 1887–1934, *Quai St Michel, Paris*, purchased from the artist, 1928

Smart, Edgar Rowley 1887–1934, *'Wheatsheaf Hotel'*, gift from the Manchester Athenaeum Graphic Club and friends of the artist, 1934

Smart, Edgar Rowley 1887–1934, *Landscape: A Mountain Valley with a Church*, bequeathed by W. H. Spurr, 1960

Smart, Edgar Rowley 1887–1934, *The Mill, Giverny*, purchased from the artist, 1927

Smith, David Murray 1865–1952, *On the Sussex Downs*, purchased from the Sculptors, Painters and Gravers Exhibition, 1914, © the copyright holder

Smith, Donald b.1934, *Estate V*, purchased from the artist, 1968, © the copyright holder

Smith, Jack 1928–2011, *Shimmer: Red and Orange*, gift from the Contemporary Art Society, 1965, © the artist/courtesy Flowers Gallery, London

Smith, James H. active 1781–1789, *Sir Thomas Egerton, Bt, as an Archer in Heaton Park*, purchased from the Watts family, 1958

Smith, Mary W. active 1947–1956, *Girl with a Book*, purchased from the artist, 1956, © the copyright holder

Smith, Matthew Arnold Bracy 1879–1959, *Pomegranates*, gift from Mrs Essil Elmslie Rutherston, 1928, © by permission of the copyright holder

Smith, Matthew Arnold Bracy 1879–1959, *Dahlias*, purchased from Arthur Tooth and Sons Ltd, 1931, © by permission of the copyright holder

Smith, Matthew Arnold Bracy 1879–1959, *Model Reclining*, purchased from Arthur Tooth and Sons Ltd, 1934, © by permission of the copyright holder

Smith, Matthew Arnold Bracy 1879–1959, *Reclining Female Nude*, bequeathed by Lord Sidney Bernstein, 1995, © by permission of the copyright holder

Smith, Ray b.1949, *Celebration*, gift from the Contemporary Art Society, 1986, © the artist

Smith, Richard b.1931, *Grey/Blue (Coathanger)*, gift from the Contemporary Art Society, 1992, © the artist/courtesy Flowers Gallery, London

Smith, Thomas c.1720–1767, *View from Durdham Down, near Bristol*, gift from Mrs Mary Greg, 1919

Snyders, Frans 1579–1657, *The Leopards*, bequeathed by Mrs W. Wood, 1908

Soens, Jan 1547/1548–1611/1614, *The Holy Family with the Infant Baptist*, purchased from P. & D. Colnaghi & Co. Ltd, 1961

Solomon, Simeon 1840–1905, *Study: Female Figure*, gift from Guy Knowles, 1933

Solomon, Simeon 1840–1905, *The Magic Crystal (Study: Male Figure)*, gift from Guy Knowles, 1933

Somerset, Richard Gay 1848–1928, *A Surrey Pastoral*, gift from Joseph Broome, 1904

Somerset, Richard Gay 1848–1928, *Conway Quay*, bequeathed by William Rothwell, 1896

Somerset, Richard Gay 1848–1928, *Evening*, bequeathed by William Rothwell, 1896

Somerset, Richard Gay 1848–1928, *On the Elwy, Denbighshire*, purchased from the Autumn Exhibition, 1883

Sorgh, Hendrik Martensz. 1609/1611–1670, *A Fish Stall by a Harbour*, bequeathed by Mr and Mrs Edgar Assheton Bennett, 1979

Sorgh, Hendrik Martensz. 1609/1611–1670, *Kitchen Interior with a Man Bringing Fish for Sale*, bequeathed by Mr and Mrs Edgar Assheton Bennett, 1979

Sorgh, Hendrik Martensz. 1609/1611–1670, *Fishing Boats in a Choppy Sea*, bequeathed by Mr and Mrs Edgar Assheton Bennett, 1979

Sorrell, Alan 1904–1974, *Marching Down to the Station*, gift from HM Government, War Artists Advisory Committee, 1947, © the artist's estate

Souch, John c.1593–1645, *Sir Thomas Aston at the Deathbed of His Wife*, gift from the National Art Collections Fund, 1927

Southall, Joseph Edward 1861–1944, *A Bucket of Salt Water*, gift from Charles Lambert Rutherston, 1925, © reproduced with permission of the Barrow family

Southall, Joseph Edward 1861–1944, *The Lickey, Worcestershire*, gift from Charles Lambert Rutherston, 1925, © reproduced with permission of the Barrow family

Soyer, Paul Constant 1823–1903, *A Young Artist*, transferred from the Horsfall Museum Collection, 1918

Spear, Ruskin 1911–1990, *Airgraphs on Drying Drums in the Dark Room*, gift from HM Government, War Artists Advisory Committee, 1947, © the artist's estate/Bridgeman Art Library

Speed, Harold 1872–1957, *Dr David Little Operating for Cataract*, gift from Mrs Little, 1919, © the copyright holder

Spencelayh, Charles 1865–1958, *The White Rat*, purchased from Messrs Palmer, Howe & Co., 1926, © the artist's estate/Bridgeman Art Library

Spencelayh, Charles 1865–1958, *Generation to Generation*, gift from Robert H. Ackerly, 1954, © the artist's estate/Bridgeman Art Library

Spencer, Gilbert 1892–1979, *Blackmoor Vale*, purchased from Mrs Marchant, 1932, © the artist's estate/Bridgeman Art Library

Spencer, Gilbert 1892–1979, *Burdens Farm with Melbury Beacon*, purchased from Leicester Galleries, 1943, © the artist's estate/Bridgeman Art Library

Spencer, Gilbert 1892–1979, *The Cottage Window*, purchased from the Artists of Today exhibition, 1937, © the artist's estate/Bridgeman Art Library

Spencer, Gilbert 1892–1979, *Twyford Dorset*, purchased from Arthur Tooth and Sons Ltd, 1937, © the artist's estate/Bridgeman Art Library

Spencer, Jean 1942–1998, *4 Part Painting (Nuremberg)*, gift from Mrs Marion Waters, 2002, © the artist's estate

Spencer, Jean 1942–1998, *4 Part Painting (Nuremberg)*, gift from Mrs Marion Waters, 2002, © the artist's estate

Spencer, Jean 1942–1998, *4 Part Painting (Nuremberg)*, gift from Mrs Marion Waters, 2002, © the artist's estate

Spencer, Jean 1942–1998, *4 Part Painting (Nuremberg)*, gift from Mrs Marion Waters, 2002, © the artist's estate

Spencer, Liam David b.1964, *Cakebread Street (Sunshine after Rain)*, purchased from the artist, 2002, © the artist

Spencer, Liam David b.1964, *Chapel Street And Blackfriars, 2001*, on loan from a private individual, © the artist

Spencer, Liam David b.1964, *City of Manchester Stadium*, gift from Lynda Healey, Manchester City Council, 2011, © the artist

Spencer, Stanley 1891–1959, *The Boatbuilder's Yard, Cookham*, purchased from the artist, 1936, © the estate of Stanley Spencer 2013. All rights reserved DACS

Spencer, Stanley 1891–1959, *A Village in Heaven*, purchased from Arthur Tooth and Sons Ltd, 1937, © the estate of Stanley Spencer 2013. All rights reserved DACS

Spencer, Stanley 1891–1959, *Cookham Moor*, purchased from Arthur Tooth and Sons Ltd, 1937, © the estate of Stanley Spencer 2013. All rights reserved DACS

Spender, John Humphrey 1910–2005, *Still Life with Pears*, purchased from the Redfern Gallery, 1947, © the Humphrey Spender Archive

Spenlove-Spenlove, Frank 1866–1933, *The Little White Cross*, purchased from the artist, 1904

Spenlove-Spenlove, Frank 1866–1933, *In the Shadow of the Church, Dordrecht, Holland*, purchased from the 21st Autumn Exhibition, 1904

Spindler, Louis Pierre 1800–1889, *Eliza Crosfield*, gift from Neil Pearson, 1971

Spindler, Louis Pierre 1800–1889, *William Crosfield*, gift from Neil Pearson, 1971

Stamper, James William 1873–1947, *Wallflowers*, purchased from an exhibition, 1926, © the copyright holder

Stanfield, Clarkson Frederick 1793–1867, *The Last of the Crew*, bequeathed by Dr David Lloyd Roberts, 1920

Stanhope, John Roddam Spencer 1829–1908, *Eve Tempted*, gift from John Slagg, 1883

Stanhope, John Roddam Spencer 1829–1908, *The Waters of Lethe by the Plains of Elysium*, gift from the artist, 1889

Stanzione, Massimo 1585–1656, *Salome with the Head of John the Baptist*, purchased from Thomas Agnew and Sons Ltd, 1958

Stark, James 1794–1859, *A Barge on the Yare: Sunset*, bequeathed by Mr James Thomas Blair, 1917

Stark, James 1794–1859, *Landscape in Norfolk*, purchased from Thomas Agnew and Sons Ltd, 1903

Stark, James 1794–1859, *Landscape with a Path Between Cottages*, bequeathed by Mr James Thomas Blair, 1917

Steen, Jan 1625/1626–1679, *The Rommelpot: Interior with Three Figures*, bequeathed by Mr and Mrs Edgar Assheton Bennett, 1979

Steer, Philip Wilson 1860–1942, *Summer at Cowes*, gift from the National Art Collections Fund, 1970

Steer, Philip Wilson 1860–1942, *A Young Girl in a White Dress*, bequeathed by George Beatson Blair, 1947

Steer, Philip Wilson 1860–1942, *The Mill, Bridgnorth*, gift from Charles Lambert Rutherston, 1925

Steer, Philip Wilson 1860–1942, *A Lady in Black*, gift from Charles Lambert Rutherston, 1925

Steer, Philip Wilson 1860–1942, *Summer*, purchased from the

French Gallery, 1932

Steer, Philip Wilson 1860–1942, *The Mauve Dress*, purchased from Charles Jackson, 1930

Steer, Philip Wilson 1860–1942, *The Horseshoe Bend of the Severn*, purchased from the Goupil Gallery, 1923

Steer, Philip Wilson 1860–1942, *The Deserted Quarry, Ironbridge*, purchased from the Goupil Gallery, 1929

Steer, Philip Wilson 1860–1942, *Mist over the Needles*, purchased from Charles Jackson, 1929

Steer, Philip Wilson 1860–1942, *Return of the Fishing Fleet*, bequeathed by George Beatson Blair, 1947

Steer, Philip Wilson 1860–1942, *The Ferry, Avonmouth*, gift from Charles Lambert Rutherston, 1925

Steer, Philip Wilson 1860–1942, *The Embarkment*, bequeathed by George Beatson Blair, 1947

Steggles, Harold 1911–1971, *Essex Landscape*, purchased from the Lefevre Galleries, 1931, © the copyright holder

Steggles, Walter James 1908–1997, *Norfolk Small Holding*, gift from the Contemporary Art Society, 1946, © Walter Steggles Bequest

Steggles, Walter James 1908–1997, *The Quay, Walberswick*, gift from the Contemporary Art Society, 1977, © Walter Steggles Bequest

Stephenson, Cecil 1889–1965, *Scrolls I*, purchased from Fischer Fine Art Ltd, 1977, © the artist's estate

Stevens, Harry 1919–2008, *Kite in the Sea*, gift from Miss Margaret Pilkington, 1970, © the copyright holder

Stevenson, William Lennie b.1911, *Still Life*, purchased from W. L. Stevenson, 1955, © the copyright holder

Stokes, Adrian Scott 1854–1935, *Snow in the Tyrol*, bequeathed by Mr James Thomas Blair, 1917

Stokes, Adrian Scott 1854–1935, *November in the Dolomites*, purchased from the 21st Autumn Exhibition, 1904

Stone, Frank 1800–1859, *Self Portrait*, gift from Miss Esther Wright, 1954

Stone, Henry 1616–1653, *Thomas Fairfax, 3rd Baron Fairfax*, purchased from Shepherd Bros, 1903

Stone, Marcus C. 1840–1921, *Two's Company, Three's None*, bequeathed by Mr James Thomas Blair, 1917

Stone, Marcus C. 1840–1921, *A Girl in a Garden*, bequeathed by Mr James Thomas Blair, 1917

Stone, Marcus C. 1840–1921, *The Lost Bird*, purchased from The Fine Art Society

Stone, Marcus C. 1840–1921, *Reverie*, bequeathed by Mr James Thomas Blair, 1917

Stone, Marcus C. 1840–1921, *A Passing Cloud*, bequeathed by Mr

James Thomas Blair, 1917

Storck, Abraham Jansz. 1644–1708, *Coast Scene with Shipping Anchored Off-Shore and Figures on a Beach in the Foreground*, bequeathed by Mr and Mrs Edgar Assheton Bennett, 1979

Storck, Abraham Jansz. 1644–1708, *Shipping off Amsterdam*, gift from Mrs Robert Hatton, 1908

Stott, Edward William 1859–1918, *Feeding the Ducks*, bequeathed by George Beatson Blair, 1947

Stott, Edward William 1859–1918, *Noonday*, bequeathed by Mr James Thomas Blair, 1917

Stott, Edward William 1859–1918, *Sunday Morning*, purchased from Mr Charles A. Jackson, 1913

Stott, Edward William 1859–1918, *The Bird Cage*, bequeathed by Mr James Thomas Blair, 1917

Stott, Edward William 1859–1918, *The Old Gate*, purchased from Mr Charles A. Jackson, 1912

Stott, Edward William 1859–1918, *The Riverbank*, purchased from Thomas Agnew and Sons Ltd, 1908

Stott, William 1857–1900, *The Eiger*, purchased from Millie D. Stott, 1912

Stott, William 1857–1900, *A Summer's Day*, gift from Frederick William Jackson, 1915

Stott, William 1857–1900, *Awakening of the Spirit of the Rose*, gift from Alderman W. J. Rothwell, 1914

Stott, William 1857–1900, *Ravenglass*, bequeathed by George Beatson Blair, 1947

Stralen, Antoni van c.1594–1641, *Skating Scene with Numerous Figures on the Ice and an Island Fort*, bequeathed by Mr and Mrs Edgar Assheton Bennett, 1979

Strang, Ian 1886–1952, *Mount Kemmel*, purchased from the Exhibition of War Paintings and Drawings, 1920, © the copyright holder

Strang, William 1859–1921, *John Masefield*, purchased from the Paterson Gallery, 1930

Strang, William 1859–1921, *A Belgian Peasant Girl*, purchased, 1915

Strang, William 1859–1921, *Panchita Zorolla*, gift from Mrs Oscar Samson, 1944

Streater, Robert (attributed to) 1621–1679, *Brancepeth Castle and the Church of St Brandon, County Durham*, purchased from the Rutland Gallery, 1967

Stringer, Daniel 1754–1806, *Self Portrait*, purchased at Sotheby's, 1986

Stringer, Thomas 1722–1790, *'Driver' with Owner and Groom*, transferred from the Parks Department, Manchester City Council, 1979

Stringer, Thomas 1722–1790, *View, Supposedly of Poynton Hall, Cheshire*, purchased from Covent Garden Gallery, 1981

Stringer, Thomas 1722–1790, *Huntsman in a Landscape*, transferred from the Parks Department, Manchester City Council, 1979

Strudwick, John Melhuish 1849–1937, *When Apples Were Golden and Songs Were Sweet but Summer Had Passed Away*, purchased from the Autumn Exhibition, 1906

Stuart, Charles active 1854–1904, *Still Life with Grapes, Brambles and Bird's Nest*, bequeathed by Miss Florence Harrison, 1971

Stubbs, George 1724–1806, *Cheetah and Stag with Two Indians*, purchased at Sotheby's, 1970

Suddaby, Rowland 1912–1972, *Still Life*, purchased from the Redfern Gallery, 1936, © the artist's estate

Sugars, Fanny 1856–1933, *My Mother*, gift from the artist and family, 1933

Sutherland, Graham Vivian 1903–1980, *Press for Making Shells*, gift from HM Government, War Artists Advisory Committee, 1947, © estate of Graham Sutherland

Sutherland, Graham Vivian 1903–1980, *Bird in Landscape*, purchased from the Redfern Gallery, 1955, © estate of Graham Sutherland

Sutton, Philip b.1928, *Orange and Blue Still Life*, purchased from Roland, Browse and Delbanco, 1960, © Philip Sutton. All rights reserved, DACS 2013

Swan, John Macallan 1847–1910, *Miss Alexandra Ionides*, gift from Mrs Alexander C. Ionides, 1934

Swimmer, Thomas b.1932, *Village in Russia*, gift from Miss Margaret Pilkington, 1970, © the copyright holder

Swiss School *Landscape with Bathers*, bequeathed by George Beatson Blair, 1947

Swynnerton, Annie Louisa 1844–1933, *The Town of Siena*, bequeathed by Mrs Louisa Mary Garrett, 1936

Swynnerton, Annie Louisa 1844–1933, *The Reverend William Gaskell*, bequeathed by Mrs M. E. Gaskell, 1914

Swynnerton, Annie Louisa 1844–1933, *S. Isabel Dacre*, gift from the sitter, 1932

Swynnerton, Annie Louisa 1844–1933, *Interior of San Miniato, Florence*, bequeathed by Mrs Louisa Mary Garrett, 1936

Swynnerton, Annie Louisa 1844–1933, *An Italian Mother and Child*, bequeathed by Mrs Louisa Mary Garrett, 1936

Swynnerton, Annie Louisa 1844–1933, *The Dreamer*, gift from Miss F. R. Wilkinson, 1936

Swynnerton, Annie Louisa 1844–1933, *The Olive Gatherers*, gift from Miss F. R. Wilkinson, 1936

Swynnerton, Annie Louisa 1844–1933, *Rain Clouds, Monte*

Gennaro, bequeathed by Mrs Louisa Mary Garrett, 1936

Swynnerton, Annie Louisa 1844–1933, *The Southing of the Sun*, purchased from the artist, 1923

Swynnerton, Annie Louisa 1844–1933, *Mrs A. Scott-Elliot and Children*, purchased from Mrs Marjorie A. Scott-Elliot, 1923

Swynnerton, Annie Louisa 1844–1933, *Montagna Mia*, bequeathed by the artist, 1934

Swynnerton, Annie Louisa 1844–1933, *Adoration of the Infant Christ* (after Perugino), bequeathed by the artist, 1934

Swynnerton, Annie Louisa 1844–1933, *Crossing the Stream* (unfinished), bequeathed by Mrs Louisa Mary Garrett, 1936

Swynnerton, Annie Louisa 1844–1933, *Illusions*, bequeathed by Mrs Louisa Mary Garrett, 1936

Swynnerton, Annie Louisa 1844–1933, *Italian Landscape*, bequeathed by Dr Jane Walker, CH, LLD, 1939

Swynnerton, Annie Louisa 1844–1933, *The Vagrant*, bequeathed by the artist, 1934

Tait, Arthur Fitzwilliam 1819–1905, *London Road, Manchester*, purchased from Mr Michael Fulder, 2007

Tait, Arthur Fitzwilliam 1819–1905, *Victoria Street, Manchester*, purchased from Mr Michael Fulder, 2007

Tal-Coat, Pierre 1905–1985, *French Village*, gift from Sir Thomas D. Barlow, 1952, © the copyright holder

Tal-Coat, Pierre 1905–1985, *Landscape with a Rainbow*, gift from Sir Thomas D. Barlow, 1952, © the copyright holder

Talmage, Algernon 1871–1939, *The Old Hunter*, purchased from Mr Charles A. Jackson, 1926

Tanguy, Yves 1900–1955, *Echelles*, bequeathed by Lord Sidney Bernstein, 1995, © ARS, NY and DACS, London 2013

Tavaré, Frederick Lawrence 1847–1930, *Robinson's Bank, Smithy Door*, gift from E. L. Compston, 1938

Taylor, Doris 1890–1978, *Springtime Group*, purchased from the artist, 1932, © the copyright holder

Taylor, Doris 1890–1978, *Fruit Bowl*, purchased from the artist, 1941, © the copyright holder

Taylor, Leonard Campbell 1874–1969, *Battledore*, bequeathed by Mr James Thomas Blair, 1917, © the artist's estate/Bridgeman Art Library

Ten Kate, Herman Frederik Carel 1822–1891, *Interior of a Dutch Inn*, purchased from A. Staal, 1931

Teniers II, David 1610–1690, *Peasants Playing Cards and Skittles in a Yard*, bequeathed by Mr and Mrs Edgar Assheton Bennett, 1979

Teniers II, David 1610–1690, *The*

Dentist, bequeathed by Mr and Mrs Edgar Assheton Bennett, 1979
Teniers II, David 1610–1690, *Cottage in a Landscape*, bequeathed by Mrs Elizabeth Hatton Wood, 1908
Tennant, John F. 1796–1872, *The Old Squire*, transferred from the Horsfall Museum Collection, 1918
Terborch II, Gerard 1617–1681, *Gerbrand Pancras, Formerly Known as Hendrick Casimir II, Prince of Nassau-Dietz*, bequeathed by Mr and Mrs Edgar Assheton Bennett, 1979
Terborch II, Gerard 1617–1681, *Cornelis Vos, Burgomaster of Deventer*, bequeathed by Mr and Mrs Edgar Assheton Bennett, 1979
Thomson, John 1835–1878, *Study of a Head*, gift from Thomas Armstrong, 1906
Thomson, John 1778–1840, *Craigmillar Castle (near Edinburgh)*, gift from Mrs Roger Oldham, 1916
Thomson, John Leslie 1851–1929, *Changing Pasture*, purchased from the artist, 1901
Thornhill, James 1675/1676–1734, *Time, Truth and Justice*, purchased from Dr A. Scharf, 1964
Thornhill, James 1675/1676–1734, *The Victory of Apollo*, purchased from Dr A. Scharf, 1964
Thornhill, James 1675/1676–1734, *Time, Prudence and Vigilance*, purchased from Dr A. Scharf, 1964
Thornton, Alfred Henry Robinson 1863–1939, *Monday Morning*, purchased from Mrs A. Thornton, 1943
Tibble, Geoffrey Arthur 1909–1952, *The Studio*, purchased from Arthur Tooth and Sons Ltd, 1946, © the copyright holder
Tibble, Geoffrey Arthur 1909–1952, *Woman at a Table*, purchased from Arthur Tooth and Sons Ltd, 1946, © the copyright holder
Tilborgh, Gillis van (attributed to) 1635–1678, *The Card Players*, gift from Mrs Robert Hatton, 1908
Tisdall, Hans 1910–1997, *Moorings at Kew*, purchased from Leicester Galleries, 1946, © the copyright holder
Tisdall, Hans 1910–1997, *Still Life*, purchased from the Leger Galleries, 1946, © the copyright holder
Tissot, James 1836–1902, *Hush!*, purchased from Leicester Galleries, 1933
Tissot, James 1836–1902, *A Convalescent*, purchased from Leicester Galleries, 1925
Todd, Arthur Ralph Middleton 1891–1966, *Sub-Officer Henry E. Shaw, BEM, London Fire Service*, gift from HM Government, War Artists Advisory Committee, 1947, © the artist's estate
Todd, Frederick 1860–1942, *Warburton Church*, gift from the artist, 1927
Tomson, Arthur 1858–1905, *Apple Blossom*, gift from Mrs Arthur Tomson, 1907
Tonks, Henry 1862–1937, *Strolling Players*, purchased from P. & D. Colnaghi & Co. Ltd, 1926
Tonks, Henry 1862–1937, *The Little Invalid*, gift from Charles Lambert Rutherston, 1925
Tresham, Henry 1751–1814, *The Earl of Warwick's Vow Previous to the Battle of Towton*, purchased from Mrs F. Scharf, 1966
Trevelyan, Julian 1910–1988, *Gulls*, gift from the Leonard Cohen Fund, 1968, © the artist's estate
Troin *French Landscape*, gift from Mr Eric C. Gregory, 1946, © the copyright holder
Troyon, Constant 1810–1865, *A Pasture in Normandy*, purchased from Mr Charles A. Jackson, 1911
Tunnard, John 1900–1971, *Iconoclasm*, purchased from Miss B. Whitaker, 1961, © the copyright holder
Tunnicliffe, Charles Frederick 1901–1979, *The Small Niece*, purchased from The Manchester Academy of Fine Arts Exhibition, 1930, © estate of C. F. Tunnicliffe, OBE, RA
Tunnicliffe, Charles Frederick 1901–1979, *Young Swan*, purchased from Arthur Greatorex Ltd, 1938, © estate of C. F. Tunnicliffe, OBE, RA
Tunnicliffe, Charles Frederick 1901–1979, *Cob*, purchased from the artist, 1938, © estate of C. F. Tunnicliffe, OBE, RA
Tunnicliffe, Charles Frederick 1901–1979, *July Gulls*, purchased from the artist, 1938, © estate of C. F. Tunnicliffe, OBE, RA
Turchi, Alessandro 1578–1649, *The Flight into Egypt*, purchased from St Luke's Church, 1978
Turner, Francis Calcraft 1795–1851, *Heaton Park Races, Manchester*, bequeathed by J. T. Malpass, 1931
Turner, Joseph Mallord William 1775–1851, *Thomson's Aeolian Harp*, gift from HM Treasury, 1979
Turner, Joseph Mallord William 1775–1851, *'Now for the Painter' (Rope) – Passengers Going on Board*, gift from Frederick John Nettlefold, 1947
Tuson, Robert active c.1950–c.1960, *Flower Piece*, purchased from the artist, 1955, © the copyright holder
Tyzack, Michael 1933–2007, *Candy Man*, gift from the Contemporary Art Society, 1968, © Michael Tyzack, courtesy of Portland Gallery, London
Uhlman, Fred 1901–1985, *Near Lyme Regis*, purchased from Leicester Galleries, 1950, © the artist's estate/Bridgeman Art Library
Underwood, Leon 1890–1975, *Concrete Observation Post, Mount Kemmel*, purchased from the Exhibition of War Paintings and Drawings, 1920, © the estate of Leon Underwood, courtesy of the Redfern Gallery
unknown artist *Andieoli Giorgio (c.1465/1470–1555)*
unknown artist *Fra B. G. D'Ulma*
unknown artist *Jean Goujon (c.1510–c.1572)*
unknown artist *Lorenzo Ghilberti (c.1381–1455)*
unknown artist *Raphael D'Urbino (1483–1520)*
unknown artist *Torrigiano*
Uwins, Thomas 1782–1857, *Neapolitan Peasants at the Festa of the Madonna del Arco*, bequeathed by Sir Joseph Whitworth, 1896
Valette, Adolphe 1876–1942, *Windsor Bridge on the Irwell*, purchased from the artist, 1928
Valette, Adolphe 1876–1942, *Study of a 'Cab at All Saints'*, purchased from Capes Dunn & Co., Manchester, 2008
Valette, Adolphe 1876–1942, *Albert Square, Manchester*, purchased from the artist, 1928
Valette, Adolphe 1876–1942, *Hansom Cab at All Saints*, purchased from the artist, 1928
Valette, Adolphe 1876–1942, *Oxford Road, Manchester*, purchased from the artist, 1928
Valette, Adolphe 1876–1942, *Central Station*, purchased at Christie's, 2010
Valette, Adolphe 1876–1942, *Study for 'Albert Square'*, purchased from Capes Dunn & Co., Manchester, 1991
Valette, Adolphe 1876–1942, *Study for 'Albert Square'*, purchased from Capes Dunn & Co., Manchester, 1996
Valette, Adolphe 1876–1942, *Study for 'Albert Square'*, purchased from Capes Dunn & Co., Manchester, 1999
Valette, Adolphe 1876–1942, *Study for 'Base of Statues, Albert Square'*, purchased from Capes Dunn & Co., Manchester, 1997
Valette, Adolphe 1876–1942, *Old Cab at All Saints, Manchester*, purchased from the artist, 1928
Valette, Adolphe 1876–1942, *Bailey Bridge, Manchester*, purchased from the artist, 1928
Valette, Adolphe 1876–1942, *Castlegate, Salford*, purchased from Tib Lane Gallery, 1986
Valette, Adolphe 1876–1942, *India House, Manchester*, purchased from the artist, 1928
Valette, Adolphe 1876–1942, *Under Windsor Bridge on the Irwell, Manchester*, purchased from the artist, 1928
Valette, Adolphe 1876–1942, *Self Portrait Study*, purchased from Mr Jonathan Fildes, 2000
Valette, Adolphe 1876–1942, *York Street Leading to Charles Street, Manchester*, purchased from the artist, 1928
Valette, Adolphe 1876–1942, *Annie Barnett*, gift from the sitter, 1938
Valette, Adolphe 1876–1942, *Flowers and Fruit*, gift from Miss Annie Barnett, 1938
Valette, Adolphe 1876–1942, *Self Portrait*, gift from Miss Annie Barnett, 1938
Valette, Adolphe 1876–1942, *May Aimee Smith*, gift from Mrs Gladys Savigny, 2001
Valette, Adolphe 1876–1942, *John Henry Reynolds*, gift from the children of the sitter, 1927
Valette, Adolphe 1876–1942, *Le Puy*, purchased from Capes Dunn & Co., Manchester, 1999
Valette, Adolphe 1876–1942, *Rowley Smart*, purchased from Tib Lane Gallery, 1998
Valette, Adolphe 1876–1942, *E. H. Mooney*, bequeathed by Miss M. C. Hodgkinson, 2002
Valette, Adolphe 1876–1942, *Girl at Her Toilet*, gift from Miss Annie Barnett, 1938
Vanderbank, John 1694–1739, *Scene from 'Don Quixote': Zoraida Pretending to Swoon in the Garden*, purchased from C. Marshall Spink, 1967
Vanderbank, John 1694–1739, *Scene from 'Don Quixote': The Arrival at the Supposed Castle*, purchased from C. Marshall Spink, 1967
Vasey, Gladys 1889–1981, *Madeleine* (the artist's daughter), purchased from the artist, 1938, © the copyright holder
Vasey, Gladys 1889–1981, *Lamorna Lane, Lamorna Cove, Cornwall*, bequeathed by Mr Frank Stephens Rosser, 1957, © the copyright holder
Vasey, Gladys 1889–1981, *Lamorna Lane*, bequeathed by Mr Frank Stephens Rosser, 1968, © the copyright holder
Vaughan, John Keith 1912–1977, *Coast above Berwick I*, purchased from Leicester Galleries, 1953, © the estate of Keith Vaughan. All rights reserved, DACS 2013
Vaughan, John Keith 1912–1977, *Assembly of Figures*, gift from the Contemporary Art Society, 1957, © the estate of Keith Vaughan. All rights reserved, DACS 2013
Velde, Adriaen van de 1636–1672, *Winter Scene with a Group of Golfers on a Frozen River*, bequeathed by Mr and Mrs Edgar Assheton Bennett, 1979
Velde I, Esaias van de 1587–1630, *Landscape with Riders in a Carriage Passing a Church*, bequeathed by Mr and Mrs Edgar Assheton Bennett, 1979
Velde I, Willem van de (studio of) 1611–1693, *Sailing Vessels Passing a Coast of Sand Dunes*, bequeathed by Mr and Mrs Edgar Assheton Bennett, 1979
Velde II, Willem van de 1633–1707, *Men of War at Anchor in a Calm*, bequeathed by Mr and Mrs Edgar Assheton Bennett, 1979
Velde II, Willem van de 1633–1707, *Seascape: With a Yacht Sailing under a Rainy Sky*, bequeathed by Mr and Mrs Edgar Assheton Bennett, 1979
Velde II, Willem van de (follower of) 1633–1707, *Seascape with Yachts Moored in a Calm*, bequeathed by Mr and Mrs Edgar Assheton Bennett, 1979
Venard, Claude 1913–1999, *Still Life with Green Apple*, purchased from the Crane Gallery, 1956, © ADAGP, Paris and DACS, London 2013
Verboeckhoven, Eugène Joseph 1798–1881, *Cattle near a Lake*, bequeathed by John Edward Yates, 1934
Verboeckhoven, Eugène Joseph 1798–1881, *Sheep and Dogs*, bequeathed by Mr James Thomas Blair, 1917
Verboeckhoven, Eugène Joseph 1798–1881, *Startled*, bequeathed by John Edward Yates, 1934
Verbruggen the elder, Gaspar Peeter de 1635–1681, *Roses, Tulips, Tobacco Plants and Other Flowers in a Glass Vase*, bequeathed by Mr and Mrs Edgar Assheton Bennett, 1979
Vernet, Claude-Joseph 1714–1789, *Coast Scene with a British Man of War*, purchased from Mr and Mrs Luke Dillon-Mahon, 1977
Verveer, Salomon Leonardus 1813–1876, *Village with a Church*, bequeathed by Lady Mary Ann Boyd Dawkins, 1979
Veyrassat, Jules Jacques 1828–1893, *Returning Home*, bequeathed by Mr James Thomas Blair, 1917
Vincent, George 1796–1831, *Wooded Landscape with Figures and Gate*, gift from Alderman R. A. D. Carter, 1936
Vincent, George 1796–1831, *View near Wroxham, Norfolk*, purchased from Thomas Agnew and Sons Ltd, 1904
Vitofski, Henry 1892–1964, *The Seamstress*, purchased from the artist, 1928, © the copyright holder
Vlaminck, Maurice de 1876–1958, *Road through Trees*, purchased from the Zwemmer Gallery, 1949, © ADAGP, Paris and DACS, London 2013
Vlieger, Simon de 1601–1653, *River Estuary with Shipping on a Windy Day*, bequeathed by Mr and Mrs Edgar Assheton Bennett, 1979
Vliet, Hendrick Cornelisz. van c.1611–1675, *Portrait of a Man*, gift from Thomas Thornhill Shann, 1909
Vliet, Hendrick Cornelisz. van c.1611–1675, *Portrait of a Young Woman*, gift from Thomas Thornhill Shann, 1909
Vliet, Hendrick Cornelisz. van (after) c.1611–1675, *Interior of the Oude Kerk at Delft*, purchased from Roland, Browse and Delbanco, 1953
Vollon, Antoine 1833–1900, *Strawberries*, purchased from Mr Charles A. Jackson, 1914

Voltz, Friedrich 1817–1886, *Cattle Drinking*, transferred from the Horsfall Museum Collection, 1918

Vouet, Simon (attributed to) 1590–1649, *Apollo in His Chariot with Time*, purchased from Mrs F. Scharf, 1966

Waddington, John Barton 1835–1918, *View of Manchester from Kersal*, purchased from E. A. Burrows, 1927

Wadsworth, Edward Alexander 1889–1949, *Dunkerque*, gift from the Contemporary Art Society, 1928, © estate of Edward Wadsworth. All rights reserved, DACS 2013

Wadsworth, Edward Alexander 1889–1949, *Souvenir of Fiumicino*, purchased from the artist, 1943, © estate of Edward Wadsworth. All rights reserved, DACS 2013

Wagner, Alexander von 1838–1919, *The Chariot Race*, bequeathed by Mrs E. M. Higgins, 1898

Waite, Robert Thorne 1842–1935, *New Mown Hay*, purchased from the Autumn Exhibition, 1901

Walker, Ethel 1861–1951, *Flora*, purchased from the Lefevre Galleries, 1933, © the artist's estate/Bridgeman Art Library

Walker, Ethel 1861–1951, *Eileen*, purchased from the Lefevre Galleries, 1931, © the artist's estate/Bridgeman Art Library

Walker, Ethel 1861–1951, *An August Morning*, purchased from the artist, 1941, © the artist's estate/Bridgeman Art Library

Walker, Ethel 1861–1951, *The Bouquet of Flowers*, purchased from the artist, 1941, © the artist's estate/Bridgeman Art Library

Walker, Ethel 1861–1951, *The Miniature*, purchased from the Lefevre Galleries, 1939, © the artist's estate/Bridgeman Art Library

Wallace, Robin 1897–1952, *The Friary Wall, Norfolk*, purchased from Lockett Thompson, 1935, © the copyright holder

Wallis, Alfred 1855–1942, *Trawler and Pier*, bequeathed by Lord Sidney Bernstein, 1995

Wallis, Hugh 1871–1943, *Flowers in the Window*, purchased from Mrs Hugh Wallis, 1944, © the artist's estate

Walton, Allan 1891–1948, *Swiss Interior*, gift from Charles Lambert Rutherston, 1925, © the copyright holder

Walton, Allan 1891–1948, *Farmyard*, gift from Mr Eric C. Gregory, 1946, © the copyright holder

Walton, Allan 1891–1948, *Lowestoft Harbour*, gift from Mr Eric C. Gregory, 1946, © the copyright holder

Walton, Allan 1891–1948, *The Sand Boat*, gift from the Contemporary Art Society, 1929, © the copyright holder

Waplington, Paul Anthony

b.1938, *Basford Hill Silver Prize Band*, purchased from the artist, 1986, © the artist

Ward, Edward Matthew 1816–1879, *Byron's Early Love, 'A Dream of Annesley Hall'*, gift from Sir Charles E. Swann, 1917

Wasse, Arthur 1854–1930, *A Courtyard in Bavaria*, gift from J. W. Addleshaw, 1913

Waterhouse, John William 1849–1917, *Hylas and the Nymphs*, purchased from the artist, 1896

Waterlow, Ernest Albert 1850–1919, *Warkworth Castle, Northumberland*, purchased from the artist, 1903

Waterlow, Ernest Albert 1850–1919, *On the Mediterranean*, gift from Lady Waterlow, 1928

Watson, John Dawson 1832–1892, *Inspiration*, bequeathed by Leicester Collier, 1917

Watson, John Dawson (after) 1832–1892, *Grinling Gibbons (1648–1721)*

Watson, William d.1921, *Morning, Loch Goil*, bequeathed by Mr James Thomas Blair, 1917

Watson, William d.1921, *Morning on the Goil*, bequeathed by Mr James Thomas Blair, 1917

Watson, William Ferguson 1895–1966, *Still Life with Dead Pigeon, Finches and Falcons' Hoods*, purchased from the Leger Galleries, 1965, © the copyright holder

Watts, George Frederic 1817–1904, *The Good Samaritan*, gift from the artist, 1852

Watts, George Frederic 1817–1904, *The Honourable John Lothrop Motley*, purchased from Thomas Agnew and Sons Ltd, 1906

Watts, George Frederic 1817–1904, *Charles Hilditch Rickards*, gift from the executors of the will of C. H. Rickards, 1886

Watts, George Frederic 1817–1904, *Prayer*, purchased from Manson and Woods Christie, 1887

Watts, George Frederic 1817–1904, *Paolo and Francesca*, purchased at Christie's, 1907

Watts, George Frederic 1817–1904, *The Ulster*, gift from Charles William and Mary Cresswell Carver, 1922

Watts, George Frederic 1817–1904, *Study: Head of a Girl*, bequeathed by John Edward Yates, 1934

Watts, George Frederic 1817–1904, *The Coquette*, bequeathed by George Beatson Blair, 1947

Watts, George Frederic 1817–1904, *A Greek Idyll*, bequeathed by John Edward Yates, 1934

Waugh, Eric b.1929, *Sheep*, gift from the Leonard Cohen Fund, 1968, © the artist

Waugh, Eric b.1929, *Suffolk Farm*, gift from the Leonard Cohen Fund, 1968, © the artist

Weatherby, William c.1891–1966,

The Old Barn, purchased from the artist, 1924, © the copyright holder

Webb, James 1825–1895, *The Signal*, untraced find, 1983

Webb, James 1825–1895, *Fishing on a Squally Day*, gift, 1920

Webb, James 1825–1895, *After the Storm* (off Mont Orgueil and Gorey, Jersey), gift from R. F. Goldschmidt, 1932

Webb, James 1825–1895, *Constantinople*, bequeathed by John Edward Yates, 1934

Webb, William J. c.1830–c.1904, *The Lost Sheep*, purchased from Mr D. Croal Thomson, 1920

Weber, Philipp 1849–1921, *A Winter Evening*, transferred from the Horsfall Museum Collection, 1918

Wedgbury, David 1937–1998, *Bobby Charlton (b.1937)*, gift from the artist, 1974, © the copyright holder

Wehnert, Edward Henry (after) 1813–1868, *Andreas Mantegna (c.1431–1506)*

Weight, Carel Victor Morlais 1908–1997, *Escape of the Zebra from the Zoo during an Air Raid*, gift from HM Government, War Artists Advisory Committee, 1947, © the artist's estate/Bridgeman Art Library

Weight, Carel Victor Morlais 1908–1997, *The First Cricket Match of Spring*, purchased from Leicester Galleries, 1945, © the artist's estate/Bridgeman Art Library

Weisbrod, Richard 1906–1991, *Harbour*, gift from the Leonard Cohen Fund, 1968, © the copyright holder

Weiss, José 1859–1919, *Clear Morning*, purchased from the Goupil Gallery, 1910

West, Joan M. active 1913–c.1940, *Ennui*, purchased from Mr Charles A. Jackson, 1940, © the copyright holder

Westall, Richard 1765–1836, *The Bower of Pan*, purchased from P. & D. Colnaghi & Co. Ltd, 1971

Westcott, Philip 1815–1878, *George Cornwall Legh, MP*, gift from Thomas Agnew and Sons Ltd, 1967

Westcott, Philip 1815–1878, *Cogitating the Poor Law Bill*, transferred from the Horsfall Museum Collection, 1918

Westcott, Philip 1815–1878, *Cromwell's Protest against the Persecution of the Waldensian Ambassadors*, gift from Manchester Grammar School, 1979

Wetherbee, George Faulkner 1851–1920, *A Sylvan Stream*, purchased from the artist, 1900

Whaite, Henry Clarence 1828–1912, *The Heart of Cambria*, purchased from the artist, 1886

Whaite, Henry Clarence 1828–1912, *Just Arrived by the Sloop* (in the Conway Valley, North Wales), gift from Frederick Smallman, 1908

Whaite, Henry Clarence

1895–1978, *Walberswick, Boats on the Blythe at a Wooden Jetty*, gift from Christopher and Gillian Whaite, 1980, © the artist's estate

Whaite, Henry Clarence 1828–1912, *Gipsy Camp, Sunrise*, gift from Mrs Roberts, 1979

Whaite, Henry Clarence 1828–1912, *Llyn Dylun, the Llandudno Water Supply*, purchased from the 16th Autumn Exhibition, 1898

Wheatley, Francis 1747–1801, *A Scene in 'Twelfth Night', Act III*, purchased from C. Marshall Spink, 1953

Wheatley, John 1892–1955, *A Little Girl*, purchased from P. & D. Colnaghi & Co. Ltd, 1925, © the copyright holder

White, Ethelbert 1891–1972, *Boats at Aldeburgh*, purchased from the Redfern Gallery, 1933, © the Ethelbert White estate

White, Ethelbert 1891–1972, *Suffolk Landscape*, gift from Sir Percy Worthington and Miss M. Pilkington, 1936, © the Ethelbert White estate

Wijnants, Jan c.1635–1684, *Landscape with Cattle*, gift from Mrs McConnel, 1923

Wijnants, Jan c.1635–1684, *Wooded Landscape with Figures Walking by a Sandy Bank*, bequeathed by Mr and Mrs Edgar Assheton Bennett, 1979

Wild, David b.1931, *The River Hodder*, purchased from the artist, 1970, © the artist

Wilde, Samuel de 1748–1832, *Music*, purchased from Shepherd Bros, 1910

Wildman, William Ainsworth 1882–1950, *Oyster Dredger, Heybridge, Essex*, purchased from the artist, 1932, © the copyright holder

Wilkie, David 1785–1841, *Sir Alexander Keith*, purchased from Thomas Agnew and Sons Ltd, 1972

Wilkinson, Derek 1929–2001, *The Harbour*, purchased from the artist, 1958, © the copyright holder

Wilkinson, Derek 1929–2001, *The Beach*, purchased from The Manchester Academy of Fine Arts, 1959, © the copyright holder

Wilkinson, Derek 1929–2001, *Industrial Scene*, gift from the Leonard Cohen Fund, 1968, © the copyright holder

Wilkinson, Derek 1929–2001, *Still Life*, gift from the Leonard Cohen Fund, 1968, © the copyright holder

Wilkinson, William Henry 1856–1925, *An Italian*, gift from the pupils of the artist, 1933

Wilkinson, William Henry 1856–1925, *Self Portrait*, purchased from the artist, 1927

Williams, Terrick John 1860–1936, *The Harbour, Dieppe*, purchased from the Artists of Today exhibition, 1937

Williams, Terrick John 1860–1936, *The Rialto Market, Venice*, bequeathed by Mr Frank

Stephens Rosser, 1968

Williamson, Harold 1898–1972, *Patsy*, purchased from The Manchester Academy of Fine Arts, 1947, © the copyright holder

Willock, John Smith 1887–1976, *Seaside Circus*, purchased from The Manchester Academy of Fine Arts Exhibition, 1935, © the copyright holder

Wilson, Alexander 1803–1846, *A Horse in Platt Fields, Manchester, with Platt Hall in the Distance*, gift from Mrs Clementia Tindal-Carill-Worsley, 1963

Wilson, Frank Avray 1914–2009, *Configuration, Green and Black*, purchased from the Redfern Gallery, 1960, © the artist's estate

Wilson, Richard 1713/1714–1782, *Cicero's Villa*, purchased from Thomas Agnew and Sons Ltd, 1897

Wilson, Richard 1713/1714–1782, *Hadrian's Villa, near Tivoli*, bequeathed by Mr James Thomas Blair, 1917

Wilson, Richard 1713/1714–1782, *A Summer Evening*, purchased from Mrs Clementia Tindal-Carill-Worsley, 1969

Wilson, Richard 1713/1714–1782, *Valley of the Mawddach with Cader Idris Beyond*, purchased from Shepherd Bros, 1905

Wilson, Richard 1713/1714–1782, *The Keep of Okehampton Castle*, purchased from Thomas Agnew and Sons Ltd, 1903

Wilson, Richard (after) 1713/1714–1782, *Dolbadarn Castle and Llyn Peris*, purchased from Messrs Wilbery, 1924

Wilson, Richard (after) 1713/1714–1782, *Pembroke Castle*, gift from Mrs Robert Hatton, 1908

Wilson, Richard (follower of) 1713/1714–1782, *Italian Landscape*, purchased from Roger Oldham, 1909

Wimperis, Edmund Morison 1835–1900, *Watering Horses*, bequeathed by William Rothwell, 1896

Wimperis, Edmund Morison 1835–1900, *The Ferry*, gift from Mr James Gresham, 1917

Windus, William Lindsay 1822–1907, *The Outlaw*, gift from Sir Thomas D. Barlow, 1937

Windus, William Lindsay 1822–1907, *Samuel Teed*, gift from Major P. L. Teed, 1954

Wissing, Willem 1656–1687, *Queen Mary, Wife of William of Orange*, bequeathed by Mr James Thomas Blair, 1917

Wit, Jacob de 1695–1754, *Sketch for a Ceiling: Bacchus and Ariadne*, purchased from Dr Alfred Scharf, 1965

Witherop, Jack Coburn 1906–1984, *Washing Day, St Ives*, purchased from the artist, 1943, © the copyright holder

Wolfe, Edward 1897–1982, *Zinnias*, purchased from Mr Charles A. Jackson, 1934, © the estate of Edward Wolfe

Wolfe, Edward 1897–1982, *Ian*, gift from the guarantors of the London Artists' Association, 1934, © the estate of Edward Wolfe

Wolfe, Edward 1897–1982, *Penrhyndeudraeth*, gift from Dame Mabel Tylecote, 1985, © the estate of Edward Wolfe

Wolfe, Edward 1897–1982, *Aisha of the Kasba*, gift from the Contemporary Art Society, 1931, © the estate of Edward Wolfe

Wolfe, Edward 1897–1982, *Self Portrait*, gift from Ruth Pearson, 1985, © the estate of Edward Wolfe

Wolfe, Edward 1897–1982, *Sunflowers*, gift from Mr Eric C. Gregory, 1946, © the estate of Edward Wolfe

Wood, Christopher 1901–1930, *Poppies in a Decorated Jar*, purchased from Mr Robert H. Jackson, 1939

Wood, Christopher 1901–1930, *Loading the Boats, St Ives*, purchased from the Storran Gallery, 1936

Wood, Christopher 1901–1930, *Cumberland Landscape*, gift from the Contemporary Art Society, 1933

Wood, Christopher 1901–1930, *'Ship Inn', Mousehole*, bequeathed by Lord Sidney Bernstein, 1995

Wood, Edgar 1860–1935, *The Garden, Redcroft*, gift from The Friends of Manchester City Galleries, 1981

Wood, Edgar 1860–1935, *Italian Hilltop Farm*, gift from Mr Harry M. Fairhurst, 2007

Wood, Edgar 1860–1935, *St Mark's, Venice*, gift from The Friends of Manchester City Galleries, 1981

Wood, Ursula 1868–c.1925, *Going through the Lock*, bequeathed by Dr Jane Walker, CH, LLD, 1939

Woodrow, Joash 1927–2006, *Jacob Kramer in Hat and Coat*, gift from Mr Saul Woodrow, 2006, © the copyright holder

Wootton, John c.1682–1764, *Landscape with Fishermen*, purchased from Appleby Bros, 1953

Workman, Harold 1897–1975, *Market Carts*, purchased from The Manchester Academy of Fine Arts Exhibition, 1940, © the copyright holder

Workman, Harold 1897–1975, *Manette Street, Soho*, gift from the Royal Manchester Institution, 1936, © the copyright holder

Workman, Harold 1897–1975, *Printing Camouflage Cloth*, gift from Simpson & Godlee Ltd, 1945, © the copyright holder

Worsley, John 1919–2000, *Away Walrus from HMS 'Devonshire' at Sea*, gift from HM Government, War Artists Advisory Committee, 1947, © the artist's estate

Wouwerman, Philips 1619–1668, *Landscape with a Large Number of Peasants Merrymaking in front of a Cottage*, bequeathed by Mr and

Mrs Edgar Assheton Bennett, 1979

Wouwerman, Philips (follower of) 1619–1668, *Battle Scene*, gift from Mrs E. F. Hickman, 1931

Wright, John Michael 1617–1694, *Murrough O'Brien, 1st Earl of Inchiquin*, gift from Sir Thomas D. Barlow, 1945

Wright, Nelson 1880–1930, *A Cumberland Slate Quarry*, purchased from the artist, 1930

Wright, William Matvyn 1910–1983, *Firemen on a Roof*, gift from HM Government, War Artists Advisory Committee, 1947, © the copyright holder

Wright of Derby, Joseph 1734–1797, *Thomas Day*, purchased from the estate of Algernon Henry Strutt, 3rd Baron Belper, 1975

Wright of Derby, Joseph 1734–1797, *Portrait of a Gentleman*, purchased from Thomas Agnew and Sons Ltd, 1901

Wright of Derby, Joseph 1734–1797, *Caernarvon Castle by Moonlight*, bequeathed by William Arnold Sandby, 1905

Wright of Derby, Joseph (after) 1734–1797, *Sir Richard Arkwright*, gift from the Manchester Royal Exchange, 1968

Wyatt, Irene 1903–1987, *Summer Flowers*, gift from G. D. Hornblower, 1935, © the copyright holder

Wyatt, Maria C. active 1940–1950, *The Potteries*, purchased from The Manchester Academy of Fine Arts Exhibition, 1947, © the copyright holder

Wyllie, James W. active c.1940–c.1950, *Flowers in a Blue Jug*, gift from Edward Wolfe, 1946, © the copyright holder

Wyndham, Richard 1896–1948, *The Medway near Tonbridge*, purchased from Arthur Tooth and Sons Ltd, 1937, © the artist's estate

Yeames, William Frederick 1835–1918, *Prince Arthur and Hubert*, purchased from the Autumn Exhibition, 1883

Youngman, Nan 1906–1995, *Convolvulus*, purchased from the Manchester Society of Modern Painters and the Society of Wood Engravers, 1945, © the artist's estate

Youngman, Nan 1906–1995, *Waste Land, Tredegar, South Wales*, purchased from Leicester Galleries, 1953, © the artist's estate

Yvon, Adolphe 1817–1893, *Marshal Ney Supporting the Rear Guard during the Retreat from Moscow*, transferred from the Royal Manchester Institution, 1882

Zick, Januarius 1730–1797, *Christ Healing the Sick*, gift from the YMCA, 1961

Zoffany, Johann 1733–1810, *Venus Bringing Arms to Aeneas*, purchased from P. & D. Colnaghi & Co. Ltd, 1966

Zuccarelli, Francesco 1702–1788, *Pastoral Landscape*, gift from the

trustees of the will of Lady Marks of Broughton, 1972

Manchester Jewish Museum

Coventry, Gertrude Mary 1886–1964, *Alderman Leslie Lever (1905–1977), Lord Mayor of Manchester*, gift, © the copyright holder

Flax, J. *Manchester Central Synagogue During Shavuot*, gift, © the copyright holder

Gardener, R. S. *The Manchester Spanish and Portugese Synagogue*, gift, © the copyright holder

Midgley, Donald G. *A Hebrew Teacher*, gift, © the copyright holder

Reed *Alderman A. Moss, Lord Mayor of Manchester (1953–1954)*, presented by colleagues and friends of the sitter for services to the Manchester Victoria Memorial Jewish Hospital, © the copyright holder

Schlesinger, M. *Central Synagogue, Manchester*, © the copyright holder

Stiasteny, Anton *Gunner Elias Harris (1881–1968)*, gift, © the copyright holder

unknown artist *Abraham Lazarus Kastenburg (d.1874)*, gift

unknown artist *Memorial to Holocaust Victims*, gift

unknown artist *Abraham Moss, Lord Mayor of Manchester*, presented by the Manchester Jewish Blind Society

unknown artist *David M. Gouldman*, gift

unknown artist *Emmanuel Nove*, gift

unknown artist *H. Bornstein, Chief Cantor*, gift

unknown artist *Mark Bloom*, gift

unknown artist *Mordacae Davide Basso (b.1815)*, gift

unknown artist *Mrs David M. Gouldman*, gift

unknown artist *Portrait of an Unknown Man*

unknown artist *Reverend Professor David Myer Isaacs (1810–1879)*, gift

unknown artist *Two Orthodox Jews in Discussion*, gift

Virotski, Henry *Ephraim Marks*, gift

Manchester Metropolitan University

Adams, Alastair Christian b.1969, *Dame Sandra Burslem*, © the artist

Aherne, J. *Jerusalem Bazaar*, © the copyright holder

Craddock, A. *Cockerel and Head*, © the copyright holder

Horowitz, S. J. *Abstract*, © the copyright holder

Hyatt, John b.1958, *The Source*, © the artist

Jones, Cayman *Faces*, © the copyright holder

Morrocco, Alberto 1917–1998, *A. H. Body, Founder, Principal*

(1946–1966), © the artist's estate

Philipson, Robin 1916–1992, *Dusk*, © the artist's estate

Riley, Harold b.1934, *Sir Kenneth Green (1934–2010)*, © the copyright holder

unknown artist *Figures*

unknown artist *Figures and Buildings*

unknown artist *Landscape*

unknown artist *River Scene*

Manchester Metropolitan University Special Collections

Billyard, Kenneth Harry 1943–1977, *'Landscape Metamorphosis No.1'*, © the copyright holder

Bradbury, Emma Louise 1866–1959, *Study of Sculpture*, © the copyright holder

Bradbury, Emma Louise 1866–1959, *Study of a Male Nude**, © the copyright holder

Brannan, Peter 1926–1994, *The Barman*, © the artist's estate

Brannan, Peter 1926–1994, *Reading in Bed*, © the artist's estate

Browne, Michael J. b.1963, *Path*, © the artist

Dakin, Andrew *View from a Window**, © the copyright holder

Farleigh, John F. W. C 1900–1965, *Sunset from Tower Bridge*, © the copyright holder

Hagan-Burt, Dympna b.1968, *Drifting Off*, © the artist

Hagan-Burt, Dympna b.1968, *Looking Back*, © the artist

Hargreaves, Joan 1921–2007, *Still Life**, © the copyright holder

Hargreaves, Joan 1921–2007, *Dutch Girl**, © the copyright holder

Hargreaves, Joan 1921–2007, *Two Men at a Table**, © the copyright holder

Hargreaves, Joan 1921–2007, *Female Nude**, © the copyright holder

Hargreaves, Joan 1921–2007, *Surrey Landscape**, © the copyright holder

Hargreaves, Joan 1921–2007, *Still Life 9**, © the copyright holder

Hargreaves, Joan 1921–2007, *Still Life 5**, © the copyright holder

Hargreaves, Joan 1921–2007, *Pink Still Life**, © the copyright holder

Hargreaves, Joan 1921–2007, *Boats**, © the copyright holder

Hargreaves, Joan 1921–2007, *House with Black Shadows**, © the copyright holder

Hargreaves, Joan 1921–2007, *Boats**, © the copyright holder

Hargreaves, Joan 1921–2007, *City Painting**, © the copyright holder

Hargreaves, Joan 1921–2007, *Dancers**, © the copyright holder

Hargreaves, Joan 1921–2007, *Elvaston Crescent**, © the copyright holder

Hargreaves, Joan 1921–2007, *Family**, © the copyright holder

Hargreaves, Joan 1921–2007, *Two*

*Nudes in a Garden** (recto), © the copyright holder

Hargreaves, Joan 1921–2007, *Figures in a Park** (verso), © the copyright holder

Hargreaves, Joan 1921–2007, *Flowers in a Pot**, © the copyright holder

Hargreaves, Joan 1921–2007, *Flowers in a Vase**, © the copyright holder

Hargreaves, Joan 1921–2007, *Landscape 1**, © the copyright holder

Hargreaves, Joan 1921–2007, *Landscape 2**, © the copyright holder

Hargreaves, Joan 1921–2007, *Landscape**, © the copyright holder

Hargreaves, Joan 1921–2007, *Male Nude 1**, © the copyright holder

Hargreaves, Joan 1921–2007, *Male Nude 2**, © the copyright holder

Hargreaves, Joan 1921–2007, *Male Nude with Boxes**, © the copyright holder

Hargreaves, Joan 1921–2007, *Male Nude with Still Life**, © the copyright holder

Hargreaves, Joan 1921–2007, *Nude Woman 1**, © the copyright holder

Hargreaves, Joan 1921–2007, *Nude Woman 2**, © the copyright holder

Hargreaves, Joan 1921–2007, *Park Scene**, © the copyright holder

Hargreaves, Joan 1921–2007, *Portrait of a Lady in Red**, © the copyright holder

Hargreaves, Joan 1921–2007, *Portrait of an Unknown Lady 1**, © the copyright holder

Hargreaves, Joan 1921–2007, *Portrait of an Unknown Lady 2**, © the copyright holder

Hargreaves, Joan 1921–2007, *Portrait of an Unknown Lady 3**, © the copyright holder

Hargreaves, Joan 1921–2007, *Portrait of an Unknown Lady 4** (recto), © the copyright holder

Hargreaves, Joan 1921–2007, *Still Life** (verso), © the copyright holder

Hargreaves, Joan 1921–2007, *Seated Nude**, © the copyright holder

Hargreaves, Joan 1921–2007, *Still Life 1**, © the copyright holder

Hargreaves, Joan 1921–2007, *Still Life 2**, © the copyright holder

Hargreaves, Joan 1921–2007, *Still Life 3**, © the copyright holder

Hargreaves, Joan 1921–2007, *Still Life 4**, © the copyright holder

Hargreaves, Joan 1921–2007, *Still Life 6**, © the copyright holder

Hargreaves, Joan 1921–2007, *Still Life 7**, © the copyright holder

Hargreaves, Joan 1921–2007, *Still Life 8**, © the copyright holder

Hargreaves, Joan 1921–2007, *Still Life with a Cézanne Book**, © the copyright holder

Hargreaves, Joan 1921–2007, *Still Life with Flowers**, © the copyright holder

Hargreaves, Joan 1921–2007, *Two Male Nudes**, © the copyright holder

Hargreaves, Joan 1921–2007, *Vase of Flowers**, © the copyright holder

Hewison, Jim M. *The Hall*, © the copyright holder

Howard, Ghislaine b.1953, *Collette in Rehearsal*, © the artist

Howard, Ghislaine b.1953, *Dennis in Rehearsal*, © the artist

Hyatt, John b.1958, *No.15: Tall Tales and Short Stories from the Collection of the Angel of History*, © the artist

Hyatt, John b.1958, *Tall Tales and Short Stories from the Collection of the Angel of History #7*, © the artist

McAleer, Mary Agnes active 1970–1990, *Four Portraits of an Unknown Man**, © the copyright holder

McAleer, Mary Agnes active 1970–1990, *Four Portraits of an Unknown Woman**, © the copyright holder

McAleer, Mary Agnes active 1970–1990, *Two Figures**, © the copyright holder

Muckley, Louis Fairfax 1862–1926, *William Jabez Muckley (1829–1905)*

Picking, John b.1939, *Confessionale No.7*, © the copyright holder

unknown artist *Portrait of an Unknown Man**

Weinberger, Harry 1924–2009, *'Studio 1'*, on loan from the Manchester School of Art, © the artist's estate

Whittam, William Wright 1931–1996, *All Saints Park, Manchester*, © the copyright holder

Whittam, William Wright 1931–1996, *Female Nude**, © the copyright holder

Whittam, William Wright 1931–1996, *Female Nude**, © the copyright holder

Whittam, William Wright 1931–1996, *Figures in a Park**, © the copyright holder

Whittam, William Wright 1931–1996, *Pigeons on Pavement**, © the copyright holder

Whittam, William Wright 1931–1996, *Portrait of an Unknown Man in a White Shirt**, © the copyright holder

Whittam, William Wright 1931–1996, *Portrait of an Unknown Woman Lying on Fabric**, © the copyright holder

Wolfendon, Christopher *'69'*, © the copyright holder

Wolfendon, Christopher *The Black Death*, © the copyright holder

Wood, Edgar 1860–1935, *Tunisia*

Manchester Metropolitan University, Arts for Health Archive

Brown, Gilford b.1965, *Man on a Horse*, on loan from Langley Brown, since 2011, © the artist

Chantrey, Melvyn b.1945, *Waterfall*, gift from the artist, © the artist

Manchester Metropolitan University, Faculty of Art and Design

Woolley, Hannah *Colour Abstract*, © the copyright holder

Manchester Town Hall

Allen, Joseph William (attributed to) 1803–1852, *John Dalton*, gift from Mr David Dick

Benson, Edward 1808–1863, *Sir Joseph Heron*, gift from Thomas Hudson, 1932

Bradley, William 1801–1857, *Joseph Brotherton*, gift from John Harding, 1849

Bradley, William (attributed to) 1801–1857, *James Kershaw*, gift from anonymous subscribers, 1850

Bradley, William (circle of) 1801–1857, *Sir Thomas Potter*, gift from Alderman John Brooks, 1842

Cartledge, William 1891–1976, *Sir William Kay*, © the copyright holder

Cartledge, William 1891–1976, *Alderman James Henry Swales*, gift from the sitter, 1927, © the copyright holder

Desanges, Louis William 1822–1906, *The Earl of Derby*, gift from The Derby Memorial Committee, 1877

Dugdale, Thomas Cantrell 1880–1952, *W. B. Pritchard*, © Joanna Dunham

Faulkner, Benjamin Rawlinson 1787–1849, *William Nield*, gift from anonymous subscribers, 1849

Gabain, Ethel Leontine 1883–1950, *Dame Mary Latchford Kingsmill Jones*, © the artist's estate

Grant, Francis (attributed to) 1803–1878, *Sergeant R. B. Armstrong, QC, MP*, gift from anonymous subscribers, 1870

Guttenberg *William Cundiff Hooke, Richard* 1820–1908, *Benjamin Nicholls*, gift from anonymous subscribers, 1863

Hooke, Richard 1820–1908, *Ivie Mackie*, purchased from anonymous subscribers, 1863

Johnson, Herbert 1848–1906, *John Hinchcliffe*, gift from A. J. Balfour, 1891

Knight, John Prescott 1803–1881, *Sir Joseph Heron*, gift, 1870

Knight, John Prescott 1803–1881, *John Bright*

Lecomte-Vernet, Charles Émile Hippolyte 1821–1900, *Henry Julius Leppoc*, gift from anonymous subscribers, 1877

Mooney, Edward Hartley 1877–1938, *Edward Holt*, gift from members and ex-members of the Manchester City Council and Officials, 1928

Mooney, Edward Hartley 1877–1938, *George Westcott*

Mostyn, Thomas Edwin 1864–1930, *John Foulkes Roberts*, gift from anonymous subscribers, 1898

Mostyn, Thomas Edwin 1864–1930, *Sir William Henry Talbot*, gift from anonymous subscribers, 1907

Muckley, William Jabez 1829–1905, *Thomas Goadsby*, gift from Mrs Goadsby, 1867

Munns, Henry Turner 1832–1898, *Abel Heywood*

Munns, Henry Turner 1832–1898, *Sir John Harwood*, gift from anonymous subscribers, 1892

Munns, Henry Turner 1832–1898, *Sir Anthony Marshall*, gift from anonymous subscribers, 1895

Noakes, Michael b.1933, *Her Majesty Queen Elizabeth II (b.1926)*, gift, © the artist

Patten, George 1801–1865, *Mark Phillips*, gift from anonymous subscribers, 1852

Patten, George 1801–1865, *Alexander Kay*, gift from anonymous subscribers, 1850

Patten, George 1801–1865, *John Potter*, gift from anonymous subscribers, 1850

Patten, George 1801–1865, *William Benjamin Watkins*, gift from anonymous subscribers

Patten, George 1801–1865, *George Wilson*, gift from anonymous subscribers, 1851

Patten, George 1801–1865, *Charles James Stanley Walker*, gift from anonymous subscribers, 1852

Patten, George 1801–1865, *Elkanah Armitage*, gift from anonymous subscribers

Penny, Edward 1714–1791, *James, Lord Strange*

Percy, William 1820–1893, *John Grave*, gift from The Grave Testimonial Committee, 1876

Reynolds, Samuel William 1773–1835, *Alderman Sir Thomas Potter*

Reynolds, Samuel William 1773–1835, *Richard Potter*

Sidley, Samuel 1829–1896, *Daniel Adamson*

Snyders, Frans 1579–1657, *Landscape with Birds and Animals*

unknown artist *Abel Heywood*

unknown artist *Alderman Sir Thomas Baker*

unknown artist *Charles Behrens*

unknown artist *James Bake*, gift from Sara Vose, 1877

unknown artist *Portrait of an Unknown Gentleman*

unknown artist *R. A. D. Carter*

unknown artist *Sir John Mark*, gift, 1956

unknown artist *Sir Joseph Heron*, gift from Mr Thomas Hudson, 1932

unknown artist *Sir Philip Dingle*

unknown artist *The Central Executive Cotton Famine Relief Committee*

unknown artist *William Booth*

Vasey, Gladys 1889–1981, *Thomas Henry Adams*, gift from the Associated Society of Locomotive Engineers and Firemen, © the copyright holder

Williams, Margaret Lindsay 1888–1960, *Elizabeth II (b.1926)*, © the copyright holder

Williamson, Harold 1898–1972, *Douglas Gosling*, © the copyright holder

Museum of Science and Industry

B., R. *Mary George, Director of the Electrical Association for Women (1956–1976)**, gift from the Electricity Council, 1990, © the copyright holder

Baxter, Gib *Avro Vulcan en route to the Falklands**, © the copyright holder

Copnall, Frank Thomas 1870–1949, *Percy Norris**, gift from Mr Brian D. Norris, 1970, © the copyright holder

Eastman, Frank S. 1878–1964, *A. V. Roe**, © the copyright holder

Garratt, Agnes M. 1867–1944, *While at Alloa, Scotland*, gift from Mrs M. Mumford, 1984, © the copyright holder

Garratt, Herbert William 1864–1913, *Cavalier** (recto), gift from Mrs M. Mumford, 1984

Garratt, Herbert William 1864–1913, *Cavalier* (verso), gift from Mrs M. Mumford, 1984

Garratt, Herbert William 1864–1913, *Ship in a Stormy Sea**, gift from Mrs M. Mumford, 1984

Garratt, Herbert William 1864–1913, *View of a Ship from the Coast at Worthing**, gift from Mrs M. Mumford, 1984

Garratt, Herbert William 1864–1913, *Ship at Sea**, gift from Mrs M. Mumford, 1984

Garratt, Herbert William 1864–1913, *0-6-0+0-6-0 Garratt Locomotive**, gift from Mrs M. Mumford, 1978

Garratt, Herbert William 1864–1913, *Great Eastern Railway Locomotive No.603**, gift from Mrs M. Mumford, 1978

Garratt, Herbert William 1864–1913, *Steam Locomotive No.310**, gift from Mrs M. Mumford, 1978

Garratt, Herbert William 1864–1913, *View of York Station**, gift from Mrs M. Mumford, 1978

Garratt, Herbert William 1864–1913, *View through the Front Window of a Steam Locomotive**, gift from Mrs M. Mumford, 1978

Harris, Alfred Peter b.1932, *1830 Warehouse and Liverpool Road Station**, © the copyright holder

Jagger, David (attributed to) 1891–1958, *Dr S. Z. de Ferranti, FRS**, gift from Ferranti International plc, 1996, © the artist's estate

Kay, Rupert active 1973–1978, *Pott Street Pumping Station**, purchased

from the artist, 1978, © the copyright holder

Miller, Edmund b.1929, *'The Quiet Test-Pilot'**, gift from Mr P. Clegg, 1989, © the artist

Miller, Edmund b.1929, *Airborne Pioneers*, gift from Mr. P. Clegg, 1987, © the artist

Miller, Edmund b.1929, *Roy Chadwick**, gift from Mr. P. Clegg, 1992, © the artist

T., R. *Firgrove Mill Engine*, 1907, gift from Mr A. Kane, District General Manager of British Telecommunications, 1988, © the copyright holder

unknown artist *Richard Johnson (1809–1881)*, gift from Mr P. Johnson, 2010

unknown artist *Charles Beyer**

unknown artist *Aerial View of a Factory on the River Avon**

National Football Museum

Adamson, Sean *Ball Game*, © the copyright holder

Avery, Stuart J. C. *Pride of the Nation*, © the copyright holder

Beaton, Cecil Walter Hardy 1904–1980, *Footballers*, on loan from The Priory Collection, © National Portrait Gallery, London

Beaton, Cecil Walter Hardy 1904–1980, *The Tackle*, on loan from The Priory Collection, © National Portrait Gallery, London

Brand, Doris *Boots (They Were Christopher's)*, purchased from the FIFA Collection, © the copyright holder

Brandao, Joyce *Football at Rio de Janeiro*, purchased from the FIFA Collection, © the copyright holder

Bratby, John Randall 1928–1992, *Jimmy Hill*, on loan from a private collection (?), © the artist's estate/ Bridgeman Art Library

Brown, Reginald *Wembley 1923*, on loan from the Neville Evans Collection, © the copyright holder

Browne, Michael J. b.1963, *The Art of The Game*, on loan from Eric Cantona, © the artist

Buza, Kustim *Sunset*, on loan from the Football Association Collection, © the copyright holder

Cains, Gerald Albert b.1932, *Saturday Taxpayers*, purchased from the Langton Collection, © the artist

Chart, Daphne c.1910–2006, *Clapham Common*, purchased from the Langton Collection, © the copyright holder

Colquhoun, Ithell 1906–1988, *The Game of The Year*, purchased from the FIFA Collection, © the artist's estate

Coverley-Price, Victor 1901–1988, *Study of Textures*, purchased from the FIFA Collection, © the copyright holder

Deykin, Henry Cotterill 1905–1989, *Aston Villa v West Bromwich Albion*, on loan from The Priory Collection, © the copyright holder

Deykin, Henry Cotterill 1905–1989, *Wembley Cup Final 1951*, purchased from the FIFA Collection, © the copyright holder

Edwards, Peter Douglas b.1955, *Bobby Charlton*, on loan from a private collection (?), © the artist

Elford, N. *Portsmouth 1, Manchester United 1, Fratton Park, 1924*, on loan from The Priory Collection, © the copyright holder

Freeth, Hubert Andrew 1913–1986, *Watford Dressing Room*, © Freeth family

Goodman *Everton F. C.*, © the copyright holder

Hackney, Arthur 1925–2010, *Spectators Returning Home After Port Vale v Accrington Stanley*, © the copyright holder

Hall, Clifford 1904–1973, *Football Match*, on loan from The Priory Collection, © the copyright holder

Higgs, J. *A Huddersfield Town Footballer Meets King George V*, purchased from the FIFA Collection, © the copyright holder

Holwell, Chris *Phew What a Scorcher/Maradona Goal*, purchased from the FIFA Collection, © the copyright holder

Horridge *Aston Villa*, © the copyright holder

Howell, Chris *Goal Mouth Scramble*, © the copyright holder

Jennings, Chris *Via Goldoni, Milano, 1908*, purchased from the FIFA Collection, © the copyright holder

Lambert, Albert *At the Match*, on loan from The Priory Collection, © the copyright holder

Lancaster, Edward *Village Football*, © the copyright holder

M., G. O. *In the Dressing Room*, purchased from the FIFA Collection, © the copyright holder

Martin, Benito Quinquela 1890–1977, *Rincon de la Boca*, © the copyright holder

Pearce, William H. *A Tense Moment*, on loan from The Priory Collection, © the copyright holder

Petts, J. *The Goalkeeper*, FIFA Collection, © the copyright holder

Powell, John *Soccer in the Suburbs*, on loan from The Priory Collection, © the copyright holder

Riordon, Eric 1906–1948, *Canadian Tour, 1950*, on loan from the Football Association Collection, © the copyright holder

Samuelson, Peter 1912–1996 *Football Match*, on loan from The Priory Collection, © the artist's estate/Bridgeman Art Library

Scott, Septimus Edwin 1879–1962, *Big Match*, © the copyright holder

Slater, Paul b.1953 *Burnley F. C.*, © the copyright holder

Smith, Paul *The Day Before War Broke Out (A Football Match, 1939)*, © the copyright holder

unknown artist *Fureball*, purchased from the FIFA Collection, © the copyright holder

unknown artist *Penalty*, © the

copyright holder

unknown artist *Tom Finney*, © the copyright holder

unknown artist *Willie Cunningham in Preston North End Kit*, on loan from the Neville Evans Collection, © the copyright holder

unknown artist *Camp Ball*, purchased from the FIFA Collection

unknown artist *William Charles Cuff*, © the copyright holder

unknown artist *John Charles*, on loan from The Priory Collection, © the copyright holder

unknown artist *Village Green Soccer*, purchased from the FIFA Collection, © the copyright holder

Vaudou, Gaston 1891–1957, *A Soccer Match*, purchased from the FIFA Collection, © ADAGP, Paris and DACS, London 2013

Webster, Thomas George 1800–1886, *Football*, purchased from the FIFA Collection

Webster, Thomas George 1800–1886, *A Football Game*, purchased from the FIFA Collection

Webster, Thomas George (after) 1800–1886, *Football*, on loan from The Priory Collection

People's History Museum

Alston, W. P. *Aneurin Bevan (1897–1960)*, gift, 1993, © the copyright holder

Ashford, J. *Railway Worker Holding Bunch of Red Roses**, gift, c.1980, © the copyright holder

Ashton, J. *Two Workers and White Dove**, gift, 1980s, © the copyright holder

Bernasconi, George Henry 1841–1916, *Merchant Shipping Bill Banner*, gift from Mrs Flinn, 1990

Brooks, Ern 1911–1993, *Still Life, 'Daily Worker' Newspaper**, gift from the Communist Party of Great Britain, 1993, © the copyright holder

Brooks, Ern 1911–1993, *Zeus and Europa**, gift from the Communist Party of Great Britain, 1997, © the copyright holder

Carr, Dorothy *Mining Village (possibly Spennymoor)*, gift from the artist, 1997, © the copyright holder

Carr, Dorothy *Spennymoor**, gift from the artist, 1997, © the copyright holder

Carr, Dorothy *Spennymoor**, gift from the artist, 1997, © the copyright holder

Dixon, William *Tin-Plate Workers' Banner, Liverpool**, gift from the Manufacturing, Science, Finance (MSF) trade union/J. Carr, 1989

Easton, A. F. *Mrs Florence Willard, Founder Member of TULC and National Museum of Labour History (now People's History Museum)*, gift, c.1980, © the copyright holder

Eisler, Georg 1928–1998, *Miners'*

Strike, 1984–1985*, gift from the artist, 1989, © Georg and Alice Eisler Foundation/Georg Eisler Archive, Vienna

Galeotti, Renzo *James Klugmann (1912–1977)*, gift from the Communist Party of Great Britain, 1993, © DACS 2013

Gibbons, Geoff P. active 1984–1990, *Solidarity, 1984–1985**, gift from the artist, 1990, © the copyright holder

Glover, Margaret b.c.1940, *Lord Fenner Brockway: Towards Tomorrow*, gift from the artist, 1991, © the copyright holder

Gray, Stuart *Hatted and Bearded Man**, gift, 1980s, © the copyright holder

Hancock, Samuel Harry 1862–1932, *Landlord and Tenants*, gift from Mr Andrew Wood, 2011

Healey, Christine 1945–2010, *Faces of Barbara Castle**, gift from the artist, 1994, © the copyright holder

Healey, Christine 1945–2010, *Faces of Foot**, gift from the artist, 1994, © the copyright holder

Locket, D. *Coal Mining, 1985*, gift from the artist, 1986, © the copyright holder

Midgely, John *Professional Footballers' Association Banner*, on loan from the Professional Footballers' Association, since 1991, © the copyright holder

Moscheles, Felix Stone 1833–1917, *Robert Cunningham Graham (?)*, gift, c.1980

Rowe, Cliff 1904–1989, *Girl with Skipping Rope*, gift from the artist, © the artist's estate

Rowe, Cliff 1904–1989, *Woman Sitting on Doorstep*, gift from the artist, © the artist's estate

Rowe, Cliff 1904–1989, *Woman with Birdcage in Window*, gift from the artist, © the artist's estate

Rowe, Cliff 1904–1989, *Two Women and Pram*, gift from the artist, © the artist's estate

Rowe, Cliff 1904–1989, *Two Young Girls on Doorstep*, gift from the artist, © the artist's estate

Rowe, Cliff 1904–1989, *Child Knocking on Door*, gift from the artist, © the artist's estate

Rowe, Cliff 1904–1989, *Sorting Pencils*, gift from the artist, © the artist's estate

Rowe, Cliff 1904–1989, *Impulse Panel*, gift from the artist, © the artist's estate

Rowe, Cliff 1904–1989, *Man on Long Boot Machine*, gift from the artist, © the artist's estate

Rowe, Cliff 1904–1989, *Gloved Machine Operator*, gift from the artist, © the artist's estate

Rowe, Cliff 1904–1989, *Woman at Bottle Machine*, gift from the artist, © the artist's estate

Rowe, Cliff 1904–1989, *Woman Looking Through a Microscope*, gift from the artist, © the artist's estate

Rowe, Cliff 1904–1989, *Woman Machinist*, gift from the artist, ©

the artist's estate

Rowe, Cliff 1904–1989, *Centrifugal Pump*, gift from the artist, © the artist's estate

Rowe, Cliff 1904–1989, *Man with Goggles at Machine*, gift from the artist, © the artist's estate

Rowe, Cliff 1904–1989, *Pulping Machine*, gift from the artist, © the artist's estate

Rowe, Cliff 1904–1989, *Still Life with Spectacles*, gift from the artist, © the artist's estate

Rowe, Cliff 1904–1989, *Black Singer*, gift from the artist, © the artist's estate

Rowe, Cliff 1904–1989, *Street Corner*, gift from the artist, © the artist's estate

Rowe, Cliff 1904–1989, *Acrobats*, gift from the artist, © the artist's estate

Rowe, Cliff 1904–1989, *Child in Pushchair* (unfinished), gift from the artist, © the artist's estate

Rowe, Cliff 1904–1989, *Dancer in Two Positions*, gift from the artist, © the artist's estate

Rowe, Cliff 1904–1989, *Emblematic Figure and Bird*, gift from the artist, © the artist's estate

Rowe, Cliff 1904–1989, *Ships Moored Together*, gift from the artist, © the artist's estate

Rowe, Cliff 1904–1989, *Southend*, gift from the artist, © the artist's estate

Rowe, Cliff 1904–1989, *Man at Conveyor Machine*, gift from the artist, © the artist's estate

Rowe, Cliff 1904–1989, *Old Lighthouse, Harwich*, gift from the artist, © the artist's estate

Rowe, Cliff 1904–1989, *Boat Hulls*, gift from the artist, © the artist's estate

Rowe, Cliff 1904–1989, *Section of Machine Part*, gift from the artist, © the artist's estate

Rowe, Cliff 1904–1989, *Shapes*, gift from the artist, © the artist's estate

Rowe, Cliff 1904–1989, *Millworker in Headscarf*, gift from the artist, © the artist's estate

Rowe, Cliff 1904–1989, *Astronaut*, gift from the artist, © the artist's estate

Rowe, Cliff 1904–1989, *Baker*, gift from the artist, © the artist's estate

Rowe, Cliff 1904–1989, *Bearded Scientist*, gift from the artist, © the artist's estate

Rowe, Cliff 1904–1989, *Bike Racers Cornering*, gift from the artist, © the artist's estate

Rowe, Cliff 1904–1989, *Bootmaking*, gift from the artist, © the artist's estate

Rowe, Cliff 1904–1989, *Buoys on Quay*, gift from the artist, © the artist's estate

Rowe, Cliff 1904–1989, *By Chance*, gift from the artist, © the artist's estate

Rowe, Cliff 1904–1989, *Casting*, gift from the artist, © the artist's estate

Rowe, Cliff 1904–1989, *Chemist*,

gift from the artist, © the artist's estate

Rowe, Cliff 1904–1989, *Child on Rocking Horse*, gift from the artist, © the artist's estate

Rowe, Cliff 1904–1989, *Crane Operator*, gift from the artist, © the artist's estate

Rowe, Cliff 1904–1989, *Drying Enamel Plates*, gift from the artist, © the artist's estate

Rowe, Cliff 1904–1989, *Electrical Engineer*, gift from the artist, © the artist's estate

Rowe, Cliff 1904–1989, *Engine Assembler*, gift from the artist, © the artist's estate

Rowe, Cliff 1904–1989, *Female Glass Worker*, gift from the artist, © the artist's estate

Rowe, Cliff 1904–1989, *Female Guitarist*, gift from the artist, © the artist's estate

Rowe, Cliff 1904–1989, *Fireside*, gift from the artist, © the artist's estate

Rowe, Cliff 1904–1989, *Fishing Boat*, gift from the artist, © the artist's estate

Rowe, Cliff 1904–1989, *Fishing Boat on the Stocks*, gift from the artist, © the artist's estate

Rowe, Cliff 1904–1989, *Fruit Basket*, gift from the artist, © the artist's estate

Rowe, Cliff 1904–1989, *Glass Blower*, gift from the artist, © the artist's estate

Rowe, Cliff 1904–1989, *Glassblower at Red Furnace*, gift from the artist, © the artist's estate

Rowe, Cliff 1904–1989, *Guitarist*, gift from the artist, © the artist's estate

Rowe, Cliff 1904–1989, *Hospital Laundry Workers*, gift from the artist, © the artist's estate

Rowe, Cliff 1904–1989, *Human Pattern*, gift from the artist, © the artist's estate

Rowe, Cliff 1904–1989, *Industrial Plant*, gift from the artist, © the artist's estate

Rowe, Cliff 1904–1989, *Kentish Town*, gift from the artist, © the artist's estate

Rowe, Cliff 1904–1989, *Kentish Town, 1937*, gift from the artist, © the artist's estate

Rowe, Cliff 1904–1989, *Loco Cleaners*, gift from the artist, © the artist's estate

Rowe, Cliff 1904–1989, *Man and Machine* (unfinished), gift from the artist, © the artist's estate

Rowe, Cliff 1904–1989, *Man and Microscope*, gift from the artist, © the artist's estate

Rowe, Cliff 1904–1989, *Man at Boot Machine*, gift from the artist, © the artist's estate

Rowe, Cliff 1904–1989, *Man at Metal Press*, gift from the artist, © the artist's estate

Rowe, Cliff 1904–1989, *Man Drawing Out Molten Glass*, gift from the artist, © the artist's estate

Rowe, Cliff 1904–1989, *Man*

Leaning Over Woman, gift from the artist, © the artist's estate
Rowe, Cliff 1904–1989, *Man Pouring Liquid into Tank*, gift from the artist, © the artist's estate
Rowe, Cliff 1904–1989, *Man Shaping a Bottle*, gift from the artist, © the artist's estate
Rowe, Cliff 1904–1989, *Men and Women in Doorway*, gift from the artist, © the artist's estate
Rowe, Cliff 1904–1989, *Men Hoisting Machine Section*, gift from the artist, © the artist's estate
Rowe, Cliff 1904–1989, *Mexican Guerrillas*, gift from the artist, © the artist's estate
Rowe, Cliff 1904–1989, *Operating Theatre Nurse*, gift from the artist, © the artist's estate
Rowe, Cliff 1904–1989, *Pipe Cutter*, gift from the artist, © the artist's estate
Rowe, Cliff 1904–1989, *Plating Bicycle Frames*, gift from the artist, © the artist's estate
Rowe, Cliff 1904–1989, *Railway Wheeltapper*, gift from the artist, © the artist's estate
Rowe, Cliff 1904–1989, *Removal Men*, gift from the artist, © the artist's estate
Rowe, Cliff 1904–1989, *Riveters*, gift from the artist, © the artist's estate
Rowe, Cliff 1904–1989, *Roofer*, gift from the artist, © the artist's estate
Rowe, Cliff 1904–1989, *Scientist at Lab Bench*, gift from the artist, © the artist's estate
Rowe, Cliff 1904–1989, *Sorting Tobacco Leaves*, gift from the artist, © the artist's estate
Rowe, Cliff 1904–1989, *Street Scene* (unfinished), gift from the artist, © the artist's estate
Rowe, Cliff 1904–1989, *Sun Furnace*, gift from the artist, © the artist's estate
Rowe, Cliff 1904–1989, *Textile Worker*, gift from the artist, © the artist's estate
Rowe, Cliff 1904–1989, *Textile Workers*, gift from the artist, © the artist's estate
Rowe, Cliff 1904–1989, *The Steps*, gift from the artist, © the artist's estate
Rowe, Cliff 1904–1989, *The Three Graces*, gift from the artist, © the artist's estate
Rowe, Cliff 1904–1989, *Three Men Building Frame*, gift from the artist, © the artist's estate
Rowe, Cliff 1904–1989, *Three Toy Bears*, gift from the artist, © the artist's estate
Rowe, Cliff 1904–1989, *Three Women Talking*, gift from the artist, © the artist's estate
Rowe, Cliff 1904–1989, *Two Bicycle Makers*, gift from the artist, © the artist's estate
Rowe, Cliff 1904–1989, *Village Harbour*, gift from the artist, © the artist's estate
Rowe, Cliff 1904–1989, *Weaver*, gift from the artist, © the artist's

estate
Rowe, Cliff 1904–1989, *White Roses*, gift from the artist, © the artist's estate
Rowe, Cliff 1904–1989, *Woman Cleaning Loco Boiler*, gift from the artist, © the artist's estate
Rowe, Cliff 1904–1989, *Woman Cleaning Loco Boiler*, gift from the artist, © the artist's estate
Rowe, Cliff 1904–1989, *Woman Cleaning Loco Boiler*, gift from the artist, © the artist's estate
Rowe, Cliff 1904–1989, *Woman Cleaning Loco Boiler*, gift from the artist, © the artist's estate
Rowe, Cliff 1904–1989, *Woman in Bottling Plant*, gift from the artist, © the artist's estate
Rowe, Cliff 1904–1989, *Woman Machinist*, gift from the artist, © the artist's estate
Rowe, Cliff 1904–1989, *Woman Millworker*, gift from the artist, © the artist's estate
Rowe, Cliff 1904–1989, *Woman on Moped*, gift from the artist, © the artist's estate
Rowe, Cliff 1904–1989, *Woman Potter*, gift from the artist, © the artist's estate
Rowe, Cliff 1904–1989, *Woman Reclining on Bed*, gift from the artist, © the artist's estate
Rowe, Cliff 1904–1989, *Woman Sat at Machine Controls*, gift from the artist, © the artist's estate
Rowe, Cliff 1904–1989, *Woman Silkscreen Printer*, gift from the artist, © the artist's estate
Rowe, Cliff 1904–1989, *Woman Sunbathing in Park*, gift from the artist, © the artist's estate
Rowe, Cliff 1904–1989, *Woman Working*, gift from the artist, © the artist's estate
Rowe, Cliff 1904–1989, *Women and Pram*, gift from the artist, © the artist's estate
Scott, Maureen b.1940, *The History of Labour*, gift, 1980s, © the artist
Stone, Marcus active 1934–1951, *Aneurin Bevan (1897–1960)*, gift, 1991, © the copyright holder
Stone, Marcus active 1934–1951, *Clement Attlee (1883–1967)*, on loan from the Labour Party, since 1992, © the copyright holder
Stone, Marcus active 1934–1951, *Emmanuel Shinwell (1884–1986)*, on loan from the Labour Party, since 1992, © the copyright holder
Stone, Marcus active 1934–1951, *Herbert Morrison (1888–1965)*, on loan from the Labour Party, since 1992, © the copyright holder
unknown artist *Skeleton*, gift from Eron Johnson, 2004
unknown artist *Friendly United Mechanics Cabinet Emblem**, gift from A. Langley, 1992
unknown artist *Success To Miners Banner**, gift from Buxton Museum & Art Gallery/Derbyshire Museums, 2006
unknown artist *Plumbers' Banner**, gift from Amicus, 1998

unknown artist *Shoemakers' Banner**, gift from Mrs M. Cuddon, 1997
unknown artist *Shoemakers' Apron**, gift from Mrs M. Cuddon, 1997
unknown artist *Typographical Association Banner* (recto), gift, c.1980
unknown artist *Typographical Association Banner* (verso), gift, c.1980
unknown artist *Co-operative Smiths Banner**, gift from GMB trade union, 2004
unknown artist *The Sunderland Employers Banner*, gift, c.1980
unknown artist *Dockers Union Banner* (recto), gift, c.1980
unknown artist *Dockers Union Banner* (verso), gift, c.1980
unknown artist *Arthur Henderson (1863–1935)*, on loan from the Labour Party, since 2010
unknown artist *National Builders Labourers And Construction Workers Society Banner* (recto), gift, c.1920
unknown artist *National Builders Labourers And Construction Workers Society Banner* (verso), gift, c.1980
unknown artist *National Union of Railwaymen Smithfield Branch Banner* (recto), gift, c.1980
unknown artist *National Union of Railwaymen Smithfield Branch Banner* (verso), gift, c.1980
unknown artist *Harry Pollitt (1890–1960)*, gift from the Communist Party of Great Britain, 1993
unknown artist *Fellowship is Life I*, gift, c.1980
unknown artist *Fellowship is Life II*, gift, c.1980
unknown artist *Liberty Fraternity & Peace**, gift, c.1980
unknown artist *The Tolpuddle Martyrs**, gift, c.1980
unknown artist *National Federation of Women Workers Banner*, gift, c.1980
unknown artist *Taking Scabs To Work*, gift, c.1985
unknown artist *Metalworkers and Engineers from the Thirteenth Century to the Nineteenth Century**, gift, 1993
unknown artist *Dick Kerrs (1917–1960)**, gift from the Women's Centre, Preston, 1993
unknown artist *Robert Blatchford (1851–1943)*, on loan from the Labour Party, 2010
unknown artist *William Rust (1903–1949), Editor of 'Daily Worker' Newspaper*, gift from the Communist Party of Great Britain, 1993
Wallhead, Richard Collingham , *Merthyr Independent Labour Party Banner*, gift from ILP Publications, 1991
Waudby, A. J. *Operative Bricklayers Society Emblem**, gift, c.1980

Royal Northern College of Music

Bradford, Dorothy 1918–2008, *Allegri String Quartet, Rodewald, Liverpool, 20 October 1964*, © the artist's estate
Bradford, Dorothy 1918–2008, *Quartet*, © the artist's estate
Cartledge, William 1891–1976, *Adolph Brodsky (1851–1929)*, © the copyright holder
Davies, Austin (attributed to) 1926–2012, *Gordon Green*, © the copyright holder
Durkin, Tom possibly 1928–1990, *Country Scene*, © the copyright holder
Fischer, Paula 1873–1950, *Carl Fuchs (1845–1951)*, © the copyright holder
Gregson, Julie '*La Rondine*', © the copyright holder
Hood, Barbara M. b.1915, *Eva Turner (1892–1990), as Turandot*, © the copyright holder
Howorth, Ray 1914–1985, *Hilda Collens (1883–1956)*, © the copyright holder
Purser, Sarah Henrietta 1848–1943, *Carl Fuchs (1845–1951)*, © the copyright holder
unknown artist *Charles Hallé (1819–1895)*
unknown artist *Greek Scene*

The Christie NHS Foundation Trust

Brown, Nicola *Landscape*, © the copyright holder
Cyprus, Chris b.1971, *Canal Scene at Night*, © the artist
Cyprus, Chris b.1971, *Landscape with Cows*, © the artist
Cyprus, Chris b.1971, *Woodland*, © the artist
Cyprus, Chris b.1971, *Tatton Park*, © the artist
Dunn, Kevin Lancelot b.1962, *Landscape*, © the artist
Dunn, Kevin Lancelot b.1962, *Landscape*, © the artist
Dunn, Kevin Lancelot b.1962, *Lindisfarne, View to the Mainland*, © the artist
Dunn, Kevin Lancelot b.1962, *Bow Lane, Manchester*, © the artist
Dunn, Kevin Lancelot b.1962, *Lizard Street, Manchester*, © the artist
Dunn, Kevin Lancelot b.1962, *Parliament Building, Budapest*, © the artist
Fox, Doreen b.1953, *Seascape*, © the artist
Fox, Doreen b.1953, *Seascape*, © the artist
George, Kevin *The Christie Hospital*, © the copyright holder
Greenhalgh, Gillian A. b.1950, *People in a Garden*, © the artist
Kushnick, Patricia b.1940, *Landscape*, © the artist
Kushnick, Patricia b.1940, *Dream Candy*, © the artist
Kushnick, Patricia b.1940, *Dream*

Farm, © the artist
Kushnick, Patricia b.1940, *Flowers*, © the artist
Kushnick, Patricia b.1940, *Halos and Flowers*, © the artist
Lily, Rooney b.1950, *Portrait of an Unknown Woman*, © the artist
Lily, Rooney b.1950, *Portrait of an Unknown Woman*, © the artist
Mountford, Patricia Ann b.1957, *Landscape*, © the artist
Mountford, Patricia Ann b.1957, *Scaffolding*, © the artist
Mountford, Patricia Ann b.1957, *Flowers*, © the artist
Mountford, Patricia Ann b.1957, *Flowers*, © the artist
Mountford, Patricia Ann b.1957, *Flowers*, © the artist
Mountford, Patricia Ann b.1957, *Flowers*, © the artist
Murray, Gill b.1940, *Landscape*, © the artist
Murray, Gill b.1940, *Landscape*, © the artist
Murray, Gill b.1940, *Woodland in Snow*, © the artist
Murray, Gill b.1940, *Woodland Scene*, © the artist
Murray, Gill b.1940, *Beach Scene*, © the artist
Murray, Gill b.1940, *Beach Scene*, © the artist
Murray, Gill b.1940, *Mountains*, © the artist
Oliver, Jo *Flowers*, © the copyright holder
Routledge, Jacki b.1957, *Seascape*, © the artist
Siraj, Zia b.1941, *Dervishes*, © the artist
Tait, Eileen *Above the Clouds*, © the copyright holder
Tait, Eileen *Autumn*, © the copyright holder
Tait, Eileen *Spring*, © the copyright holder
Tait, Eileen *Summer*, © the copyright holder
Tait, Eileen *Winter*, © the copyright holder
unknown artist *The Christie*
unknown artist *Landscape*
unknown artist *Landscape*
unknown artist *Landscape*
unknown artist *Landscape*
unknown artist *Landscape*
unknown artist *Fish*
unknown artist *Fish*
unknown artist *Landscape*
unknown artist *Landscape*
unknown artist *Landscape*
unknown artist *Landscape*
unknown artist *Tulips*
unknown artist *Peacock*
unknown artist *Venice*
Walker, Anne b.1959, *Sunflowers*, © the artist
Walker, Anne b.1959, *Sunflowers*, © the artist
Walker, Anne b.1959, *Sunflowers*, © the artist
Walker, Anne b.1959, *Portrait of an Unknown Child*, © the artist
Walker, Anne b.1959, *Portrait of an Unknown Man*, © the artist

Walker, Anne b.1959, *Portrait of an Unknown Woman*, © the artist
Walker, Anne b.1959, *Portrait of an Unknown Woman*, © the artist
Walker, Anne b.1959, *Portrait of an Unknown Woman*, © the artist
Walker, Anne b.1959, *Portrait of an Unknown Woman*, © the artist
Walker, Anne b.1959, *Portrait of an Unknown Woman*, © the artist
Walker, Anne b.1959, *Portrait of Unknown Children*, © the artist
Walker, Anne b.1959, *Woodland Scene*, © the artist
Wilkinson, Pat b.1964, *Fire*, © the artist
Wilkinson, Pat b.1964, *Ice*, © the artist
Wilkinson, Pat b.1964, *Up*, © the artist
Yeoman, Neill b.1966, *Trees*, © the artist
Yeoman, Neill b.1966, *Portrait of an Unknown Woman*, © the artist

The Portico Library and Gallery

Benjamin, Norman *The Portico Library*, donated by the artist, © the copyright holder
Bernieri, Luigi c.1862–1944, *Joseph Sunlight*, © the copyright holder
Bernieri, Luigi c.1862–1944, *Portrait of an Unidentified Lady of the Sunlight Family*, © the copyright holder
Smith, Phill W. active 1890–1932, *Portrait of an Unidentified Lady of the Sunlight Family*, © the copyright holder

The University of Manchester

Ashurst, Stephen b.1956, *Christopher Rose-Innes*, © the artist
Ashurst, Stephen b.1956, *Professor Graham Wood, UMIST (1961–2000), Britain's First Professor of Corrosion Science (1972–1997)*, © the artist
Ashurst, Stephen b.1956, *Brian Launder (b.1939)*, © the artist
Ashurst, Stephen b.1956, *Lord Alliance*, © the artist
Ashurst, Stephen b.1956, *Professor John Gartside, Professor Alan Gilbert and Professor Sir Martin Harris*, © the artist
Ashurst, Stephen b.1956, *Professor Edwin Smith, Head of Department, UMIST (1962–1990)*, © the artist
Ashurst, Stephen b.1956, *Professor Kenneth Entwhistle, Head of Department, UMIST (1962–1990)*, © the artist
Ashurst, Stephen b.1956, *The Four Deans*, © the artist
Ashurst, Stephen b.1956, *Professor Tom Hinchcliffe and Dr Roger Pannone*, © the artist
Ashurst, Stephen b.1956, *Sir Terry Leahy*, © the artist
Atack, David b.1949, *Professor H. C. A. Hankins, Principal and Vice-Chancellor (1984–1995)*, © the artist

Atack, David b.1949, *Professor R. F. Boucher, Principal and Vice-Chancellor (1995–2000)*, © the artist
Blease, G. D. b.1970, *Landscape*, © the artist
Chadwick, Heidi b.1973, *Descent 1*, © the artist
Chadwick, Heidi b.1973, *Descent 2*, © the artist
Chirnside, J. active 1957–1979, *David Cardwell, Acting Principal (1951–1953)*, © the copyright holder
Chirnside, J. active 1957–1979, *Joe Burgess, Secretary and Registrar of UMIST (1954–1973)*, © the copyright holder
Close *Portrait of an Unknown Scientist*, © the copyright holder
Collier, John 1850–1934, *Osborne Reynolds*
Coventry, Gertrude Mary 1886–1964, *Norman Smith*, © the copyright holder
Darmesteter, Helena 1849–1940, *Michael Sadler, Professor of History and Administration of Education*
Eley, William b.1938, *Legs*, © the artist
Eley, William b.1938, *Herta*, © the artist
Gunn, Herbert James 1893–1964, *The Right Honourable David Alexander Edward Lindsay*, © estate of the artist
Gunn, Herbert James 1893–1964, *Sir Walter Hamilton Moberly (1881–1974)*, © estate of the artist
Gunn, Herbert James 1893–1964, *The Right Honourable Frederick James Marquis*, © estate of the artist
Herkomer, Hubert von 1849–1914, *The Right Honourable Viscount Morley of Blackburn, Chancellor of the Victoria University of Manchester*, gift from Convocation, 1913
Herkomer, Hubert von 1849–1914, *Alfred Angus Nield, Chairman of the Council of Owen College (1864–1887)*
Hussain, Shameela *Kshitij (Unlimited Horizon)*, © the copyright holder
Isherwood *Edinburgh*, © the copyright holder
Isherwood *Southport Beach*, © the copyright holder
Jellicoe, Colin b.1942, *Two Figures in a Landscape*, © the copyright holder
Kettle, Alice b.1961, *Design I, Martin Harris Building, University of Manchester*, © the copyright holder
Kettle, Alice b.1961, *Design II, Martin Harris Building, University of Manchester*, © the copyright holder
Korur, Philippe Murat b.1986, *Pointing Fingers*, © the copyright holder
Lazell, Katherine *Flight*, © the copyright holder
Lovatt, William active 1824–1836, *John Owens*
Minor, E. *Abstract*, © the copyright holder

Minor, E. *Shapes*, © the copyright holder
Myers, William H. 1890–1924, *Hans Renold*
Nancollis, Robert b.1947, *Man as Bird**, © the artist
Nancollis, Robert b.1947, *Man with Crocodile on His Head**, © the artist
Nancollis, Robert b.1947, *Quality Not Quantity Is Our Motto*, © the artist
Nancollis, Robert b.1947, *Witton Albion*, © the artist
Noakes, Michael b.1933, *Lord Bowden of Chesterfield, Principal (1953–1976)*, © the artist
Noakes, Michael b.1933, *Professor Sir Rowland Smith, Chancellor (1996–2002)*, © the artist
Richardson-Jones, Keith 1925–2005, *Counterpoint Red/Green*, © the artist's estate
Riley, Harold b.1934, *The Urchin*, © the copyright holder
Sclettia *Text Book*, © the copyright holder
Scott, Megan *Untitled*, © the copyright holder
Servion, Peter *Abstract*, © the copyright holder
Stubley, Trevor 1932–2010, *Professor Sir Mark Henry Richmond*, © the artist's estate
unknown artist *Livesley*
unknown artist *A. W. Ward, Principal of Owens College (1895–1897)*
unknown artist *Abstract*
unknown artist *Abstract 1*
unknown artist *Abstract 2*
unknown artist *Abstract 3*
unknown artist *Abstract 4*
unknown artist *Abstract 5*
unknown artist *Daniel John Leech*
unknown artist *George Faulkner*
unknown artist *J. G. Greenwood, Principal of Owen's College and First Vice-Chancellor of the Victoria University*
unknown artist *John Dalton, Vice Principal, Manchester Mechanics Institute, UMIST (1839–1841)*
unknown artist *John Henry Renolds, First Principal of the Manchester School of Technology, UMIST (1902–1912)*
unknown artist *Joseph Jordan*
unknown artist *Joseph Jordan*
unknown artist *Landscape*
unknown artist *Lord L. Turnberg*
unknown artist *Portrait of an Unknown Academic*
unknown artist *Portrait of an Unknown Man*
unknown artist *Portrait of an Unknown Man*
unknown artist *Portrait of an Unknown Man*
unknown artist *Professor Julius Dreschfeld*
unknown artist *Professor Ross*
unknown artist *Samuel Elsworth Cottam, Secretary of the Manchester Mechanics Institute (1832–1838)*
unknown artist *Sir Henry E. Roscoe (1833–1915), Professor of Chemisty (1857–1886)*

unknown artist *Sir Martin Harris*
unknown artist *Sir William Dawkins*
unknown artist *Sir William Mansfield Cooper*
unknown artist *William Crawford Williamson, Professor of Natural History (1851–1892)*
unknown artist *William Henry, Supported the Foundation of the Manchester Mechanics Institute, 1824*
Ward, John Stanton 1917–2007, *Emeritus Professor Sir Anthony Llewellyn Armitage*, © the artist's estate/Bridgeman Art Library
Whittam, William Wright 1931–1996, *Building 60*, © the copyright holder
Wilson, Alastair *Kilburn's Machines*, © the copyright holder

Victoria Baths Trust

Worsley, John 1919–2000, *John Henry 'Rob' Derbyshire (1878–1938)*, on loan from the Amateur Swimming Association, © the artist's estate

Whitworth Art Gallery, The University of Manchester

Adams, Norman 1927–2005, *Golgotha*, © the artist's estate
Adams, Norman 1927–2005, *Time Piece*, © the artist's estate
Aldrich, Richard b.1975, *Cold Sand*, © courtesy of the artist and Bortolami Gallery
Andrews, Michael 1928–1995, *The Blue and Yellow of the Yacht Club*, © the estate of Michael Andrews, courtesy of James Hyman Gallery, London
Appelbee, Leonard 1914–2000, *Study of a Lobster*, © the copyright holder
Auerbach, Frank Helmuth b.1931, *Head of Laurie Owen*, © the artist
Ayres, Gillian b.1930, *Reef* (detail), © the artist
Ayres, Gillian b.1930, *Galatea*, © the artist
Bacon, Francis 1909–1992, *Lucian Freud*, © the estate of Francis Bacon. All rights reserved. DACS 2013
Beaton, Cecil Walter Hardy 1904–1980, *Hal Burton*, © National Portrait Gallery, London
Beaumont, Frederick Samuel 1861–1954, *Mr Horsfall*, © the copyright holder
Bidauld, Jean Joseph Xavier 1758–1846, *Monte Cavo from Lake Albano*
Birch, Samuel John Lamorna 1869–1955, *The Wave*, © the artist's estate
Blackadder, Elizabeth V. b.1931, *Still Life with Flowers*, © the artist
Bomberg, David 1890–1957, *Composition with Figures*, © the estate of David Bomberg. All rights reserved, DACS 2013

Boshier, Derek b.1937, *Megaloxenophobia*, © the artist/courtesy Flowers Gallery, London
Bradshaw, Brian b.1923, *The Croal at Churchgate, Bolton*, © the artist
Brown, Ford Madox 1821–1893, *Execution of Mary, Queen of Scots*
Bussy, Simon 1870–1954, *The Black Panther*, © the copyright holder
Castiglione, Giovanni Benedetto 1609–1664, *A Patriarchal Journey*
Caulfield, Patrick 1936–2005, *Smokeless Coal Fire*, © the estate of Patrick Caulfield. All rights reserved, DACS 2013
Clausen, George 1852–1944, *Willow Tree*, © Clausen estate
Clérisseau, Charles Louis 1722–1820, *Capriccio with Classical Ruins*
Clough, Prunella 1919–1999, *Anchor and Float*, © estate of Prunella Clough 2013. All rights reserved, DACS
Collier, John 1850–1934, *S. Wilkins*
Collins, William 1788–1847, *Coast Scene*
Conroy, Stephen b.1964, *The Red Room*, © the artist
Constable, John 1776–1837, *Study of Clouds*
Cook, Ben b.1967, *TV2*, © the artist
Cooper, Gladys 1899–1975, *A Day among the Crocuses*, © the copyright holder
Cox the elder, David 1783–1859, *Landscape with Sheep*
Cozens, Alexander 1717–1786, *Setting Sun*
Crane, Thomas 1808–1859, *Walter Crane as a Child*
Crane, Walter 1845–1915, *Beatrice and Lionel Crane*
Davie, Alan b.1920, *Elephant's Eyeful*, © the artist
De Chirico, Giorgio 1888–1978, *The Philosopher*, © DACS 2013
De Wint, Peter 1784–1849, *Study of Sorrel, Cow Parsley and Willow Saplings*, gift from Thomas Agnew and Sons through Hammond Smith
Downton, John 1906–1991, *Girl Conducting*, © Whitworth Art Gallery
Dughet, Gaspard 1615–1675, *View of Tivoli*
Dutch School *River Scene*
Faed, Thomas 1826–1900, *'What shall I say to him?'*
Fedden, Mary 1915–2012, *Fruit at Christmas*, © The Estate of Mary Fedden, care of Portland Gallery, London
Feiler, Paul b.1918, *Overlapping Forms Brown*, © the artist/Bridgeman Art Library
Forbes, Stanhope Alexander 1857–1947, *Châteaudun, Street Scene*, © the artist's estate/Bridgeman Art Library
Freud, Lucian 1922–2011, *Man's Head (Self Portrait I)*, © estate of Lucian Freud
Frost, Terry 1915–2003, *Blue, Red*

Lime Art active since 1973 &
**Minehead Resource Centre
Painting Group** & **Prime, Len**
Dinner by the Sea, © the copyright
holder
Lime Art active since 1973 &
**Minehead Resource Centre
Painting Group** & **Wells, Kay**
Catch a Leaf to get a Wish, © the
copyright holder
Lime Art active since 1973 &
**Minehead Resource Centre
Painting Group** & **Wells, Kay**
Playing by a Waterfall, © the
copyright holder
Lime Art active since 1973 & **Platt
Lane Planning Group** & **Smith,
Dorothy** *Cottages and Boats*
Lime Art active since 1973 & **Platt
Lane Planning Group** & **Smith,
Dorothy** *Leaf Pattern*
Lime Art active since 1973 & **Platt
Lane Planning Group** & **Smith,
Dorothy** *Leaves*
Lime Art active since 1973 & **Platt
Lane Planning Group** &
Stephenson, Sue *Leaves Leaf
Pattern*
Todd, Anna b.1964, *High Tea at
the Cricket Match*, © the copyright
holder
unknown artist *Skye*

Collection Addresses

Manchester

Central Manchester University Hospitals NHS
  Foundation Trust
Oxford Road, Manchester M13 9WL
Telephone 0161 276 1234

Chetham's Library
Long Millgate, Manchester M3 1SB
Telephone 0161 834 7961

Greater Manchester County Record Office
56 Marshall Street, New Cross, Manchester M4 5FU
Telephone 0161 832 5284

Greater Manchester Police Museum & Archives
57a Newton Street, Manchester M1 1ET
Telephone 0161 856 3287/4500

John Rylands Library, The University of Manchester
150 Deansgate, Manchester M3 3EH
Telephone 0161 306 0555

Manchester City Galleries
Manchester Art Gallery, Mosley Street
Manchester M2 3JL
Telephone 0161 235 8888

Manchester Jewish Museum
Cheetham Hill Road, Manchester M8 8LW
Telephone 0161 834 9879

Manchester Metropolitan University:

> Manchester Metropolitan University,
>   Ormond Building
> All Saints, Manchester M15 6BR
> Telephone 0161 247 2000

> Manchester Metropolitan University,
>   All Saints Building
> All Saints, Manchester M15 6BH

> Manchester Metropolitan University,
>   Didsbury Campus
> 799 Wilmslow Road, Didsbury,
> Manchester M20 2RR
> Telephone 0161 247 1385

Manchester Metropolitan University Special Collections
Sir Kenneth Green Library, All Saints,
Manchester M15 6BH
Telephone 0161 247 6107

Manchester Metropolitan University,
  Arts for Health Archive
Righton Building, Cavendish Street,
Manchester M15 6BG
Telephone 0161 247 1091

Manchester Metropolitan University,
  Faculty of Art and Design
212 Chatham Building, Cavendish Street,
Manchester M15 6BR
Telephone 0161 247 1005

Manchester Town Hall
Albert Square, Manchester M60 2LA
Telephone 0161 234 5000

Museum of Science and Industry
Liverpool Road, Castlefield, Manchester M3 4FP
Telephone 0161 832 2244

National Football Museum
Urbis Building, Cathedral Gardens, Manchester M4 3BG
Telephone 0161 605 8200

People's History Museum
Left Bank, Spinningfields, Manchester M3 3ER
Telephone 0161 838 9190

Royal Northern College of Music
124 Oxford Road, Manchester M13 9RD
Telephone 0161 907 5200

The Christie NHS Foundation Trust
Wilmslow Road, Manchester M20 4BX
Telephone 0161 446 3000

The Portico Library and Gallery
57 Mosley Street, Manchester M2 3HY
Telephone 0161 236 6785

The University of Manchester
Manchester
Telephone 0161 306 6000

Victoria Baths Trust
Hathersage Road, Chorlton-on-Medlock,
Manchester M13 0FE
Telephone 0161 224 2020

Whitworth Art Gallery, The University of Manchester
Oxford Road, Manchester M15 6ER
Telephone 0161 275 7450

Withington Community Hospital
Nell Lane, West Didsbury, Manchester M20 2LR
Telephone 0161 434 5555

Acknowledgements

The Public Catalogue Foundation would like to thank the individual artists and copyright holders for their permission to reproduce for free the paintings in this catalogue. Exhaustive efforts have been made to locate the copyright owners of all the images included within this catalogue and to meet their requirements. Copyright credit lines for copyright owners who have been traced are listed in the Further Information section.

The Public Catalogue Foundation would like to express its great appreciation to the following organisations for their kind assistance in the preparation of this catalogue:

Bridgeman Art Library
Flowers East
Marlborough Fine Art
National Association of Decorative & Fine Arts Societies (NADFAS)
National Gallery, London
National Portrait Gallery, London
Royal Academy of Arts, London
Tate

Index of Artists

In this catalogue, artists' names and the spelling of their names follow the preferred presentation of the name in the Getty Union List of Artist Names (ULAN) as of February 2004, if the artist is listed in ULAN.

The page numbers next to each artist's name below direct readers to paintings that are by the artist; are attributed to the artist; or, in a few cases, are more loosely related to the artist being, for example, 'after', 'the circle of' or copies of a painting by the artist. The precise relationship between the artist and the painting is listed in the catalogue.

The Public Catalogue Foundation

The Public Catalogue Foundation is a registered charity. It was launched in 2003 to create a photographic record of the entire national collection of oil, tempera and acrylic paintings in public ownership in the United Kingdom.

Whilst our public galleries and civic buildings hold arguably the greatest collection of oil paintings in the world, over 80 per cent of these are not on view. Few collections have a complete photographic record of their paintings let alone a comprehensive illustrated catalogue. What is publicly owned is not publicly accessible.

The Foundation is publishing a series of fully illustrated, county-by-county catalogues that will cover, eventually, the entire national UK collection. To date, it has published over 30 volumes, presenting over 72,000 paintings.

In partnership with the BBC, the Foundation will make its database of the entire UK collection of 200,000 oil paintings available online through a new website called *Your Paintings*. The website was launched in the summer of 2011.

Your Paintings (*www.bbc.co.uk/arts/yourpaintings*) offers a variety of ways of searching for paintings as well as further information about the paintings and artists, including links to the participating collections' websites. For those interested in paintings and the subjects they portray *Your Paintings* is an unparalleled learning resource.

Collections benefit substantially from the work of the Foundation, not least from the digital images that are given to them for free following photography, and from the increased recognition that the project brings. These substantial benefits come at no financial cost to the collections.

The Foundation is funded by a combination of support from individuals, charitable trusts, companies and the public sector although the latter provides less than 20 per cent of the Foundation's financial support.

Supporters

Master Patrons

The Public Catalogue Foundation is greatly indebted to the following Master Patrons who have helped it in the past or are currently working with it to raise funds for the publication of their county catalogues. All of them have given freely of their time and have made an enormous contribution to the work of the Foundation.

Peter Andreae *(Hampshire)*
Sir Henry Aubrey-Fletcher, Bt, Lord Lieutenant of Buckinghamshire *(Buckinghamshire)*
Sir Nicholas Bacon, DL, High Sheriff of Norfolk *(Norfolk)*
Sir John Bather, Lord Lieutenant of Derbyshire *(Derbyshire)*
The Hon. Mrs Bayliss, JP, Lord Lieutenant of Berkshire *(Berkshire)*
Ian Bonas *(County Durham)*

Peter Bretherton *(West Yorkshire: Leeds)*
Michael Brinton, Lord Lieutenant of Worcestershire *(Worcestershire)*
Sir Hugo Brunner, KCVO, JP *(Oxfordshire)*
Mr John Bush, OBE, Lord-Lieutenant of Wiltshire *(Wiltshire)*
Lady Butler *(Warwickshire)*
Richard Compton *(North Yorkshire)*
George Courtauld, DL, Vice Lord Lieutenant of Essex *(Essex)*

The Countess of Darnley, Lord
Lieutenant of Herefordshire
(Herefordshire)
The Marquess of Downshire (North
Yorkshire)
Martin Dunne, Lord Lieutenant of
Warwickshire (Warwickshire)
Sir Henry Elwes, KCVO, Lord-
Lieutenant of Gloucestershire
(Gloucestershire)
Jenny Farr, MBE, DL (Nottinghamshire)
John Fenwick (Tyne & Wear
Museums)
Mark Fisher, MP (Staffordshire)
Patricia Grayburn, MBE, DL (Surrey)
The Earl of Halifax, KStJ, JP, DL
(East Riding of Yorkshire)
Lord Roy Hattersley, PC (South
Yorkshire: Sheffield
Algy Heber-Percy, Lord Lieutenant
of Shropshire (Shropshire)
The Lady Mary Holborow, Lord
Lieutenant of Cornwall (Cornwall)
Sarah Holman (Warwickshire)
Tommy Jowitt (West Yorkshire)
Alderman Sir David Lewis, The Rt
Hon. The Lord Mayor of London,
2007–2008 (The City of London)

Sir Michael Lickiss (Cornwall)
Magnus Linklater (Scotland)
Lord Marlesford, DL (Suffolk)
Dr Bridget McConnell (Glasgow)
Lady Sarah Nicholson (County
Durham)
Malcolm V. L. Pearce, MP (Somerset)
Sir John Riddell, Lord
Lieutenant of Northumberland
(Northumberland)
Venetia Ross Skinner (Dorset)
The Most Hon. The Marquess of
Salisbury, PC, DL (Hertfordshire)
Julia Somerville (Government Art
Collection)
Tim Stevenson, OBE, Lord
Lieutenant of Oxfordshire
(Oxfordshire)
Phyllida Stewart-Roberts, OBE (East
Sussex)
Lady Juliet Townsend, Lord
Lieutenant of Northamptonshire
(Northamptonshire)
Leslie Weller, DL (West Sussex)
Sir Samuel C. Whitbread, KCVO,
Lord Lieutenant of Bedfordshire
(Bedfordshire)

Financial support

The Public Catalogue Foundation is particularly grateful to the following organisations and individuals who have given it generous financial support since the project started in 2003.

National Sponsor

Christie's

Benefactors (£10,000–£50,000)

The 29th May 1961 Charitable Trust
Arts Council England
The Barbour Trust
Binks Trust
City of Bradford Metropolitan
District Council
Deborah Loeb Brice Foundation
The Bulldog Trust
A. & S. Burton 1960 Charitable Trust
Christie's
City of London Corporation
The John S. Cohen Foundation
Covent Garden London
Creative Scotland
Department for Culture, Media and
Sport

Sir Harry Djanogly, CBE
Mr Lloyd Dorfman
Dunard Fund
The Elmley Foundation
Fenwick Ltd
Fidelity UK Foundation
Marc Fitch Fund
The Foyle Foundation
J. Paul Getty Jr Trust
Hampshire County Council
The Charles Hayward Foundation
Peter Harrison Foundation
Mr Robert Hiscox
Hiscox plc
David Hockney, CH, RA
ICAP plc

The Jordan Charitable Foundation
Kent County Council
The Linbury Trust
The Manifold Trust
Paul Mellon Centre for Studies in
    British Art
The Mercers' Company
Robert Warren Miller
Mr & Mrs A. Mittal
The Monument Trust
Miles Morland
Allan and Carol Murray
National Gallery Trust
Stavros Niarchos Foundation
Norfolk County Council
Northern Rock Foundation
Nottingham City Council
Malcolm V. L. Pearce, MP
P. F. Charitable Trust
The Pilgrim Trust

Provident Financial
RAB Capital plc
The Radcliffe Trust
Renaissance East Midlands
Renaissance West Midlands
Renaissance Yorkshire
Saga Group Ltd
Scottish Government
The Bernard Sunley Charitable
    Foundation
Townsend Family Trust
University College, London
University of Leeds
The Walker Trust
The Wolfson Foundation
Sir Siegmund Warburg's Voluntary
    Settlement
Garfield Weston Foundation
Mr & Mrs A. H. Wilkinson
The Wixamtree Trust

**Series Patrons
(Minimum donation of £2,500)**

James & Lindsay Adam
Sir John Bather
Harry Bott
Janey Buchan
Mrs Rhona Callander
Dr Peter Cannon-Brookes
The John S. Cohen Foundation
Bushey Museum in memory of
    Lavender Watson
Mr Lloyd Dorfman
Lord Douro
Jenny Farr, MBE, DL
Mrs Greta Fenston
The FIRS Trust
Glasgow Museums
Patricia Grayburn, MBE, DL
G. Laurence Harbottle
R. K. Harrison Insurance Services
    Limited
Paul & Fiona Hart
Paul & Kathrine Haworth
Lord & Lady Heseltine
Patrik Holden & Lin Hinds
Neil Honebon

Michael Jacobson
Grace Jenkins
Dr David Johnson, DL
The Keatley Trust
John Kendall, Esq.
Michael A. Lambert, CBE
David & Amanda Leathers
Miles Morland
Allan & Carol Murray
North East Regional Museums Hub
The University of Northampton
Nottingham Civic Society
Richard & Amika Oldfield
The Roper Family Charitable Trust
Adam Sedgwick
Sir Harry & Lady Soloman
Stuart M. Southall
Simon Still
Chloe Teacher
University of Surrey
David & Cissy Walker
Tony Wilkinson
Mr & Mrs Jo Windsor
Mr & Mrs Charles Wyvill

**Catalogue Patrons
(£1,000–£10,000)**

The 29th May 1961 Charitable Trust
ACE Study Tours
Adams & Remers
Marcus & Kate Agius
The AIM Foundation
D. C. R. Allen
John Alston, CBE

Amberley Castle
The Astor Foundation
The Aylesford Family Charitable
    Trust
Chairman of Cornwall County
    Council, Mrs Doris Anson, OBE, JP
Archant Ltd

G. F. Armitage Family Charitable
  Trust
Mr Ian Askew
Aurelius Charitable Trust
The Bacon Charitable Trust
Lawrence Banks, CBE, DL
Barlow Robbins LLP
Mr James & Lady Emma Barnard
Basingstoke and Deane Borough
  Council
Bath & North East Somerset District
  Council Heritage Services
Robert Baxter, DL
Birmingham Common Good Trust
Sir Christopher Bland
Johnnie Boden
The Charlotte Bonham-Carter
  Charitable Trust
H. R. Pratt Boorman Family
  Foundation
A. J. H. du Boulay Charitable Trust
The Bowerman Charitable Trust
Viscountess Boyd Charitable Trust
Lord & Lady Bradbury
Bramdean Asset Management LLP
Peter Bretherton
Brewin Dolphin
J. & M. Britton Charitable Trust
Mrs T. Brotherton-Ratcliffe
Janey Buchan
Mr & Mrs Patrick Burgess
Mr & Mrs Mark Burrell
Arnold J. Burton Charitable Trust
Bushey Museum in Memory of
  Lavender Watson
Mrs Anne Cadbury, OBE, JP, DL
Roger Cadbury
C. J. R. & Mrs C. L. Calderwood
Sir Ralph Carr-Ellison
Mr & Mrs J. Chambers
Chichester District Council
His Honour Richard Cole, DL &
  Mrs Sheila Cole
The Timothy Colman Charitable
  Trust
Mr & Mrs Derek Coombs
The Helen Jean Cope Trust
Mr & Mrs Ian Copesteak
Cornwall County Council
Mr S. J. D. Corsan

Graeme Cottam & Gloriana Marks
  de Chabris
Coutts Charitable Trust
David Crane Trust
Elaine Craven, Earl Street
  Employment Consultants Ltd
Harriett Cullen
Culture North East
Rt Hon. Viscount Daventry
N. Davie-Thornhill
Brigadier Mike Dauncey, DSO, DL
De La Rue Charitable Trust
Mr Robert Dean
Deborah Gage (Works of Art) Ltd
Derek Johns Ltd, London
Derby City Council
Derby High School Trust Ltd
Derbyshire Building Society
Derbyshire Community Foundation
  (The Ashby Fund)
J. N. Derbyshire Trust
The Duke of Devonshire's Charitable
  Trust
S. Dewhirst Charitable Trust
Sir Harry Djanogly, CBE
Dorset County Council
Lord Douro
Professor Patrick & Dr Grace
  Dowling
Dunn Family Charitable Trust
East Sussex County Council
Eastbourne Borough Council
EEMLAC, through the Association
  for Suffolk Museums
Lord & Lady Egremont
Sir John & Lady Elliott
Andrew & Lucy Ellis
Peter & Judy Ellwood
Essex County Council
John & Felicity Fairbairn
Fairfield Charitable Trust
Jenny Farr, MBE, DL
John Feeney Charitable Trust
The Trustees of the Finnis Scott
  Foundation
The Fishmongers' Company
David & Ann FitzWilliam-Lay
Elizabeth & Val Fleming
The Follett Trust
Richard & Elizabeth Fothergill

Christopher & Catherine Foyle
Freemasons of Derbyshire
The Friends of Historic Essex
The Friends of the Laing Art Gallery
The Friends of the Royal Pavilion,
    Art Gallery & Museums, Brighton
The Friends of Southampton's
    Museums, Archives and Galleries
The Friends of Sunderland Museums
The Friends of York Art Gallery (E. J.
    Swift Bequest)
Philip Gibbs
The Hon. H. M. T. Gibson's Charity
    Trust
Lewis & Jacqueline Golden
The Goldsmiths' Company
Gorringes
Charles Gregson
The Grocers' Company
The Gulland Family
David Gurney
Philip Gwyn
Sir Ernest Hall
The Earl of Halifax, KStJ, JP, DL
The W. A. Handley Charity Trust
The Hartnett Charitable Trust
Hazlitt, Gooden & Fox Ltd
Heartwood Wealth Management Ltd
The Trustees of the King Henry VIII
    Endowed Trust, Warwick
The Rt Hon. the Lord Heseltine, CH,
    PC & Lady Heseltine
The Lady Hind Trust
Hobart Charitable Trust
Edward and Anna Hocknell
David Hockney CH, RA
Patrick Holden & Lin Hinds
Mrs Michael Hollingbery
The Holman Family
Mr & Mrs A. Holman-West
The Honourable Company of
    Gloucestershire
The Hope Scott Trust
David & Prue Hopkinson
Major & Mrs Bill Hutchinson
His Honour Gabriel Hutton
Isle of Wight Council
The J. and S. B. Charitable Trust
Alan & Penny Jerome
James & Lucilla Joll Charitable Trust

Mr & Mrs Peter Jones
Tommy Jowitt
The Keatley Trust
Kent Messenger Group
Garrett Kirk, Jr
Mr John Kirkland, OBE & Mrs
    Sheila Kirkland
Robert Kirkland
Kirklees Council
The David Laing Foundation
Landau Foundation
Lord Lea of Crondall, OBE
The Leche Trust
Leeds Art Collections Fund
Leeds City Council
Leeds Philosophical and Literary
    Society
The Hon. David Legh, DL
Lord Leverhulme's Charitable Trust
Mr & Mrs John Lewis
Mark & Sophie Lewisohn
Tom Lugg & the Lane Family
The Orr Mackintosh Foundation
The MacRobert Trust
Maidstone Borough Council
John Manser
Mr & Mrs Derek Mapp
Walter & Barbara Marais
The Marlay Group
Marshall Charitable Trust
Stephen & Carolyn Martin
Tom & Anne Martin
The Medlock Charitable Trust
The Piet Mendels Foundation
MLA East of England
MLA North East of England
Museums Galleries Scotland
Mr Paul Myners
Rupert Nabarro
Nancie Massey Charitable Trust
Newcastle City Council
Bryan Norman
Lord & Lady Northampton
The University of Northampton
NP Aerospace Ltd
Oakmoor Trust
Jasper & Virginia Olivier
The Orr Mackintosh Foundation
Mr Christopher Oughtred
The Owen Family Trust

Sir Idris Pearce
Roger Neville Russ Peers
The Pennycress Trust
Perkins Family
The Lord & Lady Phillimore
Mrs Margaret Pollett
Simon & Ursula Pomeroy
The Portland Family
Portsmouth City Council
George Pragnell Ltd
The Prince Philip Trust Fund for the
    Royal Borough of Windsor and
    Maidenhead
Provident Financial plc
Mr John Rank
Rathbone Investment Management
    Ltd
The Hans and Märit Rausing
    Charitable Trust
Roger & Jane Reed
Renaissance North East
Renaissance South East
Renaissance South West
Michael Renshall, CBE, MA, FCA
Sir John Riddell
Sir Miles & Lady Rivett-Carnac
Rockley Charitable Trust
Rolls-Royce plc
The Roper Family Charitable Trust
Rothschild Foundation
Royal Cornwall Museum
Graham & Ann Rudd
Sir Nigel Rudd
Russell New
The J. S. & E. C. Rymer Charitable
    Trust
The Earl St Aldwyn
The Sammermar Trust
Scarfe Charitable Trust
Andrew & Belinda Scott
The Trustees of the Finnis Scott
    Foundation
Shaftesbury PLC
Mr W. Sharpe
The Shears Foundation
Robert Shields, DL
Smith & Williamson

South West of England Regional
    Development Agency
Caroline M. Southall
Stuart M. Southall
Southampton City Council
The Jessie Spencer Trust
Hugh & Catherine Stevenson
Mrs Andrew Stewart-Roberts, OBE
Mr Michael Stone
Mr Peter Stormonth Darling
The Stratford-upon-Avon Town
    Trust
Strutt and Parker
Suffolk County Council, through the
    Association for Suffolk Museums
Surrey County Council
The John Swire 1989 Charitable
    Trust
The Tanner Trust
Tennants Auctioneers
Tesco Charity Trust
The Thistle Trust
Prof. Caroline Tisdall
Trusthouse Charitable Foundation
Gladwyn Turbutt
TWM Business Partners
Tyne & Wear Museums
University College Falmouth
University of Derby
University of Essex
David & Grizelda Vermont
Wakefield Metropolitan District
    Council
Robert & Felicity Waley-Cohen
The Peggy Walker Charitable Trust
The Walland Trust Fund
John Wates Charitable Trust
Leslie Weller, DL
The Welton Foundation
West Sussex County Council
Mr & Mrs David Wigglesworth
Wilkin & Sons Ltd
Mr & Mrs Jo Windsor
Peter Wolton Charitable Trust
Michael J. Woodhall, FRICS
Sir Philip Wroughton
Mrs Angela Yeoman

First published in 2013 by The Public Catalogue
Foundation, Printed Catalogue Division,
8 Frederick's Place, London, EC2R 8AB

© 2013 The Public Catalogue Foundation,
registered charity number 1096185. Company
limited by guarantee incorporated in England and
Wales with number 4573564. VAT registration
number 833 0131 76. Registered office: The
Courtyard, Shoreham Road, Upper Beeding,
Steyning, West Sussex, BN44 3TN.

We wish to thank the individual artists and all
the copyright holders for their permission to
reproduce the works of art. Exhaustive efforts have
been made to locate the copyright owners of all the
images included within this catalogue and to meet
their requirements. Any omissions or mistakes
brought to our attention will be duly attended to
and corrected in future publications. Owners of
copyright in the paintings illustrated who have
been traced are listed in the Further Information
section.

Photographs of paintings are © the collections that
own them, except where otherwise acknowledged.

Forewords to each collection are © the respective
authors.

**The responsibility for the accuracy of the
information presented in this catalogue lies solely
with the holding collections. Suggestions that
might improve the accuracy of the information
contained in this catalogue should be sent to the
relevant collection and emailed to
info@thepcf.org.uk.**

Any copy of this book issued by the publisher is
sold subject to the condition that it shall not by way
of trade or otherwise be lent, re-sold, hired out or
otherwise circulated without the publisher's prior
consent in any form of binding or cover other than
that in which it is published and without a similar
condition, including these words, being imposed
on a subsequent purchaser.

© All Rights Reserved. No part of this publication
may be reproduced or transmitted in any form or
by any means, electronic or mechanical, including
photocopy, recording or any other information
storage and retrieval system, without prior
permission in writing from the publisher.

ISBN 978-1-909475-21-2

Designed by Sally Jeffery

Printed in the UK by Gomer Press Ltd on paper
sourced from sustainable forests